D1030321

ELECTRONIC STRUCTURE
OF MOLECULES

Electronic Structure
of Molecules

Diatomic Molecules, Small Molecules
Saturated Hydrocarbons, Conjugated Molecules
Molecules of Biochemical Interest

BY

RAYMOND DAUDEL

PERGAMON PRESS

OXFORD · LONDON · EDINBURGH · NEW YORK
TORONTO · PARIS · BRAUNSCHWEIG

Pergamon Press Ltd., Headington Hill Hall, Oxford
4 & 5 Fitzroy Square, London W.1
Pergamon Press (Scotland) Ltd., 2 & 3 Teviot Place, Edinburgh 1
Pergamon Press Inc., 44–01 21st Street, Long Island City, New York 11101
Pergamon of Canada, Ltd., 6 Adelaide Street East, Toronto, Ontario
Pergamon Press S.A.R.L., 24 rue des Écoles, Paris 5^e
Vieweg & Sohn GmbH, Burgplatz 1, Braunschweig

First English edition 1966

This is a translation of the original French *Structure électronique
des molécules* published by Gauthier-Villars, Paris in 1962

2527/66

Contents

258161

Preface

BASED on the third-year course in Molecular Theoretical Physics given by the author at the Sorbonne, this book constitutes an introduction to the study of the "Electronic Structure of Molecules" and associated molecular properties.

The theoretical methods employed in the following chapters have mostly been described in another book in this series, *Les Fondements de la Chimie Théorique*.† Any new techniques which have been evolved since the appearance of the above book are described as and when they are used.

We could not in a work of this size deal with the whole range of problems touching on the structure of molecules. We shall confine ourselves to the study of the properties of an isolated molecule in the absence of any external fields. We are concerned only with phenomena associated with the "motion" of electrons in the field of nuclei assumed to be fixed. We shall not mention, therefore, either the infrared spectrum or the radio spectrum of molecules.

In spite of this restriction there is still too much material. We have had to confine ourselves to the study of certain classes of molecules which are indicated in the sub-title of the book. Nevertheless, reference will be made to over a thousand reports in the present volume.

R. DAUDEL

† English translation, *The Fundamentals of Theoretical Chemistry*, in preparation, Pergamon Press.

One-electron systems: Hydrogen ion-molecule, Various kinds of molecular orbitals

POSSIBLE one-electron systems include the hydrogen atom and iso-electronic atoms studied in the first book (Chapter I) together with the hydrogen ion-molecule and isoelectronic molecules.

We shall not return to the former systems. We must, however, complete the examination of the ion-molecule. In the limit, the wave function of the molecule ion constitutes a typical example of a *molecular orbital*. Different methods of calculation are compared with a view to the derivation of the wave functions of molecular orbitals for other molecules.

1. REVISION OF BURRAU'S METHOD

Burrau's method which was explained in the first book (p. 125) has been applied to the study of both ground and excited [1] states of the molecule.

Figure 1 shows the electric energy $U(r_{AB})$ as a function of r_{AB}, the distance between the nuclei, as given by these calculations. Note that there are states, other than the ground state, for which the corresponding curve passes through a minimum, i.e. the stable excited states.

Figure 2 shows the curves of equal electron density for the ground state. As one might expect, the points of maximum density coincide with the nuclei and the electrons of the ion-molecule occur chiefly "between" the nuclei.

The curve *a* on Fig. 3 shows the variation of the wave function along the line of the nuclei. The wave functions given by Burrau's method do not have analytic form, but analytic formulae giving good approximations to Burrau's function for the ground state have been

ESM 1

proposed, e.g. James's approximation [2]

$$\phi = N e^{-Z\xi}[1 + a\eta^2]$$

where N is a normalising coefficient and where

$$\xi = \frac{r_A + r_B}{r_{AB}} \qquad \eta = \frac{r_A - r_B}{r_{AB}}$$

$$Z = 1{\cdot}35 \qquad a = 0{\cdot}448$$

(This corresponds to an electric dissociation energy of 2.272 eV.)

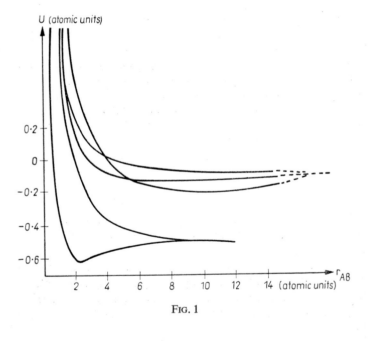

FIG. 1

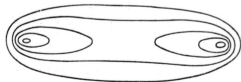

FIG. 2. Curves of equal electron density in a plane passing through the line of nuclei of the molecule H_2^+.

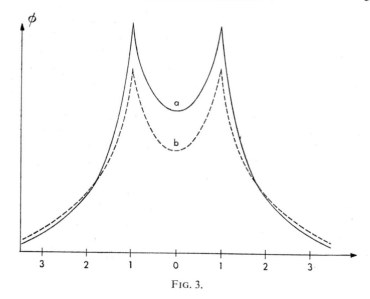

FIG. 3.

Also Guillemin and Zener's approximation[3]:

$$\phi = N' \, e^{-Z\xi} \cosh a\eta$$

where N' is another normalising coefficient.

2. THE METHOD OF LINEAR COMBINATIONS OF ATOMIC ORBITALS

A general examination of the method of linear combinations of atomic orbitals has already been carried out in the first book (Chapter 5, Section 28). It is interesting to apply this method in the case of the ion-molecule of hydrogen where it is possible to obtain a better grasp of the physical significance of this approximation.

The unique molecular orbital φ coincides here with the approximate wave function ϕ, and, therefore, the ground state can be represented by:

$$\phi = \varphi = N(1s_A + 1s_B)$$

where N is a normalising coefficient, and $1s_A$ and $1s_B$ denote the K orbitals of the hydrogen atoms associated with nuclei A and B respectively.

Consider a point near A and distant from B. At this point the electron is influenced mainly by A, the influence of B being negligible. It is therefore reasonable to assume that the wave function at this point approximates to $1s_A$. In the orbital φ the effect of the function $1s_B$ is negligible compared with that of $1s_A$; the function φ behaves like $1s_A$. Similar reasoning can be applied to points near B.

Summing up, the orbital φ gives a good approximation to the exact function in the neighbourhood of the nuclei. The function φ along the line of nuclei is shown by the curve b of Fig. 3. It can be seen that its behaviour near the nuclei resembles that of Burrau's function, but it decreases more rapidly towards the middle of the line of the nuclei and more slowly outside the molecule. In other words the function does not take sufficient account of the increase of electric field produced "between" the nuclei in the establishment of a chemical bond.

The energy U can be calculated easily from the expression

$$U = \int \phi \, \mathfrak{H} \, \phi \, dv$$

$$= N^2 \int (1s_A + 1s_B) \left[-\frac{h^2}{8\pi^2 m} \varDelta + \frac{e^2}{r_{AB}} - \frac{e^2}{r_A} - \frac{e^2}{r_B} \right] \times$$

$$\times \; (1s_A + 1s_B) \, dv.$$

Figure 4 allows this function to be compared with that obtained with Burrau's method. The minimum for this can be seen to occur at $U_{AB} = 1\cdot32$ Å (instead of $1\cdot06$) which corresponds to a dissociation energy of $1\cdot77$ eV, too small by approximately 1 eV, confirming that the chemical bond is not sufficiently well represented [4].

Following a method which was indicated several times in the first book (e.g. p. 58), we shall now introduce an undeterminate factor in the coefficient of the exponential of $1s$ as follows:

$$- Zr/a_0$$

and find the value of Z which minimises the minimum of $U(r_{AB})$. This gives [5]

$$Z = 1\cdot23.$$

This gives a minimum at

$$r_{AB} = 1\cdot06 \text{ Å}$$

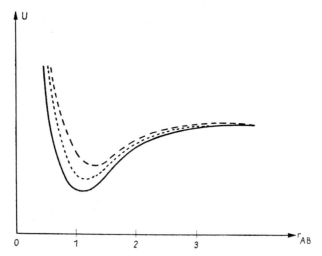

FIG. 4. The energy U as a function of r_{AB}. The unbroken line refers to Burrau's calculation. The broken and dotted lines correspond to the L.C.A.O. method without and with variation of Z.

corresponding to

$$D_e = 2 \cdot 25 \text{ eV}.$$

Figure 4 shows how the function behaves in this case. In order to increase, slightly more, the density between the nuclei which is still too small, we add to the preceding functions the functions $2p_z$ which have positive regions between the nuclei and negative regions outside the molecule (z being the axis of the nuclei).

We shall therefore put:

$$\phi = \varphi = N(1s_A + \lambda 2p_{zA} + 1s_B - \lambda 2p_{zB})$$

where the z-axis is directed from A to B.

Explicitly we have

$$\varphi = N\left(e^{\frac{-Zr_A}{a_0}} + \lambda r_A \cos\theta_A\, e^{\frac{-Z'r_A}{a_0}} + e^{\frac{-Zr_B}{a_0}} - \lambda r_B \cos\theta_B\, e^{\frac{-Z'r_B}{a_0}}\right)$$

Z, Z' and λ being parameters.

Minimising the energy[6] gives

$$Z = 1 \cdot 247 \qquad Z' = 1 \cdot 868$$
$$\lambda = 0 \cdot 145 \qquad r_{AB} = 1 \cdot 06$$

D_e is then $2 \cdot 73$ eV.

These are very close to Burrau's results.

Another way to increase the density between the nuclei consists of displacing the centre of the exponentials e^{-zr/a_0} a distance x from the nuclei[7].

Figure 5 gives an idea of the variation of density along the nuclei. Minimisation of energy gives

$$x = 0.061 \text{ Å}; \quad Z = 1.23; \quad r_{AB} = 1.05 \text{ Å}$$

corresponding to $D_e = 2.66$ eV.

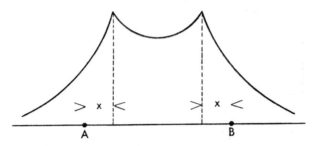

Fig. 5. Electron density along the line of nuclei (Hurley's calculation).

Finally, some authors[9] have sought to replace the hydrogen-type orbitals by the Gaussian functions

$$x^l y^m z^n e^{-ar^2}$$

which lead to easily calculated integrals. Unfortunately, if two Gaussian functions centred on A and B are introduced, an almost zero energy is obtained. It is necessary to introduce a combination of a large number of Gaussian functions to represent the bond, thus replacing a problem in analysis by one in algebra.

3. METHOD OF THE UNITED ATOMS

The method of combinations of atomic orbitals consists essentially of finding the form the wave function would have had if the nuclei had been an infinite distance apart.

Conversely, if the two nuclei were considered coincident at the centre M of the bond, we should then have

$$\phi = k \, e^{-\frac{2r}{a_0} M}.$$

The use of this idea is the basis of the method of the united atom. The above function gives rather poor results[10]. Some improvement is made by replacing the factor 2 in the exponential by Z which is determined by variation. This method is only really interesting for the study of excited states.

4. NOTATION FOR STATES OF HOMONUCLEAR MOLECULES: IN PARTICULAR H_2^+

We have already discussed the notation of states of atoms (first book, p. 15). The notation of states of molecules is derived in a similar manner as a function of quantities measurable at the same time as the energy.

It is useful to recall that the necessary and sufficient condition for two operators A and B to commute is that they have a complete set of eigenfunctions in common[11].

Hence, when the energy is not degenerate, an eigenfunction of the Hamiltonian is also an eigenfunction of all the operators commuting with it. All the corresponding quantities will be measurable simultaneously with the energy.

In the case of degenerate levels, we can always find an eigenfunction of the Hamiltonian which is an eigenfunction of an operator which commutes with it; however, this eigenfunction is not necessarily an eigenfunction of another operator which commutes with the Hamiltonian. Therefore, at least one quantity is measurable at the same time as the energy.

In the case of homonuclear diatomic molecules (i.e. formed by two identical nuclei), $\mathfrak{L}^2$ does not commute with the Hamiltonian whilst $\mathfrak{L}_z$ does.

The wave functions can be chosen so that

$$\mathfrak{L}_z = M\hbar.$$

We shall denote the state

$$\Sigma, \Pi, \Delta, \quad \text{etc.} \ldots$$

accordingly as

$$M = 0, \quad \pm 1, \quad \pm 2 \ldots$$

The multiplicity $2S + 1$ associated with spin will appear as a superscript to the left of the symbol, as in the case of atoms.

It is easy to show that any symmetry operator commutes with the Hamiltonian. In the case of a homonuclear diatomic molecule, one can consider an inversion i symmetrical about O, the centre of the line of nuclei, a reflection σ_v, about a plane passing through the line of nuclei Oz, and a reflection σ_d about a plane through O and perpendicular to Oz.

Let $\Re_i$, $\Re_{\sigma v}$, $\Re_\sigma$ be the corresponding operators. They commute with $\mathfrak{H}$. Let us demonstrate this is the case of σ_v for a one-electron system.

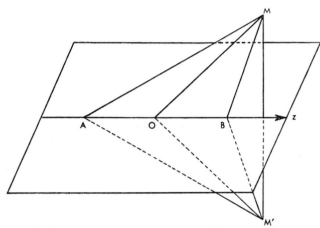

FIG. 6. Reflection σ_v.

Let M and M' be two symmetrical points in an operation σ_v (Fig. 6). By definition

$$\Re_{\sigma_v}\Psi(M) = \Psi(M').$$

Now

$$\mathfrak{H} = \mathfrak{T} + \mathfrak{F}_{AM} + \mathfrak{F}_{BM} + \mathfrak{F}_{AB}$$

where $\mathfrak{T}$ is the kinetic operator and $\mathfrak{F}$ the different parts of the potential operator.

Hence:

$$\mathfrak{H}\Re_{\sigma_v}\Psi(M) = \mathfrak{T}\Psi(M') + \mathfrak{F}_{AM}\Psi(M') + \mathfrak{F}_{BM}\Psi(M')$$
$$+ \mathfrak{F}_{AB}\Psi(M') \ldots \tag{1}$$

Now

$$\mathfrak{H}\Psi(M) = \mathfrak{T}\Psi(M) + \mathfrak{F}_{AM}\Psi(M) + \mathfrak{F}_{BM}\Psi(M) + \mathfrak{F}_{AB}\Psi(M),$$

therefore

$$\Re_{\sigma_v}\mathfrak{H}\Psi(M) = \mathfrak{T}\Psi(M') + \mathfrak{F}_{AM'}\Psi(M') + \mathfrak{F}_{BM'}\Psi(M')$$
$$+ \mathfrak{F}_{AB}\Psi(M')\ldots \tag{2}$$

But by symmetry

$$\mathfrak{F}_{AM'} = \mathfrak{F}_{AM} \qquad \mathfrak{F}_{BM'} = \mathfrak{F}_{BM}.$$

Obviously, the left-hand side of (1) equals the left-hand side of (2). Therefore:

$$\mathfrak{H}\Re_{\sigma_v} = \Re_{\sigma_v}\mathfrak{H}.$$

Note, moreover, that if $\Re$ is a symmetry operator

$$\Re^2\Psi(M) = \Re\Psi(M') = \Psi(M)\ldots \tag{3}$$

Suppose α is an eigenvalue of $\Re$; i.e. by definition

$$\Re\psi(M) = \alpha\psi(M)$$

and hence

$$\Re^2\psi(M) = \alpha^2\psi(M)\ldots \tag{4}$$

Comparing (3) and (4) gives

$$\alpha^2\psi(M) = \psi(M),$$

i.e. $\alpha = \pm 1$.

These are the eigenvalues of the symmetry operators. The table below shows the notations used to characterise the non-degenerate states of a homonuclear molecule (Σ states) against the eigenvalues of the symmetry operators.

Notation		i	σ_v	σ_d
Σ_g^+	or Σ_g	$+1$	$+1$	$+1$
Σ_g^-	or Σ_g^*	$+1$	-1	-1
Σ_u^+	or Σ_u^*	-1	$+1$	-1
Σ_u^-	or Σ_u	-1	-1	$+1$

There is a choice of two notations, the $+$ or $-$ indicating the sign of the eigenvalues of σ_v and the presence or absence of an asterisk indicating that of σ_d. In all cases g and u are used. They characterise the inversion i and are derived from "gerade" (even) and "ungerade" (odd).

For degenerate states, it can be seen that the wave function can be chosen to act as an eigenfunction of $\mathcal{L}_z$ and one of the symmetry operators. The inversion operator is usually chosen. The states are then denoted by $^{2s+1}\Pi_g$, $^{2s+1}\Pi_u$, $^{2s+1}\Delta_g$, $^{2s+1}\Phi_g$, $^{2s+1}\Phi_u$, ... without the other supplementary sign.

These symmetry considerations are very useful when one wishes to investigate the nature of approximate functions characterising a given state.

The function $1s_A + 1s_B$ which has been used above to characterise H_2^+ is symmetric with respect to i, σ_v and σ_d.

This function, independent of angle φ, obviously corresponds to the eigenvalue, $M = 0$, of the eigenfunction $e^{iM\varphi}$ of the operator $\mathcal{L}_z$. It therefore corresponds to a $^2\Sigma_g^+$ of the molecule H_2^+.

Hence, the fundamental state of H_2^+ is $^2\Sigma_g^+$. The table below gives the notation of states representable by L.C.A.O. functions.

The last column of the table gives two current notations of the molecular orbitals under consideration. The first is derived from the notation of the atomic orbitals in it. This is preceded by a symbol associated with the value of $\mathcal{L}_z$ and the symmetry. Small Greek letters are used to characterise an orbital, i.e. a function of one point (capitals are used for quantities which may depend on several electrons).

Orbital	Notation of state	Eigenvalues for				Notation of orbital	
		i	σ_v	σ_d	$\mathcal{L}_z$		
$1s_A + 1s_B$	$^2\Sigma_g^+$	$+1$	$+1$	$+1$	0	$\sigma_g\,1s$ or	$1s\sigma_g$
$1s_A - 1s_B$	$^2\Sigma_u^+$	-1	$+1$	-1	0	$\sigma_u^*\,1s$ or	$2p\sigma_u^*$
$2s_A + 2s_B$	$^2\Sigma_g^+$	$+1$	$+1$	$+1$	0	$\sigma_g\,2s$ or	$2s\sigma_g$
$2s_A - 2s_B$	$^2\Sigma_u^+$	-1	$+1$	-1	0	$\sigma_u^*\,2s$ or	$3p\sigma_u^*$

The second notation uses the same symbol, which is now preceded by another symbol indicating the state which would represent the orbital if the nuclei were considered coincident (method of the united atom); (further details will be found in Section 8).

CHAPTER II

Two-electron systems: Helium atom and hydrogen molecule, Interaction between electrons

5. FURTHER REMARKS ON THE HELIUM ATOM

We have seen (first book, Chapter 2) that the wave equation of the helium atom can be written

$$\mathfrak{H}\Psi = -\frac{h^2}{8\pi^2 m}[\Delta_1\Psi + \Delta_2\Psi] + \left[-\frac{2e^2}{r_1} - \frac{2e^2}{r_2} + \frac{e^2}{r_{12}}\right]\Psi$$

$$= W\Psi.$$

Using the method of atomic orbitals, the states of helium can be represented to a first approximation (first book, p. 41) by

$$\Phi = \psi_{n,l,m}(x_1, y_1, z_1)\, \psi_{n',l',m'}(x_2, y_2, z_2)$$

where ψ are hydrogen-type functions.

The method is called *the independent model* as it neglects the interaction between the electrons, i.e. considers them independent. This leads to a representation of the fundamental state as

$$\Phi = Ks(1)\, Ks(2) = \left(\frac{Z^3}{\pi a_0^3}\right) e^{-\frac{Zr_1}{a_0}}\, e^{-\frac{Zr_2}{a_0}}$$

with $Z = 2$ (first book, p. 58).

If the operator e^2/r_{12} is neglected, the corresponding energy is

$$\int \Phi\left(\mathfrak{H} - \frac{e^2}{r_{12}}\right)\Phi\, dv \quad \text{and equals } -108\cdot24 \text{ eV}.$$

Using the complete operator one finds

$$\int \Phi\mathfrak{H}\Phi\, dv = -74\cdot41 \text{ eV}.$$

Also, if Z is considered as a variable, a minimisation of the energy is given for $Z = 2 - (\frac{5}{16})$, the corresponding energy being -77.07 eV (first book, p. 58).

One can consider, therefore, that a start has been made to represent the effect of the term e^2/r_{12} in function form and the quantity 5/16 can be interpreted as *the screening effect* due to one of the electrons partially masking the nuclei for the other.

If we conserve only the general form of the function, e.g.

$$\Phi = \psi(1)\,\psi(2)$$

where ψ is an indeterminate function and then seek the best form of ψ, we are led to the *self-consistent field method*.

The form of this method in the general case has already been established. It would be easy to apply it in the particular case of the fundamental state of helium. It would, however, be interesting to solve this problem from first principles as this simple example demonstrates the method of calculation very clearly.

We know (first book, p. 10) that if

$$\mathfrak{H}\Psi = W\Psi$$

the functional

$$J = \int \Psi^*(\mathfrak{H}\Psi - W\Psi)\,dv$$

possesses a zero first variation.

A variation $\delta\Psi$ in Ψ produces a corresponding variation in J:

$$\Delta J = \int \delta\Psi^*[\mathfrak{H}\Psi - W\Psi]\,dv$$
$$+ \int \Psi^*[\mathfrak{H}\,\delta\Psi - W\,\delta\Psi]\,dv + \delta\Psi^*[\mathfrak{H}\,\delta\Psi - W\,\delta\Psi]\,dv.$$

The first variation is therefore

$$\delta J = \int \delta\Psi^*[\mathfrak{H}\Psi - W\Psi]\,dv + \int \Psi^*[\mathfrak{H}\,\delta\Psi - W\,\delta\Psi]\,dv$$

which can be written

$$\delta J = 2\mathrm{R} \int \delta\Psi^*[\mathfrak{H}\Psi - W\Psi]\,dv$$

since $\mathfrak{H}$ is a Hermitian operator and where R denotes "real part of".

We know that the fundamental state of helium is representable by a real function. We must therefore find a function Φ such that

$$\int \delta\Phi[\mathfrak{H}\Phi - W\Phi]\,dv = 0 \qquad (1)$$

and the method of the self-consistent field consists of reducing the variation of Φ to a value which preserves the form of a product of two orbitals. For the fundamental state, therefore,

$$\Phi + \delta\Phi = [\psi(1) + \delta\psi(1)] [\psi(2) + \delta\psi(2)].$$

Substituting in (1) and eliminating the second order terms in δ,

$$\int \psi(1)\, \delta\psi(2)\, [\mathfrak{H}\psi(1)\, \psi(2) - W\psi(1)\, \psi(2)]\, dv$$

$$+ \int \psi(2)\, \delta\psi(1)\, [\mathfrak{H}\psi(2)\, \psi(1) - W\psi(2)\, \psi(1)]\, dv = 0.$$

Since the two integrals are obviously equal, we have

$$\int \psi(1)\, \delta\psi(2)\, [\mathfrak{H}\psi(1)\, \psi(2) - W\psi(1)\, \psi(2)]\, dv = 0. \qquad (2)$$

The operator $\mathfrak{H}$ can be written

$$\mathfrak{H} = \mathfrak{H}^N(1) + \mathfrak{H}^N(2) + \frac{e^2}{r_{12}}$$

where

$$\mathfrak{H}^N(1) = -\frac{h^2}{8\pi^2 m}\, \Delta_1 - \frac{2e^2}{r_1},$$

$$\mathfrak{H}^N(2) = -\frac{h^2}{8\pi^2 m}\, \Delta_2 - \frac{2e^2}{r_2}.$$

Equation (2) leads to

$$\int \delta\psi(2)\, dv_2 \left\{ [\psi(1)\, \mathfrak{H}^N(1)\, \psi(1)\, dv_1]\, \psi(2) + \mathfrak{H}^N(2)\, \psi(2) \right.$$

$$\left. + \left[\int \psi^2(1)\, \frac{e^2}{r_{12}}\, dv_1\right] \psi(2) - W\psi(2) \right\} = 0.$$

Since $\delta\psi$ is arbitrary, the integrand must be zero:

$$\left[\mathfrak{H}^N(2) + \int \psi^2(1)\, \frac{e^2}{r_{12}}\, dv_1 \right] \psi(2) = (W - C)\, \psi(2) = E\psi(2), \qquad (3)$$

where

$$C = \int \psi(1)\, \mathfrak{H}^N(1)\, \psi(1)\, dv_1.$$

This is obviously the self-consistent field equation which ψ must obey for Φ to be an approximation to Ψ in the sense of this method.

The determination of $\psi^{(12)}$ leads to

$$W = -77 \cdot 80 \text{ eV},$$

but the function ψ does not have an analytic form. Various authors have proposed analytic expressions approximating to ψ. The most recent work on this subject has been that of Roothaan[13]. It consists of constructing the family of functions

$$F(r) = \sqrt{(\zeta^3/\pi)} \, [a_0 + a_1\zeta r + a_2(\zeta r)^2] \, e^{-\xi r}$$

and calculating the coefficients by variation. The energy then found is within three hundred-thousandths of Wilson's figure and the function obtained is very near that of the self-consistent field.

Approximately $0 \cdot 8$ eV remains to be found. One of the inconveniences of the above methods becomes apparent in the following reasoning.

If ψ has a maximum at the point M in space, the function

$$\Psi(M, M) = \psi(M) \, \psi(M)$$

becomes dominant in the neighbourhood of the point. There will therefore be some important configurations where two electrons coincide which is physically inadmissible because of the coulomb repulsion between them. This inconvenience can be removed by choosing a function of the form

$$F(r_1) \, F'(r_2) + F(r_2) \, F'(r_1),$$

e.g.[14]

$$N \left[e^{-\frac{Z'r_1}{a_0}} \, e^{-\frac{Z''r_2}{a_0}} + e^{-\frac{Z'r_2}{a_0}} \, e^{-\frac{Z''r_1}{a_0}} \right].$$

Minimisation yields an energy of

$$-77 \cdot 86 \text{ eV} \quad \text{for} \quad Z' = 2 \cdot 15 \quad \text{and} \quad Z'' = 1 \cdot 19.$$

It is more efficient to use a function of the type

$$F(r_1) \, F(r_2) f(r_{12})$$

(designated by the name *correlated atomic orbitals*) in which $f(r_{12})$ is an increasing function of r_{12} such that the importance of configurations where r_{12} is zero is relatively decreased[15].

Roothaan has used the functions

$$F = [a_0 + a_1\zeta r + a_2(\zeta r)^2]\, e^{-\zeta r}$$
$$f = 1 - [b_0 + b_1(\zeta r_{12}) + b_2(\zeta r_{12})^2]\, e^{-\eta \zeta r_{12}}$$

and obtained by variation: $W = 78 \cdot 59$ eV (only $0 \cdot 01$ eV from the experimental value).

It will be recalled that Hylleraas constructed excellent wave functions by this explicit introduction of the variable r_{12} (first book, p. 36).

Also, we must not forget the method of configuration interaction which we have applied in the case of the helium atom on various occasions (first book, pp. 45, 48, 57, 72).

The following table is a résumé of the results obtained for the energy of the fundamental states of helium.

Method used	Energy in eV
Wave function and operator of the independent model	$-108 \cdot 24$
Wave functions of the independent model, complete operator	$-74 \cdot 4$
Interaction of configurations on two terms	$-76 \cdot 998$
Variation of Z	$-77 \cdot 07$
Analytic self-consistent field (Roothaan)	$-77 \cdot 8$
Self-consistent field (Hartree)	$-77 \cdot 8$
Function $e^{-\frac{Z'r_1}{a_0}}\, e^{-\frac{Z''r_2}{a_0}} + e^{-\frac{Z'r_2}{a_0}}\, e^{-\frac{Z''r_1}{a_0}}$	$-77 \cdot 86$
f_1 (Hylleraas)	$-78 \cdot 59$
Pluvinage's method (see first book)	$78 \cdot 5$
f_2	$78 \cdot 55$
f_3 (or its extension by configuration interaction)	$78 \cdot 59$
Correlated orbitals	$78 \cdot 59$
f_4	$78 \cdot 60$
Experimental	$78 \cdot 60$

6. FURTHER REMARKS ON THE HYDROGEN MOLECULE

We will now return to the hydrogen molecule as it is the simplest case of a molecule with interaction between electrons. We shall use our knowledge of the helium atom to introduce electron interaction, and of the hydrogen ion molecule for the effect of two nuclei.

The independent model method, which we have previously discussed in the case of helium, leads to the representation of the fundamental state of the molecule of hydrogen:

$$\phi = \varphi(1)\, \varphi(2)$$

(see also first book, pp. 151 and 163).

In this formula the φ are called the molecular orbitals and we can treat them as in the case of the hydrogen molecule ion. For example, a linear combination of atomic orbitals can be used for φ:

$$\varphi = N(1s_A + 1s_B).$$

The energy, calculated with the complete operator, is a minimum for

$$r_{AB} = 0.850 \text{ Å}$$

(the experimental value of the interatomic distance is 0·74 Å), corresponding to a dissociation energy:

$$D_e = 2.681 \text{ eV}^{(16)} \quad \text{(experimental value 4·72 eV)}.$$

The space wave function ϕ can be written (first book, p. 164)

$$\phi = s^+\{1s_A(1)\, 1s_B(2) + 1s_A(2)\, 1s_B(1) + 1s_A(1)\, 1s_A(2)$$
$$+ 1s_B(1)\, 1s_B(2)\}.$$

As r_{AB} tends to infinity, products of the form

$$1s_A(M)\, 1s_B(M)$$

tends to zero.

The normalising coefficient becomes

$$s^+ = \tfrac{1}{4}$$

and the energy, for example, can be written

$$U = \int \phi \mathfrak{H} \phi \, dv = \tfrac{1}{2} \int 1s_A(1)\, 1s_B(2)\, \mathfrak{H}\, 1s_A(1)\, 1s_B(2)\, dv_1 \, dv_2$$
$$+ \tfrac{1}{2} \int 1s_A(1)\, 1s_A(2)\, \mathfrak{H}\, 1s_A(1)\, 1s_A(2)\, dv_1 \, dv_2.$$

The energy, therefore, can be represented as the arithmetic mean of the energies of two hydrogen atoms and that of ions H^- and H^+.

With the ground state, dissociation takes place between atoms and not ions. Now electrochemical data show that

$$H^- + H^+ \rightarrow 2H + 12\cdot8 \text{ eV}.$$

As r_{AB} tend to infinity, the curve of U (Fig. 7) as calculated from the above ϕ increases more rapidly than the actual curve. Therefore, the function ϕ gives a very bad representation of the molecule H_2 for large values of r_{AB}.

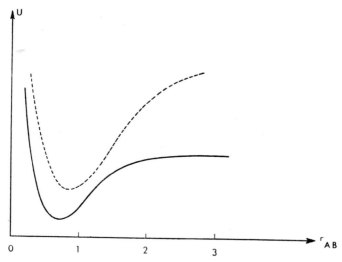

FIG. 7. Variation of U with r_{AB} for the hydrogen molecule. The results of James and Coolidge's calculation are given by the unbroken line and the L.C.A.O. approximation by the dotted line.

If Z is allowed to vary, the energy D_e increases to $3\cdot47$ eV and r_{AB} decreases to $0\cdot73$ Å (first book, p. 164). The value of Z corresponding to minimum energy U is $1\cdot193$. It is important to note that the value of Z which minimises the energy depends on r_{AB}. Thus, we must not use the value $1\cdot193$ for all r_{AB} in calculating the energy. Otherwise, we obtain curve b of Fig. 8 which is much sharper than the correct curve a, as for every value of r_{AB} the value of U obtained by varying Z is less than that obtained using a fixed Z. This observation assumes importance when one wishes to evaluate a force constant.

ESM 2

Coulson[16] has utilised various forms of φ which resembles those proposed by James in the case of the molecule ion. The following table gives the value of D_e obtained for different choices of φ.

Form of φ	D_e in eV
$e^{-\frac{Z(r_A+r_B)}{a_0}}(1 + a\eta^2)$	3·096
$e^{-\frac{Z(r_A+r_B)}{a_0}}(1 + a\eta^2 + b\xi)$	3·53
$e^{-\frac{Z(r_A+r_B)}{a_0}}(1 + a\eta^2 + b\xi + c\xi^2)$	3·54
$e^{-\frac{Z(r_A+r_B)}{a_0}}(1 + a\eta^2 + b\xi + c\xi^2 + d\xi\eta^2)$	3·603

Coulson[16] has estimated that if the φ are calculated by the self-consistent field method, the energy D_e is increased to 3·63 eV. We have already noted that a configuration interaction carried out over two terms starting from orbitals $1s_A$ and $1s_B$ gives Weinbaum's function.

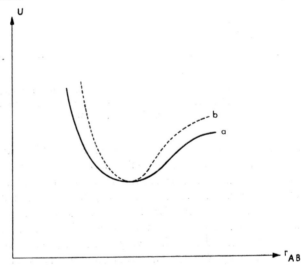

FIG. 8. The energy U as a function of r_{AB} in the L.C.A.O. approximation with: (a) Z allowed to vary for each r_{AB}; (b) Z fixed at 1·193 for all r_{AB}.

Eleven terms constructed on the atomic orbitals $1s$, $2s$ and $2p$ have been used recently. By allowing Z to vary, the energy D_e is increased to 4·30 eV [17] (approximately 0·4 eV from the experimental value).

In analogy with the helium atom, a second method of studying the hydrogen molecule consists of using functions of the form

$$F(r_1) \, F'(r_2) + F'(r_1) \, F(r_2).$$

The use of

$$F = 1s_A \quad \text{and} \quad F' = 1s_B$$

reduces to the function of Heitler and London (first book, p. 133). The introduction of an indeterminate factor Z in the atomic orbitals gives Wang's function (first book, p. 134).

Rosen [18] introduced into this procedure *polarised atomic orbitals* by a function $2p$ as has already been done in the case of the molecule ion. Thus:

$$F = e^{-\frac{Zr_A}{a_0}} \, (1 + \lambda r_A \cos \theta_A),$$

$$F' = e^{-\frac{Zr_B}{a_0}} \, (1 - \lambda r_B \cos \theta_B).$$

If Z is given the value 1, D_e becomes 3·34 eV. By varying Z, D_e decreases to 4·2 eV. Gurnee and Magee [19] have used orbitals centred a distance X from the nuclei, as in the case of the molecule ion (Chapter I, Section 2). Minimisation is given for $X = 0.07a_0$, $Z = 1.17$. This gives $D_e = 4.16$ eV, i.e. a good value of the bonding energy.

To these last two methods which aim, as in the H_2^+ case, at increasing the electron density between the two nuclei, can be added three others with the same effect but which bring in different procedures.

Inui's [20] method consists of setting

$$F = e^{-Zr_A} e^{-Z'r_B},$$

$$F' = e^{-Zr_B} e^{-Z'r_A}.$$

This choice leads to $D_e = 4.04$ eV. Coulson and Fischer [21] utilised *semi-localised orbitals*, i.e. consisting of a principal part centred on one of the nuclei and a complementary part centred on the other.

$$F = 1s_A + \lambda \, 1s_B,$$

$$F' = 1s_B + \lambda \, 1s_A.$$

This reduces to Weinbaum's function.

This result, however, can be improved by combining this method with that of Inui, i.e. one sets

$$F = e^{-Z r_A} e^{-Z' r_B} + \lambda e^{-Z r_B} e^{-Z' r_A},$$

$$F' = e^{-Z r_B} e^{-Z' r_A} + \lambda e^{-Z r_A} e^{-Z' r_B}.$$

and obtains[22]

$$D_e = 4 \cdot 20 \text{ eV}.$$

We will mention two more methods of improving Weinbaum's function. Lennard-Jones and Pople[23] have set

$$\phi = 1s_A(1) \, 1s_B(2) \, [1 + \alpha Z^2 r_{A1} r_{B2} \sin \theta_{A1} \sin \theta_{B2} \cos(\varphi_1 - \varphi_2)]$$

$$+ \, 1s_A(2) \, 1s_B(1) \, [1 + \alpha Z^2 r_{A2} r_{B1} \sin \theta_{A2} \sin \theta_{B1} \cos(\varphi_2 - \varphi_1)]$$

$$+ \, \gamma[1s_A(1) \, 1s_A(2) + 1s_B(1) \, 1s_B(2)]$$

and obtained $D_e = 4 \cdot 16$ eV.

Hirschfelder and Linnett[24] with the function

$$\phi = 1s_A(1) \, 1s_B(2) \, [1 + \alpha Z^2(x_{A1} x_{B2} + y_{A1} y_{B2}) + \beta Z^2 z_{A1} z_{B2}]$$

$$+ \, 1s_A(2) \, 1s_B(1) \, [1 + \alpha Z^2(x_{A2} x_{B1} + y_{A2} y_{B1}) + \beta Z^2 z_{A2} z_{B1}$$

$$+ \, \gamma[1s_A(1) \, 1s_A(2) + 1s_B(1) \, 1s_B(2)]$$

found $D_e = 4 \cdot 25$ eV.

Just as in the case of the helium atom, and for the same reasons, a third way of constructing the wave function is to use correlated orbitals.

Frost and Braunstein[25], for example, chose

$$\phi = [1s_A(1) + 1s_B(1)] \, [1s_A(2) + 1s_B(2)] \, [1 + a r_{12}]$$

the $1s$ orbitals containing the parameter Z. They obtained $D_e = 4 \cdot 11$ eV.

Also, we must not forget the excellent functions of James and Coolidge who introduced the correlations in a complicated manner and which leads to a dissociation energy coincident with the experimental value.

The table opposite summarises the results obtained.

Methods using $F(r_1)F(r_2)$	Methods using $F(r_1)F'(r_2) + F(r_2)F'(r_1)$	Method using r_{12}	Value of D_e
L.C.A.O. orbitals, $Z = 1$			
Coulson's 1st function			2·681
	Heitler and London's function, $Z = 1$		3·096
	Rosen's function, $Z = 1$		3·14
			3·34
L.C.A.O. orbitals, Z varied			
Coulson's 2nd function			3·47
Coulson's 3rd function			3·53
Coulson's 4th function			3·54
			3·60
	Heitler and London's function, Z varied		3·76
Weinbaum's function	Weinbaum's function		4·0
	Rosen's function, Z varied		4·02
	Inui's function		4·04
		Frost's function	4·11
	Gurnee and Magee's function		4·16
	Lennard-Jones and Pople's function		4·16
	Mueller and Eyring's function		4·20
	Hirschfelder and Linnett's function		4·25
Aghajanian's function			4·30
		James and Coolidge's function	
		to 5 terms	4·53
		to 13 terms	4·70
		Experiment	4·72

CHAPTER III

Diatomic Molecules

7. Some General Observations

It can be stated that the principal methods of studying molecules consist of constructing wave functions in starting from what they are when the distance between the nuclei is either infinity or zero. In either case, the molecule function is often built up from the atomic orbitals of the atoms which arise at the separation, or fusion, of the nuclei.

In principle, therefore, all the types of atomic orbitals which have been mentioned can be introduced into the molecular function.

The simplest are those of Slater (first book, p. 62). They present, however, a serious disadvantage in not being orthogonal. It is possible to orthogonalise Slater's functions.

For example, let us form an orbital $2s^*$ orthogonal to Slater's $1s$ orbital. Let $2s$ be Slater's usual orbital. We shall put

$$2s^* = a1s + b2s$$

and calculate a and b so that

$$\int 1s2s^* \, dv = 0.$$

Let
$$S = \int 1s2s \, dv$$

then

$$a = -\frac{S}{\sqrt{(1 - S^2)}} \quad \text{and} \quad b = \frac{1}{\sqrt{(1 - S^2)}}.$$

Instead of using the value of Z_{eff} given by Slater's rules, we can find the value of Z_{eff} which minimises the energy of the atom. The orbitals of Morse, Young and Haurwitz mentioned in the previous book (p. 60) are obtained by a similar procedure.

The hydrogen-like orbitals are often used, with Z_{eff} calculated by Slater's rules or by minimisation. Finally, the self-consistent field's functions can also be introduced either in numerical form or by an analytic approach.

One might wonder whether it is reasonable to form a molecular orbital by choosing atomic orbitals characterised by the value of the effective atomic numbers which fit the atoms. A more natural way consists of allowing the Z_{eff} to vary, forming the nuclear orbital, and finding the values of the Z_{eff} which minimise the energy of the molecule.

If we use this method, or analogous methods, we find that in some cases the Z_{eff} are near these obtained for atoms [26] while in others they are very different [27].

Fishers-Hjalma [28] has shown that in certain cases the values of Z_{eff} which fit a molecular orbit vary with the orbital in the same molecule. This is so in the case of the ion H_2^-, where in order to describe the ground state using the two orbitals

$$1s_A + 1s_B$$
and
$$1s_A - 1s_B$$

one must choose $Z = 1{\cdot}02$ for the first and $Z = 0{\cdot}37$ for the second.

Among the methods of calculating molecular wave functions, we shall make particular use, in the case of diatomic molecules, of the self-consistent field method (L.C.A.O. approximation) and the configuration interaction method.

Whichever method of calculation is chosen, it can be used with or without empirical data. Moffitt [29] has proposed a scheme which consists of introducing empirical data associated with the atoms into which the molecule dissociates. Bingel, on the other hand, uses data derived from the atoms produced by the fusion of the nuclei [30]. Preuss [31] has proposed a combination of the two methods, Moffitt's having greater prominence where the nuclei are far apart.

8. Symmetry Orbitals. Correlation Diagrams

Consider a diatomic molecule. With the independent model, the molecular orbitals describe the movement of an electron in the field of two nuclei. They are, therefore, like wave functions. In non-degenerate cases, therefore, they should be the eigenfunctions of operators which commute with the Hamiltonian describing the movement of an electron in the independent model; in particular, with the symmetry operators. This is why it is generally interesting to study the eigenfunction orbitals of the symmetry operators associated with the molecule. They are called *symmetry orbitals*.

With homonuclear molecules, the symmetry operators are the same as those which arose in the study of the molecule H_2^+ (Section 4). Hence, the symmetry orbitals are of the same type. The following table gives the list and the two notations of the L.C.A.O. approximations of each of them.

$$1s_A + 1s_B \qquad \sigma_g 1s \qquad 1s\sigma_g$$

$$1s_A - 1s_B \qquad \sigma_u^* 1s \qquad 2p\sigma_u^*$$

$$2s_A + 2s_B \qquad \sigma_g 2s \qquad 2s\sigma_g$$

$$2s_A - 2s_B \qquad \sigma_u^* 2s \qquad 3p\sigma_u^*$$

$$\left. \begin{array}{c} 2p_{+1A} + 2p_{+1B} \\ \text{or} \\ 2p_{-1A} + 2p_{-1B} \end{array} \right\} \qquad \pi_u 2p \qquad 2p\pi_u$$

$$2p_{zA} - 2p_{zB} \qquad \sigma_g 2p \qquad 3s\sigma_g$$

$$\left. \begin{array}{c} 2p_{+1A} - 2p_{+1B} \\ \text{or} \\ 2p_{-1A} - 2p_{-1B} \end{array} \right\} \qquad \pi_g^* 2p$$

$$2p_{zA} + 2p_{zB} \qquad \sigma_u^* 2p$$

One can get an idea of the energies associated with the orbitals by following their change as the interatomic distance tends from infinity towards zero.

It is natural to think that the orbital $1s_A + 1s_B$ tends towards the orbital $1s$ of the united atom, its symmetry becoming spherical.

The orbital $1s_A - 1s_B$ is antisymmetric with respect to the operator σ_d like a p state. It is reasonable to think that this function tends to the $2p$ state of the single atom (hence the notation $2p\sigma_u^*$).

Proceeding thus, we end up with the notation given in the preceding table, and adding some empirical data, the correlation diagram (Fig.9), which shows the variation of the energies associated with the orbitals against the interatomic distance.

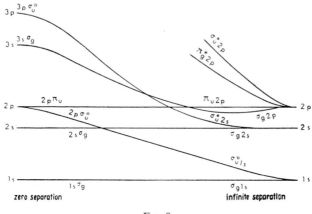

FIG. 9

A very simple first representation of homonuclear diatomic molecules can be obtained by using the first symmetry orbitals as molecular orbitals.

Table 8.1 shows the resulting "filling in" of usable orbitals to represent each ground state. This table also contains various data characteristic of each state.

Note that when an orbital is antisymmetric with respect to the operator σ_d, the plane passing through the centre of the molecule and perpendicular to the line of nuclei is a nodal surface of the function. This orbital, therefore, introduces a feeble electron density "between the nuclei". It is called antibonding. Its notation then contains an asterisk. Otherwise the orbital is said to be bonding.

Herzberg[32] has pointed out that the chemical notation of a molecule can be obtained by subtracting the number of antibonding orbitals from the number of bonding ones, an orbital being counted twice if it is used twice.

The number obtained is called *the number of non-compensated bonding electrons*. We then obtain the chemical formulas of the table, where a dash represents two binding electrons.

We are now in a position to understand the instability of the

TABLE 8.1

Orbital notation	He$_2$	He$_2^+$	Li$_2$	Be$_2$	B$_2$	C$_2$	N$_2$	N$_2^+$	O$_2$	O$_2^+$	F$_2$	Ne$_2$
$\sigma_u^* 2p$										—		××
$\pi_g^* 2p$									× ×	×	×× ××	×× ××
$\sigma_g 2p$							××	×	××	××	××	××
$\pi_u 2p$					× ×	×× ××	×× ××	×× ××	×× ××	×× ××	×× ××	×× ××
$\sigma 2s$				××	××	××	××	××	××	××	××	××
$\sigma_g 2s$			××	××	××	××	××	××	××	××	××	××
$\sigma_u^* 1s$	××	×	××	××	××	××	××	××	××	××	××	××
$\sigma_g 1s$	××	××	××	××	××	××	××	××	××	××	××	××
n	0	1	2	0	2	4	6	5	4	5	2	0
Chemical formula	He He	[He He]$^+$	Li—Li	Be Be	B—B	C=C	N≡N	[N≡N]$^+$	O=O	[O=O]$^+$	F—F	Ne Ne
Dissociation energy (in eV)	0	3·1	1·03	0	3	5·9	9·75	8·73	5·08	6·48	1·6	0
Force constant (in 10^5 dynes cm^{-1})	0	3·13	0·25	0	3·60	9·55	23·1	20·1	11·8	16·6	4·45	0
Interatomic distance (in Å)	∞	1·08	2·67		1·59	1·31	1·09	1·12	1·21	1·12	1·44	∞
Notation of ground state	$^1\Sigma_g^+$	$^2\Sigma_u^+$	$^1\Sigma_g^+$	$^1\Sigma_g^+$	$^3\Sigma_g^-$	$^3\Pi_u$	$^1\Sigma_g^+$	$^2\Sigma_g^+$	$^3\Sigma_g^-$	$^2\Pi_g$	$^1\Sigma_g^+$	$^1\Sigma_g^+$

system He_2 and the stability of the He_2^+ ion; the existence of the molecule Li_2; the non-existence of Be_2; why N_2^+ is less stable than N_2 and why O_2^+ is more stable than O_2. By an extension of Hund's rules for molecules, B_2 and O_2 possess triplet ground states and so behave like biradicals.

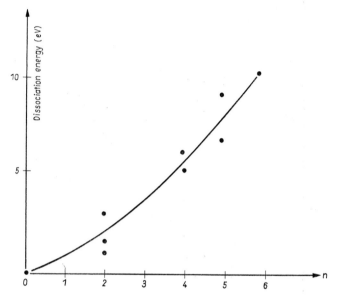

FIG. 10. Relationship between dissociation energy and the number, n, of non-compensated bond electrons.

Figures 10, 11 and 12 show how the dissociation energy, the force constant, and the interatomic distance, respectively, varies with the number of bonding electrons for the ground state of the molecules under study.

As expected, the dissociation energy and the force constant are increasing functions, and the interatomic distance is a decreasing function.

Linnett[33] has extended this method. He has shown that very exact relationships can be found between the number and nature of the non-compensated bonding electrons and the force constants, the interatomic distances, the bonding energies for a molecule, its ions and its excited states. The relationships remain the same from one molecule to another, requiring only a change in scale.

Up to now we have utilised symmetry orbitals qualitatively. Symmetry orbitals can also be used in quantitative calculations.

A product or a determinant constructed of these orbitals obviously gives a solution of the independent model equation. In the case

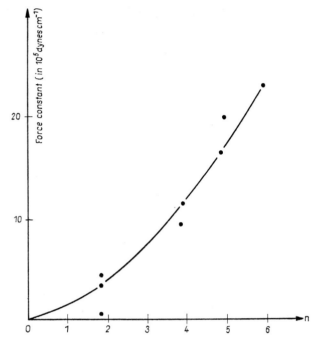

FIG. 11. Relationship between the force constant and the number, n, of non-compensated bond electrons.

of the molecule Li_2, for example, one is led to represent the ground state with the aid of the function

$$\phi = \det \sigma_g 1s(1)\, \alpha(1)\, \sigma_g 1s(2)\, \beta(2)\, \sigma_u^* 1s(3)\, \alpha(3)\, \sigma_u^* \times$$

$$\times\; 1s(4)\, \beta(4)\, \sigma_g\, 2s(5)\, \alpha(5)\, \sigma_g\, 2s(6)\, \beta(6).$$

Note that the overlap integral between the $1s$ orbitals of the two lithium atoms is very small, as only the domains associated with "L-shells" overlap appreciably in a molecule like Li_2. The normalised molecular orbitals $\sigma_g 1s$ and $\sigma_u 1s$ can be approximated:

$$\sigma_g 1s = \frac{1}{\sqrt{2}} (1s_A + 1s_B),$$

$$\sigma_u^* 1s = \frac{1}{\sqrt{2}} (1s_A - 1s_B).$$

As has been said before (first book, p. 80) the symmetry orbitals φ_i can be replaced, without changing ϕ, by linear combinations of the form,

$$\chi_l = \sum_m T_{lm} \varphi_e,$$

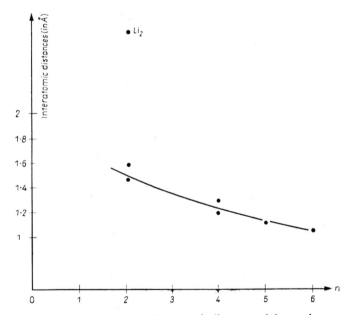

FIG. 12. Relationship between the interatomic distance and the number, n, of non-compensated bond electrons.

where

$$\sum_m T_{lm}^2 = 1,$$

$$\sum_m T_{km} T_{lm} = 0.$$

Let us choose

$$
T =
\begin{Vmatrix}
\dfrac{1}{\sqrt{2}} & 0 & \dfrac{1}{\sqrt{2}} & 0 & 0 & 0 \\[2ex]
\dfrac{1}{\sqrt{2}} & 0 & -\dfrac{1}{\sqrt{2}} & 0 & 0 & 0 \\[2ex]
0 & \dfrac{1}{\sqrt{2}} & 0 & \dfrac{1}{\sqrt{2}} & 0 & 0 \\[2ex]
0 & \dfrac{1}{\sqrt{2}} & 0 & -\dfrac{1}{\sqrt{2}} & 0 & 0 \\[2ex]
0 & 0 & 0 & 0 & 1 & 0 \\[2ex]
0 & 0 & 0 & 0 & 0 & 1
\end{Vmatrix}
$$

This give

$$
\chi_1 = 1s_A \alpha
$$
$$
\chi_2 = 1s_B \alpha
$$
$$
\chi_3 = 1s_A \beta
$$
$$
\chi_4 = 1s_B \beta
$$
$$
\chi_5 = N(2s_A + 2s_B)\alpha = L\alpha
$$
$$
\chi_6 = N(2s_A + 2s_B)\beta = L\beta,
$$

and hence:

$$
\phi = \det 1s_A(1)\,\alpha(1)\ 1s_A(2)\,\beta(2)\ 1s_B(3)\,\alpha(3)\ 1s_B(4)\,\beta(4) \times
$$
$$
\times\ L(5)\,\alpha(5)\ L(6)\,\beta(6).
$$

The orbitals $1s_A$ and $1s_B$ are thus "invariants" in the determinant. Taking the point of view previously discussed, (first book Chapter 8), these functions are given the name *core orbitals*. On the other hand, the orbit L is then called a *bonding orbital*. The concept of symmetry orbitals can be generalised to include the case of heteroatomic molecules. Similarly, correlation diagrams can be constructed [34].

Cores can also be introduced here. In the case of the molecule NO, for example, $1s_N$ and $1s_O$ can be used as core orbitals; a binding orbital of the form

$$
a2s_N + b2s_O
$$

cannot have its coefficients a and b fixed by symmetry. They can be fixed by variation. In the case of a hydride, e.g. LiH, the orbital $1s_H$ cannot be considered as a core orbital as it participates directly in the bond, and its correlation with $2s_{Li}$ is important. Only $1s_{Li}$ takes the role of a core. One may set

$$\phi = \det 1s_{Li}(1)\,\alpha(1)\,1s_{Li}(2)\,\beta(2)\,[a2s_{Li} + b1s_H]\,(3)\,\alpha(3)\,\times$$

$$\times\,[a2s_{Li} + b1s_H]\,(4)\,\beta(4),$$

where a and b can be considered as variational parameters.

9. The Method of the Self-consistent Field and of Configuration Interactions in the L.C.A.O. Approximation

A self-consistent field method can be developed, based on the use of symmetry orbitals of L.C.A.O. This method has been studied by Roothaan[35].

We shall analyse the very simple case of a function product representing a diatomic molecule with two electrons:

$$\phi = \varphi_1(1)\,\varphi_2(2).$$

The self-consistent field equations have already been derived in this case, but we shall now introduce an extra restriction such that the orbitals φ must be combinations of certain of the atomic orbitals associated with the atoms of the molecule; we then have

$$\varphi_1 = \sum_i c_{1i}\psi_i \qquad \varphi_2 = \sum_j c_{2j}\psi_j.$$

The equation of p. 13 can be written, using the appropriate notation:

$$\int \delta\varphi_1(1)\,dv_1 \left\{ \left[\int \varphi_2(2)\,\mathfrak{H}^N(2)\,\varphi_2(2)\,dv_2 \right] \varphi_1(1) + \mathfrak{H}^N(1)\,\varphi_1(1) \right.$$

$$\left. + \left[\int \varphi_2^2(2)\,\frac{e^2}{r_{12}}\,dv_2 \right] \varphi_1(1) - U\varphi_1(1) \right\} = 0.$$

Letting

$$E_1 = U - \int \varphi_2(2)\,\mathfrak{H}^N(2)\,\varphi_2(2)\,dv_2$$

we have

$$\int \delta\varphi_1(1)\,dv_1 \left\{\mathfrak{H}^N(1)\varphi_1(1) + \left[\int \varphi_2^2(2)\,\frac{e^2}{r_{12}}\,dv_2\right]\varphi_1(1) - E_1\varphi_1(1)\right\}$$
$$= 0.$$

In order to give φ the L.C.A.O. form, we impose a limitation on $\delta\varphi$; we cannot then set the bracket to zero. To continue the calculation, we set, for example:

$$\delta\varphi_1 = \delta c_{1p}\psi_p.$$

This gives, by expanding the φ and assuming that δc_{1p} is constant:

$$\delta c_{1p}\int \psi_p(1)\,dv_1 \left\{\sum_i c_{1i}\mathfrak{H}^N(1)\,\psi_i(1)\right.$$
$$\left. + \sum_i c_{1i}\psi_i(1)\left[\sum_j \sum_{j'} c_{2j}c_{2j'}\int \psi_j(2)\,\psi_{j'}(2)\,\frac{e^2}{r_{12}}\,dv_2 - E_1\right]\right\} = 0.$$

Letting

$$S_{pi} = \int \psi_p(1)\,\psi_i(1)\,dv_1$$

$$(pi/jj') = \int \psi_p(1)\,\psi_i(1)\,\frac{e^2}{r_{12}}\,\psi_j(2)\,\psi_{j'}(2)\,dv_1\,dv_2$$

we finally obtain

$$\sum_i c_{1i}\left[\int \psi_p(1)\,\mathfrak{H}^N(1)\,\psi_i(1)\,dv_1 + \sum_j\sum_{j'} c_{2j}c_{2j'}(pi/jj') - E_1S_{pi}\right] = 0$$

for each value of p.

The sum of the first two terms in the bracket is denoted by $\mathscr{H}^1_{pi}$
The equations become:

$$\sum_i c_{1i}[\mathscr{H}^1_{pi} - E_1S_{pi}] = 0.$$

Similarly:

$$\sum_j c_{2j}[\mathscr{H}^2_{qj} - E_2S_{qj}] = 0.$$

An iterative solution of the two sets of simultaneous equations gives the value of the coefficients.

In the case of a determinant containing the orbitals

$$\varphi_k = \sum_j c_{kj}\psi_j$$

used twice (complete shells), we arrive at the equations

$$\sum_i c_{ki}[\mathcal{H}_{pi} - ES_{pi}] = 0$$

with:

$$\mathcal{H}_{pi} = \sum_{\kappa} \int \psi_p(k)\, \mathfrak{H}^N(k)\, \psi_i(k)\, dv_k$$

$$+ \sum_k \sum_j \sum_{j'} c_{kj}c_{kj'} \{2(pi/jj') - (pj/ij')\}.$$

These are called Roothaan's equations.

In the case of incomplete shells (free radicals, excited states) the equations become rather difficult. Approximate methods have been proposed [36], but one can also, without extra approximations, replace these equations by the self-consistence conditions established by Lefebvre [37] which are much easier to handle. MacWeeny has proposed another view [38].

The choice of atomic orbitals to introduce into the molecular orbitals is, in principle, arbitrary, but it is natural to use the first symmetry orbitals. Details of this subject will be given later.

The symmetry orbitals can, of course, serve as a basis for the method of configuration interactions. As this has been the object of a detailed study in the L.C.A.O. (first book, p. 165) we shall not return to it.

10. Expression of Some Molecular Quantities in the L.C.A.O. Approximations

The expression of energy measurements does not pose new problems. We have seen how to obtain the total electronic energy associated with a state of a molecule. Changes in the electronic energy are know to be principally responsible for the energy transitions which give the ultraviolet and visible spectra of molecules.

The study of infrared and Hertzian spectra bring in other energy considerations, which we shall not try to study in this book, where neither the movement of the nuclei, interactions between spins and orbital movements nor interactions between the spins and the electric moments of the nuclei, have been introduced.

Ionisation energies are obtained using the self-consistent field method, either by comparing the energy of the ion with that of the neutral molecule, or more simply, by means of the energies associated with the orbitals (first book, p. 156). In the method of configuration interactions, only the first procedure is applicable.

The dissociation energy is obtained using the function $U(r)$. In fact, it is sufficient to know the minimum value of U and the value of U corresponding to an infinite separation of the atoms. The interatomic separation is obtained in the course of the calculation. The force constants can be calculated by various means. One can calculate the value of U at many points near the minimum and construct an analytic curve passing through these points, e.g. using Lagrangian interpolation. The second derivative of U with respect to r, i.e. the force constant, can be deduced from this. Also, as was shown by Bratoz[39] for both self-consistent field and configuration interactions methods, explicit formulae can be established showing the force constant as a function of derivatives of molecular integrals and of characteristic coefficients of the wave functions.

The study of electron density merits a more detailed analysis. The probability of finding electron 1 with spin ω_1 in a small volume dv_1 around a point M in a molecule is

$$dP_{\omega_1} = dv_1 \int |\phi(M, \omega_1, M_2, \omega_2, \ldots M_n, \omega_n)|^2 \, dv_2 \ldots dv_n \, d\omega_2 \ldots d\omega_n,$$

where ϕ is the wave function for the molecule. The probability of finding the same electron in dv_1 with any spin is:

$$dP = dv_1 \int |\phi|^2 \, dv_2 \ldots dv_n \, d\omega_1 \ldots d\omega_n = dv \int |\phi|^2 \frac{d\tau}{dv_1}.$$

The probability density function of finding any electron at M is therefore:

$$d(M) = \sum_i \int |\phi(M_1, \omega_1 \ldots M_{i-1}, \omega_{i-1}, M, \omega_i \ldots M_n, \omega_n)|^2 \frac{d\tau}{dv_i}$$

and the electron density is:

$$\varrho(M) = ed(M),$$

i.e. the same formula as was derived from a different point of view in the first book (p. 185). We have mentioned that another function

$$\delta(M) = \varrho(M) - \varrho^s(M)$$

can be deduced from this function†, characterising the increase or decrease of electronic density induced by the chemical bond at M.

This method is applicable to all types of wave function. An analysis of electron density has been proposed by Mulliken[40] for the case of wave functions of the self-consistent field L.C.A.O. This analysis has been extended to include the case of the configurations interaction method[41].

Consider, for example, a molecular function with two electrons of the form

$$\phi = \frac{1}{\sqrt{2}} \begin{vmatrix} \varphi_1(M_1) & \varphi_2(M_1) \\ \varphi_1(M_2) & \varphi_2(M_2) \end{vmatrix}$$

the molecular orbitals φ being orthonormal. We have

$$\phi^2 = \tfrac{1}{2}\{\varphi_1^2(M_1)\,\varphi_2^2(M_2) + \varphi_1^2(M_2)\,\varphi_2^2(M_1)\}$$
$$- \varphi_1(M_1)\,\varphi_2(M_1)\,\varphi_1(M_2)\,\varphi_2(M_2)$$

and

$$\varrho = e\{\tfrac{1}{2}\varphi_1^2(M) \int \varphi_2^2(M_2)\,dv_2 + \tfrac{1}{2}\varphi_2^2(M) \int \varphi_1^2(M_2)\,dv_2$$
$$- \varphi_1(M)\,\varphi_2(M) \int \varphi_1(M_2)\,\varphi_2(M_2)\,dv_2$$
$$+ \tfrac{1}{2}\varphi_2^2(M) \int \varphi_2^2(M_1)\,dv_1 + \tfrac{1}{2}\varphi_1^2(M) \int \varphi_2^2(M_1)\,dv_1$$
$$- \varphi_1(M)\,\varphi_2(M) \int \varphi_1(M_1)\,\varphi_2(M_1)\,dv_1\}.$$

This expression reduces immediately to

$$\varrho(M) = e[\varphi_2^2(M) + \varphi_1^2(M)]$$

using the orthonormal conditions.

This relationship generalises easily, showing that the density at a point M is e times the sum of the squares of values at M of the orbitals used in the wave function: an orbital being counted twice if it is used twice.

† In fact, in the first book, p. 193, we have considered the function: $\Delta(M) = \delta(M)/\varrho^s(M)$. The function δ is now more frequently used.

If the φ possess L.C.A.O. expressions such that

$$\varphi_1 = c_{11}\psi_1 + c_{12}\psi_2$$

$$\varphi_2 = c_{21}\psi_1 + c_{22}\psi_2,$$

where ψ_1 and ψ_2 are the orbitals associated with the two atoms 1 and 2, we have

$$\varphi_1^2 = c_{11}^2\psi_1^2 + 2c_{11}c_{12}\psi_1\psi_2 + c_{12}^2\psi_2^2.$$

The electric charge carried by orbital φ_1 in the molecule is written

$$q = \int \varphi_1^2 \, dv = [c_{11}^2 + 2c_{11}c_{12}S + c_{12}^2] \, e$$

with

$$S = \int \psi_1\psi_2 \, dv.$$

Mulliken proposed that the term

$$c_{11}^2 + c_{11}c_{12}S$$

be called the *electron population* supplied to orbital ψ_1 of the atom 1 by orbital φ_1 and

$$c_{12}^2 + c_{11}c_{12}S$$

the population for atom 2 in the same orbital. The quantities

$$q_1 = e(c_{11}^2 + c_{11}c_{12}S) \quad \text{and} \quad q_2 = e(c_{12}^2 + c_{11}c_{12}S)$$

can be thought of as the charges corresponding to these populations.
The total atomic population associated with an orbital of an atom can be obtained in a straight forward manner by summing the populations associated with each molecular orbital by reason of the expression which has been obtained for $\varrho(M)$.

Mulliken calls the quantity

$$2c_{11}c_{12}S$$

the overlap population due to orbital φ_1. As before, a simple summation gives the total population.

As a further example, consider the case of the ground state of the molecule Li_2. A calculation [42] using the self-consistent field method gives the following molecular orbitals:

$$\varphi_{1g} = 0 \cdot 99\sigma_g 1s + 0 \cdot 01\sigma_g 2s,$$

$$\varphi_{1u} = 1 \cdot 01\sigma_u 1s + 0 \cdot 09\sigma_u 2s + 0 \cdot 04\sigma_u 2p,$$

$$\varphi_{2g} = -0 \cdot 09\sigma_g 1s + 0 \cdot 66\sigma_g 2s + 0 \cdot 29\sigma_g 2p.$$

The function ϕ contains each orbital twice. We have already said that in a case of this kind we have approximately

$$\sigma_g 1s = \frac{1}{\sqrt{2}} (1s_a + 1s_b)$$

$$\sigma_u 1s = \frac{1}{\sqrt{2}} (1s_a - 1s_b),$$

where a and b denote the lithium nuclei, as $\int 1s_a \, 1s_b \, dv$ is negligible.

Let us calculate the total electron population of orbital $1s_a$, for instance. Replacing $\sigma_g 1s$ and $\sigma_u 1s$ by their expressions, we obtain:

$$\varphi_{1g} = \frac{0 \cdot 99}{\sqrt{2}} 1s_a + \cdots$$

$$\varphi_{1u} = \frac{1 \cdot 01}{\sqrt{2}} 1s_a + \cdots$$

$$\varphi_{2g} = \frac{-0 \cdot 09}{\sqrt{2}} 1s_a + \cdots$$

Since the overlap integral between $1s_a$ and $1s_b$ is negligible, the population associated with an atomic orbital in a molecular orbital is equal simply to the square of the coefficient of the atom orbital in the expansion of the molecular orbital.

Therefore, φ_{1g} produces in $1s_a$ a population of

$$\frac{(0 \cdot 99)^2}{2} \times 2$$

since it is used twice.

Hence the total population of orbital $1s_a$ is:

$$(0 \cdot 99)^2 + (1 \cdot 01)^2 + (-0 \cdot 09)^2 = 2 \cdot 01.$$

Continuing this simple calculation, we find that, in the lithium molecule, the orbitals 1s, 2s and 2p yield 2·01, 0·795 and 0·19 electrons
respectively for each nuclei where in the free atom their populations
are evidently 2, 1 and 0. The bond is responsible for, in some way,
a transfer of about 0·2 electrons from each 2s orbital to a 2p orbital.
This is the effect of polarisation which we have previously discussed
in the case of H_2 (p. 29).

Mulliken says that the *hybridisation character* of the bond of lithium is 0·19. We shall return to the subject later.

Finally we wish to express those quantities for the case of a molecule in an electric field.

Let $V(x, y, z)$ be the potential of the field and $\varrho(x, y, z)$ the electron density in the molecule. Since the molecule generally has small
dimensions, the potential V does not vary much inside the molecular domain. V can be expanded about a point O inside this domain, thus:

$$V(x, y, z) = V_0 + x \left(\frac{\partial V}{\partial x} \right)_0 + y \left(\frac{\partial V}{\partial y} \right)_0 + z \left(\frac{\partial V}{\partial z} \right)_0$$

$$+ \frac{1}{2} x^2 \left(\frac{\partial^2 V}{\partial x^2} \right)_0 + \cdots xy \left(\frac{\partial^2 V}{\partial x \, \partial y} \right)_0 + \cdots + \cdots.$$

Let us examine the first three groups of terms (scalar, vector and
tensor). The energy of interaction between the molecule and the
field is

$$E = \int \varrho V \, dv = V_0 \int \varrho \, dv + \left(\frac{\partial V}{\partial x} \right)_0 \int \varrho x \, dv + \cdots$$

$$+ \frac{1}{2} \left(\frac{\partial^2 V}{\partial x^2} \right)_0 \int \varrho x^2 \, dv + \cdots.$$

The integral $\int \varrho \, dv$ is the charge on the molecule and, since we have
assumed the molecule to be neutral, this term is zero.

The quantities

$$\mu_x = \int \varrho x \, dv$$

$$\mu_y = \int \varrho y \, dv$$

$$\mu_z = \int \varrho z \, dv$$

which form the dipolar moment (see first book, p. 185) are the principal functions in the determination of the energy.

In some cases, this vector is null (e.g. for homonuclear molecules). Then the quantities

$$Q_{x^2} = \int \varrho x^2 \, dv \qquad Q_{xy} = \int \varrho xy \, dv$$

$$Q_{y^2} = \int \varrho y^2 \, dv \qquad Q_{yz} = \int \varrho yz \, dv$$

$$Q_{z^2} = \int \varrho z^2 \, dv \qquad Q_{zx} = \int \varrho zx \, dv$$

which constitutes a definition of the quadrupolar electric moment, become preponderant.

Using the L.C.A.O. method, these quantities have a particularly simple form. We shall illustrate this for the dipolar moment. By definition:

$$\vec{\mu} = \int \varrho(M) \, \vec{r}_M \, dv_M$$

$$\varrho(M) = e \sum_i \int |\Psi(M_1 \ldots M_{i-1}, M, M_{i+1} \ldots M_n)|^2 \, \frac{d\tau}{dv_i}.$$

Therefore

$$\vec{\mu} = e \sum_i \int |\Psi|^2 \, \vec{r}_M \, d\tau.$$

If

$$\varrho(M) = \sum_j \varphi_j^2(M)$$

$$\vec{\mu} = e \sum_j \int \varphi_j^2(M) \vec{r}_M \, dv_M.$$

The total dipolar moment is thus the sum of terms which we can call the polar moment associated with each molecular orbital.

Suppose that the φ are approximated by L.C.A.O. For example,

$$\varphi_1 = c_{11}\psi_1 + c_{12}\psi_2$$

and

$$\varphi_1^2 \vec{r}_M = c_{11}^2 \psi_1^2 \vec{r}_M + 2c_{11}c_{12}\psi_1\psi_2 \vec{r}_M + c_{12}^2 \psi_2^2 \vec{r}_M$$

$$\vec{\mu}_{\phi_1} = e \int \varphi_1^2 \vec{r}_M \, dv = \{c_{11}^2 \int \varphi_1^2 \vec{r}_M \, dv + 2c_{11}c_{12} \int \psi_1\psi_2 \vec{r}_M \, dv$$

$$+ c_{12}^2 \int \psi_2^2 \vec{r}_M \, dv\}.$$

It often happens that the orbitals ψ have some symmetry elements. Suppose, for example, that one of the nuclei is a centre of symmetry for ψ^2. Let us calculate

$$\int \psi_1^2 \vec{r}_M \, dv.$$

The space can be divided equally and symmetrically with respect to nuclei 1. Then, with obvious notation

$$\vec{r}_M = \vec{r}_1 + \vec{r}_{1M}$$

$$\vec{r}_{M'} = \vec{r}_1 + \vec{r}_{1M'}$$

and

$$\vec{r}_{1M'} = -\vec{r}_{1M}$$

for reasons of symmetry.

The corresponding contributions are

$$\psi^2(M)(\vec{r}_1 + r_{1M})\, dv_M$$

and

$$\psi^2(M')(\vec{r}_1 + \vec{r}_{1M'})\, dv_{M'} = \psi^2(M)(\vec{r}_1 - \vec{r}_{1M})\, dv_M.$$

The sum of those contributions becomes

$$2\psi^2(M)\,\vec{r}_1\, dv_M,$$

which can be written:

$$\psi^2(M)\,\vec{r}_1\, dv_M + \psi^2(M')\,\vec{r}_1\, dv_{M'}.$$

The integral therefore reduces to

$$\int \psi_1^2 \vec{r}_1\, dv = \vec{r}_1,$$

since r_1 is a constant and ψ_1 is normalised. If, moreover, the distribution $\psi_1\psi_2$ has a centre of symmetry O, the corresponding integral reduces in the same manner to $\vec{r}_0 S$. It often happens that this centre is the centre of the bond (if ψ_2 translates to ψ_1, for example), i.e.

$$\vec{r}_0 = \frac{\vec{r}_1 + \vec{r}_2}{2} S$$

and

$$\vec{\mu}_{\phi_1} = c_{11}^2 \vec{r}_1 + 2c_{11}c_{12} \frac{\vec{r}_1 + \vec{r}_2}{2} S + c_{12}^2 \vec{r}_2$$

$$= e\left\{(c_{11}^2 + c_{11}c_{12}S)\,\vec{r}_1 + (c_{12}^2 + c_{11}c_{12}S)\,\vec{r}_2\right\}$$

$$= q_1\vec{r}_1 + q_2\vec{r}_2.$$

11. Some Results of Using the Self-consistent Field Method in the L.C.A.O. Approximation

We have seen (Section 9) that in this case the molecular orbitals have the form

$$\varphi_i = \sum_j c_{ij} \psi_j.$$

In principle, any number of orbitals associated with the constituent nuclei can be introduced into this expansion. In practice, in order to make the calculation realisable, only a small number are introduced. In the case of the molecule Li_2, for example, Faulkner introduced the orbitals $1s_a$, $2s_a$, $2p_{za}$, $1s_b$, $2s_b$, $2p_{zb}$ (a and b referring to the nuclei). In place of the basis formed by these six orbitals one can well choose an equivalent basis formed by the symmetry orbitals $\sigma_g 1s$, $\sigma_u 1s$, $\sigma_g 2s$, $\sigma_u 2s$, $\sigma_g 2p$, $\sigma_u 2p$ and this is why the orbitals given on p. 37 are expressed on this base. The calculations can be carried out in a way such that the self-consistent field operator has the same symmetry as the operator of the independent model. Non-zero matrix elements are then only obtained between orbitals of the same symmetry. This is why the orbitals given on p. 37 contain either only orbitals σ_u or only orbitals σ_g. Calculations have been carried out, using all the orbitals of the K and L bonds without extra approximation in cases of:

Li_2[43], N_2[44], O_2[45], F_2[46], BH[47], CH[48], NH[48], OH[50], HF[48], NO[49].

Table 11.1 compares the total energy and the dissociation energy given by these calculations with the experimental values. The dissociation energy is calculated by applying the generalised Koopmans' theorem. The error in total energy is always of the order of 1 per cent. The order of magnitude of the dissociation energy is obtained, but the error can reach 25 per cent.

In the case of the CH radical, the ionisation energy can also be obtained from the difference between the energies calculated for CH and CH^+. This gives 10·6 eV instead of 11·1 eV. The agreement between the value obtained by Koopmans' theorem and the experimental value is certainly fortuitous. This latter value is not known to give an error of less than 1 eV. As can be seen from Krauss's memoir, the loss of an electron from the CH bond clearly perturbs the re-

TABLE 11.1

	Li₂	N₂	O₂	F₂	BH	CH	CH⁺	NH	OH	HF	NO
Total calculated energy	14·848 a.u.	2953·7 eV	149·087 a.u.	197·87 a.u.	681·8 eV	38·164 a.u.	37·775 a.u.	54·78 a.u.	75·062 a.u.	99·475 a.u.	128·739 a.u.
Total experimental energy	14·995	2982·0	150·406		687	38·489	38·080	55·259	75·778	100·478	129·737
Calculated ionisation energy (eV)	4·91	14·816				11·1		11·8	10·8	12·6	9·14
Experimental ionisation energy		15·602				11·1			13·16	15·77	9·25

(a.u. denotes atomic units of energy)

TABLE 11.2

	Li₂	N₂	O₂	F₂	BH	CH	CH⁺	NH	OH	HF	NO
Calculated bonding energy	0·33 eV	1·20 eV	0·795 eV	−0·00829 a.u.	1·8 eV	1·2 eV	0·9 eV	0·5 eV	0·8 eV	1·1 eV	−1·6 eV
Experimental bonding energy	1·05	9·90	5·08	0·061	2·6	3·64	3·77	4·01	4·58	6·07	6·6
Overlap population						0·42	0·52	0·35	0·30		
Calculated polar moment					0·989	0·93		0·90	0·92	0·87	0·50
Experimental polar moment										1·91	0·2

maining orbitals. This case is therefore not favourable to the application of Koopmans' theorem†.

Table 11.2 compares the results of calculations and experiment for bonding energies and polar moments. The total overlap population is also shown. One sees that the L.C.A.O. self-consistent field method underestimates the bonding energies considerably. The bonding energies of both F_2 and NO are found to be negative. Also, no simple relationship between the bonding energy and the overlap population can be seen. Only the order of magnitude of the polar moment is obtained. It is curious to find that the polar moment is almost constant for CH, NH, OH, FH.

It is interesting to compare this polar moment with the transfer of electric charge which can be calculated using the total atomic population defined by Mulliken. Table 11.3 compares these populations separately for the atoms and the molecules.

TABLE 11.3

		CH	NH	OH	HF
Separate atoms	{X = C, N, O or F	6	7	8	9
	{H	1	1	1	1
Molecule	{X	6·0056	7·0775	8·1291	9·1515
	{H	0·9943	0·9224	0·8704	0·8452

The transfer of charge to the heavy atom is 0·0056, 0·0775, 0·1291, 0·1515 respectively. This confirms the chemical intuition that fluorine, for example, has more "electronegativity" than oxygen, both having more than nitrogen.

Therefore, there is no simple relationship between the transfer of charge and the polar moment.

Finally, Table 11.4 compares experimental data with the energies of different states, taking the lowest as the origin.

In this table, for each level, the first number refers to the calculated value and the second to the experimental value. One sees that

† J. Mulliken (*J. Chemie Physique* **46** (1949), 497) has argued that the application of Koopmans' theorem leads to ionisation energies in better agreement with experimental results than calculating them from the energies of the molecule and the ion.

J. C. Lorquet (Communications of the International Congress on Molecular Quantum Physics at Boulder, 1959) has produced a new argument where the opposite is found.

theory gives only the order of magnitude of the transition energies, but permits an ordering of the different energy levels.

TABLE 11.4

CH	CH$^+$	NH	OH
	(energies of electron levels in eV)		
$^2\Pi$ 0	$^1\Sigma^+$ 0	$^3\Sigma^-$ 0	$^2\Pi$ 0
$^2\Delta \begin{cases} 3\cdot19 \\ 2\cdot87 \end{cases}$	$^1\Pi \begin{cases} 2\cdot79 \\ 2\cdot99 \end{cases}$	$^1\Delta \begin{cases} 2\cdot24 \\ 1\cdot2 \end{cases}$	$^2\Sigma^+ \begin{cases} 5\cdot54 \\ 4\cdot05 \end{cases}$
$^2\Sigma^- \begin{cases} 4\cdot10 \\ 3\cdot22 \end{cases}$		$^1\Sigma^+ \begin{cases} 4\cdot48 \\ 2\cdot3 \end{cases}$	
$^2\Sigma^+ \begin{cases} 5\cdot06 \\ 3\cdot95 \end{cases}$		$^3\Pi \begin{cases} 5\cdot09 \\ 3\cdot69 \end{cases}$	
		$^1\Pi \begin{cases} 7\cdot74 \\ 5\cdot0 \end{cases}$	

Other approximations have been added to those which have been discussed. The most common of these consists of the introduction of a core. Such calculations have been carried out for Li$_2$[43], BeH[51], BH[47], CH[52], HF[53], CO[54], and NO[49].

Consider the radical BeH—the procedure consists normally of constructing the molecular orbitals as linear combinations of the 1s, 2s and 2pσ orbitals of beryllium and the 1s orbital (which we denote by h) of hydrogen. For simplicity, one can assume that the first orbital reduces to 1s (of beryllium) using a result that we have discussed in introducing the nature of a core.

It remains to construct the other two orbitals orthogonal to the first. A convenient procedure consists of forming the atomic orbitals, 2s*, 2pσ and h* orthogonal to 1s, using a method previously discussed, and writing

$$\varphi_1 = 1s$$

$$\varphi_2 = c_{22}2s^* + c_{23}2p\sigma + c_{24}h^*$$

$$\varphi_3 = c_{32}2s^* + c_{33}2p\sigma + c_{34}h^*.$$

Following this procedure, and introducing some small extra approximations, the total energy of BeH was calculated for four values of the interatomic distance r_{BeH}.

Table 11.5 contains the results.

TABLE 11.5

Distance r_{BeH} (in Å)	1·2500	1·3122	1·3431	1·5000
Total energy (in eV)	−412·1980	−412·2804	−412·2803	−412·1089

A Lagrangian interpolation gives the minimum at

$$r_{BeH} = 1·33 \text{ Å}$$

with value −412·28 eV.

The experimental energy is −414·74 and the equilibrium distance is 1·34 Å. The agreement is very good. The same calculation gives a dissociation energy of 2·75 eV compared with an experimental value of 2·2 eV.

Finally, the first ionisation energy is found to be 8·43 eV while experimental data leads to a value of 8·10. It can be seen that the approximations made here do not alter the value of the method in this case. Indeed, one has the impression that they improve it accidentally.

12. COMPARISONS OF RESULTS OF METHODS BASED ON THE USE OF ATOMIC ORBITALS

Various memoirs compare the results of different methods based on the use of atomic orbitals. That of Ishiguro et al.[55] on the molecule Li_2 is a model of its kind. The calculations have been carried out for 23 types of wave functions.

As before, three sets of parameters are used. Letting δ_1 and δ_2 be the coefficients of the exponentials of the K and L shells' atomic orbitals, these three sets, denoted by I, II and III, are given in Table 12.1.

TABLE 12.1

	I	II	III	IV
δ_1	2·8	2·65	2·8	2·7
δ_2	0·6	0·65	0·7	0·65

Column IV of this table corresponds to the parameters given by Slater's rules.

The total energy, calculated in the first configuration derived from the lowest symmetry orbitals, is

$$-14\cdot8010; \quad -14\cdot8268; \quad -14\cdot7999 \text{ a.u.}$$

using parameters I, II, III respectively.

Hence, the small variations of parameters envisaged here cover a variation of 0·03 a.u., i.e. of the order of 1 eV, which is not negligible. The parameters nearest to those of Slater's appear to be the best.

Table 12.2 gives the total energy and the bonding energy corresponding to five wave functions (with parameters II).

TABLE 12.2

	A	B	C	D	E	F
Total energy (a.u.)	−14·8268	−14·8388	−14·8376	−14·8401	−14·8614	−14·995
Bonding energy (a.u.)	−0·170	0·155	0·124	0·190	0·770	1·05

Column A corresponds to the preceding simple configuration. Column B corresponds to the use of a "polarised" bonding orbital with the aid of atomic orbitals $2p_z$; Column C to the L.C.A.O. self-consistent field method; Column D to the method of mesomery (approximations of Heitler and London) and Column E to a configuration interaction of eight terms. Column F contains the experimental results.

One sees that the method of Heitler and London is better than the self-consistent field method here, but only the configuration interaction method gives a reasonable figure for the bonding energy.

Table 12.3 gives the values of two transition energies obtained by methods A and E using parameters I, II and III as well as the experimental values.

Here again, method E appears to be better, but the parameters I give the best results, in agreement with the idea that the best parameters for an excited state are not necessarily identical with those for the ground state.

TABLE 12.3

		$^1\Sigma_g^+ \to {}^1\Sigma_u^+$	$^1\Sigma_g^+ \to {}^1\Pi_u$
I	A	3·00	2·19
	E	1·84	3·21
II	A	3·26	3·05
	E	1·91	3·28
III	A	3·55	3·19
	E	1·99	3·35
Experiment		1·86	2·59

The study of function Δ, introduced in the first book, also permits a useful comparison between the various methods. More exactly, we are interested in the function

$$\delta(M) = \varrho^f(M)\,\Delta(M) = \varrho(M) - \varrho^f(M).$$

A series of memoirs[56] has been devoted to this problem.

Figure 13 shows how this function varies along the line of the nuclei of the hydrogen molecule when it is calculated using the

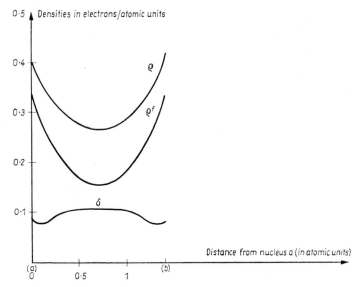

FIG. 13. Function δ for H_2 from James and Coolidge's calculation.

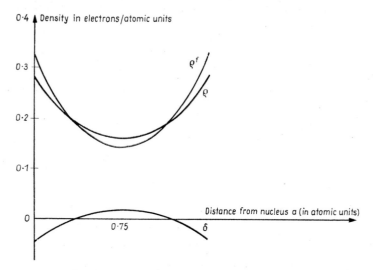

FIG. 14. Function δ for H_2 after Heitler and London.

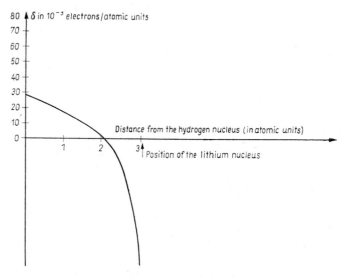

FIG. 15. Function δ for LiH.

function of James and Coolidge. It can be seen that the chemical bond induces a very great concentration of electrons along this line. Figure 14 shows the same function calculated by means of the wave function of Heitler and London. We can conclude that this function underestimates considerably this concentration of electrons, which is consistent with the underestimation of the bonding energy.

Figure 15 corresponds to the molecule LiH using a wave function calculated by I. Fischer[57] by means of a function derived from the lowest symmetry orbitals with polarisation of the last. In

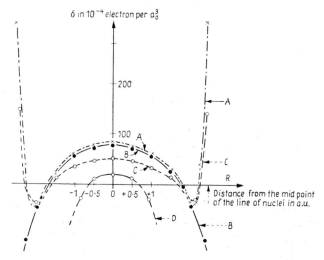

FIG. 16. Variations of function δ along the line of nuclei for Li_2 Curve A: incomplete S.C.F. calculation; Curve B: complete S.C.F. calculation; Curve C: method of configuration interactions; Curve D: result of the previous calculation by L.C.A.O. method.

this heteropolar molecule, the function δ makes evident a transfer of electrons from the lithium to the hydrogen in accord with chemical intuition which leads to writing

$$Li^{\delta+}H^{\delta-}.$$

Figure 16 compares four calculations of the function δ for the molecule Li_2. One sees that the self-consistent calculations produce a greater electron concentration than the configurations constructed from the lowest symmetry orbitals, but, on the other hand, the configuration interaction function appears to give a weaker concentration in the neighbourhood of the nuclei.

Figure 17 shows that this is not always so. This figure compares the results of self-consistent calculations and those of configuration interaction for the function δ along a perpendicular bisector of the line of nuclei. One sees that the latter function gives a greater $\delta(M)$

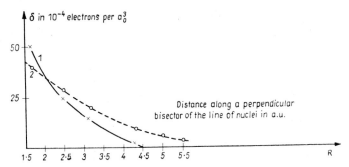

FIG. 17. Variation of δ along a perpendicular bisector of the line of nuclei: Curve 1: complete S.C.F. calculation; Curve 2: method of configuration interactions.

for distances greater than approximately one angström from the centre. *Overall*, configuration interaction gives a greater concentration of electrons "between the nuclei" than the other methods, in accordance with the fact that it gives the best value of the bonding energy.

13. SEMI-EMPIRIC FORMS BASED ON THE USE OF MOLECULAR ORBITALS

We shall discuss three such methods. The earliest, due to Moffitt[58], is called *the method of atoms in the molecule*. The essence of this method consists of substituting the energies of isolated atoms, contained in the molecule, into the energy matrices necessary for the study of that molecule. We thus introduce experimental values of atomic energies into the molecular energies. Good results have been obtained (Moffitt *loc. cit.*) by using this procedure in the case of O_2 and also with H_2[59].

In the latter case, the investigation has been carried out with both an ionic part and a covalent part. It was found necessary to introduce distinct effective atomic numbers in the two parts of this function.

Other diatomic molecules, in particular HF[60], have been studied using this procedure.

The second group of methods consists of introducing into the calculation experimental data characterising the atom, resulting from the fusion of the atoms making up the molecule as in the united atom method. This has been suggested by Bingel[61].

Finally, the technique of Preuss[62] is a synthesis of the method of Moffitt and of Bingel.

If ϕ_M is the wave function, obtained by Moffitt's method of a molecule, then it must be a better representation when the nuclei are distant. Let ϕ_B be Bingel's function for the same molecule. This will be better when the nuclei are close.

It is therefore natural to try

$$\phi = a\phi_M + b\phi_B$$

and to determine the coefficients a and b by variation for each internuclear distance; a will be large for large distances; b, on the other hand, becoming important for small distances. This is the essence of Preuss's procedure. Although very ingenious, this procedure has not as yet given the results one might expect.

14. Some Problems Connected with the Representation of Spin

In the approximation which we have been considering, the Hamiltonian operator does not contain the spin. The eigenfunctions of this Hamiltonian are not necessarily adapted to the representation of spin. In order that the wave function representing a state of the system corresponding to an eigenvalue gives a good determination of spin, it must be an eigenfunction of both the Hamiltonian and the operator $\mathfrak{S}^2$. Since $\mathfrak{S}^2$ and $\mathfrak{S}_z$ commute, for all non-degenerate levels, the eigenfunction of the Hamiltonian constructed to be also an eigenfunction of $\mathfrak{S}_z$ is necessarily one for $\mathfrak{S}^2$.

For degenerate levels, the eigenfunctions of $\mathfrak{S}^2$ can be constructed by linear combinations of those of $\mathfrak{S}_z$.

The problem of finding eigenfunctions of $\mathfrak{S}^2$ thus reverts to the manipulation of those of $\mathfrak{S}_z$.

Now, we have already seen that it is easy to construct this last eigenfunction in the important case where functions constructed on spin orbitals are used (e.g. first book, pp. 8 and 51). A product of spin orbitals, which contains p functions α and q functions β corresponds to the eigenvalue $(p - q) h/4\pi$ of $\mathfrak{S}_z$.

The corresponding determinant, a linear combination of eigenfunctions associated with this eigenvalue, is also an eigenfunction for this eigenvalue.

In the majority of cases, therefore, we shall construct the eigenfunctions of $\mathfrak{S}^2$ by transforming those of $\mathfrak{S}_z$.

We shall, therefore, proceed to show how the necessary transformation may be achieved.

Let $|Y|$ be a determinant of Slater, an eigenfunction of $\mathfrak{S}_z$. Let us form the operator

$$\Omega_k = \prod_{\substack{i=1 \\ i \neq k}}^{n} \left(\frac{\mathfrak{S}^2 - \lambda_i}{\lambda_k - \lambda_i} \right)^{\dagger},$$

where the λ_i are the eigenvalues of $\mathfrak{S}^2$, and find the function $\Omega_k |Y|$.

Let ϕ be an eigenfunction of $\mathfrak{S}^2$. Since $\mathfrak{S}_z$ commutes with $\mathfrak{S}^2$, $|Y|$ can be written as a linear combination of ϕ_e:

$$|Y| = \sum_l c_l \phi_l.$$

Obviously:

$$\Omega_k \phi_l = 0 \quad \text{if} \quad l \neq k$$

$$\Omega_k \phi_k = \phi_k.$$

Hence:

$$\Omega_k |Y| = \Omega_k \sum_l c_l \phi_l = c_k \phi_k.$$

Therefore, the operator Ω_k transforms $|Y|$ to a function proportional to ϕ_k. It projects $|Y|$ onto ϕ_k and is called in consequence the projection operator.

The problem is therefore solved if we can calculate the effect of the operator Ω on a function $|Y|$. To form Ω, all the eigenvalues of $\mathfrak{S}^2$ must be known. The action of Ω splits into operations of the form $\mathfrak{S}^2 |Y|$. We will, therefore, study how to find all the eigenvalues of $\mathfrak{S}^2$ and the result of the action of $\mathfrak{S}^2$ on $|Y|$.

† Note that even if an eigenvalue is multiple, it is only introduced once in this operator.

Let us find, for example, all the eigenvalues of $\mathfrak{S}^2$ in the three electron case. The table below gives in the first three columns the value of s associated with each orbital. Column four contains the possible values of S_{proj}.

s	s	s	S_{proj}	$S = \frac{3}{2}$	$S = \frac{1}{2}$	$S = \frac{1}{2}$
$\frac{1}{2}$	$\frac{1}{2}$	$\frac{1}{2}$	$\frac{3}{2}$	×		
$\frac{1}{2}$	$\frac{1}{2}$	$-\frac{1}{2}$	$\frac{1}{2}$	×		
$\frac{1}{2}$	$-\frac{1}{2}$	$\frac{1}{2}$	$\frac{1}{2}$		×	
$\frac{1}{2}$	$-\frac{1}{2}$	$-\frac{1}{2}$	$-\frac{1}{2}$			×
$-\frac{1}{2}$	$\frac{1}{2}$	$\frac{1}{2}$	$\frac{1}{2}$			×
$-\frac{1}{2}$	$\frac{1}{2}$	$-\frac{1}{2}$	$-\frac{1}{2}$		×	
$-\frac{1}{2}$	$-\frac{1}{2}$	$\frac{1}{2}$	$-\frac{1}{2}$	×		
$-\frac{1}{2}$	$-\frac{1}{2}$	$-\frac{1}{2}$	$-\frac{3}{2}$	×		

Using reasoning analogous to that given in the first book, p. 55, we can with the aid of the spin orbitals describe a quadruplet state $(S = \frac{3}{2})$ and two doublets $(S = \frac{1}{2})$. $\mathfrak{S}^2$ has, therefore, two equal eigenvalues at $\frac{1}{2}(1 + \frac{1}{2}) h^2/4\pi^2$ and another at $\frac{3}{2}(1 + \frac{3}{2}) h^2/4\pi^2$. We can now form the operator

$$\Omega_{1/2} = \frac{\mathfrak{S}^2 - \dfrac{15}{16}\dfrac{h^2}{\pi^2}}{\dfrac{3}{16}\dfrac{h^2}{\pi^2} - \dfrac{15}{16}\dfrac{h^2}{\pi^2}},$$

$$\Omega_{3/2} = \frac{\mathfrak{S}^2 - \dfrac{3}{16}\dfrac{h^2}{\pi^2}}{\dfrac{15}{16}\dfrac{h^2}{\pi^2} - \dfrac{3}{16}\dfrac{h^2}{\pi^2}}.$$

Continuing in this manner, the branched diagram of Fig. 18 can be constructed.

The abscissa gives the number, n, of electrons of the system. The ordinate shows the different values of S. For a given n the numbers in the circles indicate the multiplicity of each of the possible corresponding eigenvalues of $\mathfrak{S}^2$.

The operator

$$\mathfrak{S}^2 = \mathfrak{S}_x^2 + \mathfrak{S}_y^2 + \mathfrak{S}_z^2$$

can be written

$$\mathfrak{S}^2 = (\mathfrak{S}_x - i\mathfrak{S}_y)(\mathfrak{S}_x + i\mathfrak{S}_y) + \mathfrak{S}_z^2 - (h/2\pi)\,\mathfrak{S}_z$$

as (see first book, pp. 2–9)

$$(\mathfrak{S}_x - i\mathfrak{S}_y)(\mathfrak{S}_x + i\mathfrak{S}_y) = \mathfrak{S}_x^2 + \mathfrak{S}_y^2 + i(\mathfrak{S}_x\mathfrak{S}_y - \mathfrak{S}_y\mathfrak{S}_x)$$

and

$$\mathfrak{S}_x\mathfrak{S}_y - \mathfrak{S}_y\mathfrak{S}_x = -i(h/2\pi)\,\mathfrak{S}_z.$$

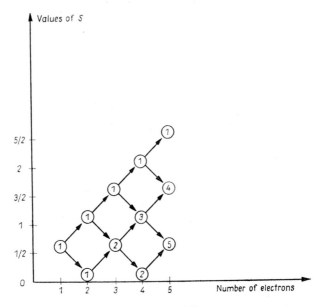

FIG. 18. Branched diagram.

The action of the different operators appearing in $\mathfrak{S}^2$ on $|Y|$ is relatively simple. We know that (first book, p. 6) for one spin coordinate say k

$$\mathfrak{S}_{xk} = \begin{Vmatrix} 0 & \frac{1}{2} \\ \frac{1}{2} & 0 \end{Vmatrix} \frac{h}{2\pi} \qquad \mathfrak{S}_{yk} = \begin{Vmatrix} 0 & -i/2 \\ i/2 & 0 \end{Vmatrix} \frac{h}{2\pi} \qquad \mathfrak{S}_{zk} = \begin{Vmatrix} \frac{1}{2} & 0 \\ 0 & -\frac{1}{2} \end{Vmatrix} \frac{h}{2\pi}$$

so that

$$\mathfrak{S}_{zk}\alpha = -\frac{h}{4\pi}\,\alpha \qquad\qquad \mathfrak{S}_{zk}\beta = -\frac{h}{4\pi}\,\beta$$

$$\mathfrak{S}_{xk}\alpha = \frac{h}{4\pi}\beta \qquad\qquad \mathfrak{S}_{xk}\beta = \frac{h}{4\pi}\alpha$$

$$\mathfrak{S}_{yk}\alpha = -\frac{ih}{4\pi}\beta \qquad\qquad \mathfrak{S}_{yk}\beta = \frac{ih}{4\pi}\alpha$$

$$(\mathfrak{S}_{xk} - i\mathfrak{S}_{yk})\alpha = 0 \qquad (\mathfrak{S}_{xk} - i\mathfrak{S}_{yk})\beta = \frac{h}{2\pi}\alpha$$

$$(\mathfrak{S}_{xk} + i\mathfrak{S}_{yk})\alpha = \frac{h}{2\pi}\beta \qquad (\mathfrak{S}_{xk} + i\mathfrak{S}_{yk})\beta = 0.$$

Let us study the effect of operator $\mathfrak{S}_z$ on a determinant constructed on three spin-orbitals:

$$|Y| = \det \varphi_1(1)\,\varphi_2(2)\,\overline{\varphi_3(3)}.$$

In the notation introduced here, the absence of a bar on a spin orbital signifies that it contains the function α and the presence of a bar indicates the function β. We have

$$\mathfrak{S}_z = \mathfrak{S}_{z1} + \mathfrak{S}_{z2} + \mathfrak{S}_{z3}$$

and

$$\mathfrak{S}_{z1}|Y| = \frac{h}{4\pi}\det \varphi_1(1)\,\varphi_2(2)\,\overline{\varphi_3(3)}$$

$$\mathfrak{S}_{z2}|Y| = \frac{h}{4\pi}\det \varphi_1(1)\,\varphi_2(2)\,\overline{\varphi_3(3)}$$

$$\mathfrak{S}_{z3}|Y| = -\frac{h}{4\pi}\det \varphi_1(1)\,\varphi_2(2)\,\overline{\varphi_3(3)}$$

whence

$$\mathfrak{S}_z|Y| = \frac{h}{4\pi}|Y|.$$

In the general case of $|Y|$ containing p functions α and q functions β, we arrive at

$$\mathfrak{S}^2|Y| = \frac{h^2}{4\pi^2}\sum_{\mathfrak{R}}\mathfrak{R}|Y| + \frac{h^2}{8\pi^2}(p-q)|Y| + \frac{h^2}{16\pi^2}(p-q)^2|Y|.$$

As in the first book, $\Re$ represents a permutation of spin functions between the spin orbitals and $\sum_{\Re}$ the summation over all possible permutations.

Let us now look at the expression

$$\Omega_{3/2} \det \varphi_1(1) \, \varphi_2(2) \, \overline{\varphi_3(3)} \, .$$

We have seen that

$$\Omega_{3/2} = \frac{4\pi^2}{3h^2} \left(\mathfrak{S}^2 - \frac{3}{16} \frac{h^2}{\pi^2} \right).$$

Let us therefore find the effect of $\mathfrak{S}^2$ on the determinant. Here $p - q = 1$. Therefore

$$\mathfrak{S}^2 |Y| = \frac{h^2}{4\pi^2} \left[\det \varphi_1(1) \, \varphi_2(2) \, \overline{\varphi_3(3)} + \det \varphi_1(1) \, \overline{\varphi_2(2)} \, \varphi_3(3) \right.$$

$$\left. + \det \overline{\varphi_1(1)} \, \varphi_2(2) \, \varphi_3(3) \right] + \frac{3}{16} \frac{h^2}{\pi^2} \det \varphi_1(1) \, \varphi_2(2) \, \overline{\varphi_3(3)}.$$

Hence:

$$\left(\mathfrak{S}^2 - \frac{3}{16} \frac{h^2}{\pi^2} \right) |Y|$$

$$= \frac{h^2}{4\pi^2} \left[\det \varphi_1(1) \, \varphi_2(2) \, \overline{\varphi_3(3)} + \det \varphi_1(1) \, \overline{\varphi_2(2)} \, \varphi_3(3) \right.$$

$$\left. + \det \overline{\varphi_1(1)} \, \varphi_2(2) \, \varphi_3(3) \right].$$

We deduce from this that

$$\Omega_{3/2} \det \varphi_1(1) \, \varphi_2(2) \, \overline{\varphi_3(3)}$$

$$= a \left[\det \varphi_1(1) \, \varphi_2(2) \, \overline{\varphi_3(3)} + \det \varphi_1(1) \, \overline{\varphi_2(2)} \, \varphi_3(3) \right.$$

$$\left. + \det \overline{\varphi_1(1)} \, \varphi_2(2) \, \varphi_3(3) \right].$$

i.e. that the function in brackets is an eigenfunction of $\mathfrak{S}^2$ for $S = \frac{3}{2}$.

CHAPTER IV

Some General Problems in the Structure
of Molecules

15. VALENCE ANGLES, HYBRIDISATION.
THEORY OF THE DIRECTED VALENCE

A. *Direct Method*

In the Born–Oppenheimer approximation, it is essential to know the equilibrium position about which the nuclei oscillate in the molecular state under study. In the diatomic case, this problem reduces to finding its separation of the nuclei. In the polyatomic case, we must know either the distance between each pair of nuclei or the distances between each nucleus and its nearest neighbour, together with the angles formed by a given nucleus and adjacent nuclei.

The most direct method of treating this problem consists of finding the position of the nuclei which corresponds to a minimum of function U. It is rarely applicable for two principal reasons. It only gives reasonable results if the wave function chosen is already very elaborate. It requires much calculation since, in general, one cannot find the minimum of U other than by calculating its value for a great many positions of the nuclei.

Boys, Cook, Reeves and Shavitt[63] have constructed a wave function for a water molecule using a linear combination of determinants corresponding to thirty configurations. Each determinant is formed by ten molecular orbitals, since the water molecule contains ten electrons. The function has been calculated from different bonding distances OH and for different angles HÔH. Table 15.1 shows the results obtained.

In general, it is preferable to compute valence angles by methods which are less obvious but which are easier to use. Before presenting

TABLE 15.1

	Results of calculation	Experimental values
Total energy (atomic units)	−75·7763	−76·4641
Bonding energy (atomic units)	0·2135	0·3544
Distance OH (in Å)	1·95	1·85
Angle HÔH	96°	104°

these, it is useful to collect together some experimental results in order to highlight the most important facts which are to be interpreted.

B. *The Geometric Structure of Molecules as Deduced by Experiment*

A number of methods give a precise idea of the geometrical organisation of molecular structures. The writing of expanded formulae, the method of stereochemistry, gives the first fundamental indications. Spectrographic techniques, electron and X-ray diffraction allow exact measurements of the distance between the nuclei and angles between the lines joining the nuclei.

Suppose that nothing is known about the molecules except for the results of the measurement of mean distances between their nuclei and the angles between the lines of the nuclei. For simplicity, we shall restrict our discussion to *distinctly differentiated molecules* like those found in gases and in certain solutions and crystals.

The first problem which presents itself to us is to define *the nearness* of two atoms. When do we say that two atoms are adjacent? The answer is not immediately obvious, particularly if we do not want to use preconceived ideas.

We therefore start by establishing the difference between adjacent and non-adjacent atoms and in a given molecule we are interested in the separation of any two atoms. We have already said that spectroscopic methods and electron and X-ray diffraction allows the measurement of these distances.

The precision with which these can be determined depends on the method and the molecule. Spectroscopic methods give very high accuracy (about 0·001 Å) for simple molecules. In carbon monoxide, CO, the interatomic distance has been evaluated thus at 1·129 Å [64].

If the molecule is complicated, however, interpretations become uncertain and diffraction methods are used instead.

They are, in general, less accurate except for highly symmetrical systems.

For diamond, the distance $C-C$ is found to be 1·54452 $\pm$ 0·00014 Å [65] using X-ray diffraction.

For more complex molecules, the accuracy of diffraction methods may vary between 0·01 and 0·05 Å. The lower limit of the error is only obtainable, in general, as a result of a large amount of effort including a *triple* Fourier series expansion.

Let us consider, for example, the carbon–carbon bond.

The distance which separates the two carbon atoms in the same molecule appears at first to vary from case to case.

Here are some examples:

In ethane   one distance CC of 1·55 $\pm$ 0·03 Å [66]
in ethylene   one distance CC of 1·33 Å [67]
in trichloroethylene   one distance CC of 1·38 Å [68]
in acetylene   one distance CC of 1·204 Å [69]
in dibromoacetylene   one distance CC of 1·20 Å [68]
in propane   two distances CC of 1·54 Å [66]
                       and one distance CC of 2·52 Å
in cyclopropane   three distances CC of 1·52 $\pm$ 0·03 Å [66]
in allene   two   distances CC of 1·34 $\pm$ 0·02 Å [66]
                       and one distance CC of 2·68 Å

Methylene cyclobutane

                       one CC distance of 1·34 Å [70]
                       four CC distances of 1·56 Å
                       two CC distances of 2·2 Å
                       two CC distances of 2·6 Å
                       one CC distance of 3·54 Å

In butane one finds:

                       three bonds CC 1·54 Å
                       two bonds CC 2·52 Å

and a CC bond with distance varying from 2·6 to 3·9 Å depending on the position of the atoms.

In naphthalene we find[71]

> four CC distances of 1·36 Å
> three CC distances of 1·39 Å
> four CC distances of 1·42 Å
> fourteen CC distances of 2·4 Å
> six CC distances of 2·8 Å
> four CC distances of 3·8 Å
> four CC distances of 4·2 Å
> two CC distances of 4·8 Å
> two CC distances of 5·1 Å

We have therefore:

> two CC distances between 1·20 and 1·29 Å
> twelve CC distances between 1·3 and 1·39 Å
> four CC distances between 1·4 and 1·49 Å
> thirteen CC distances between 1·5 and 1·59 Å
> zero CC distances between 1·6 and 2·19 Å
> two CC distances between 2·2 and 2·39 Å
> sixteen CC distances between 2·4 and 2·59 Å
> twenty-two CC distances between 2·6 and 5 Å

Figure 19 summarises these results in a histogram.

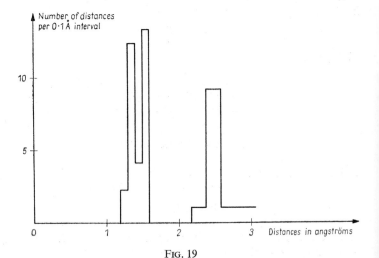

FIG. 19

This graph shows the existence of a first region of possible distances between 1·2 and 1·5 Å as well as a forbidden region (from 1·6 to 2·2 Å). Beyond 2·2 Å all distances become possible.

Although our statistics are confined to less than a hundred distances our conclusions are not essentially different from those obtained from a more extended statistical analysis.

The most important fact is the existence of a *first probable distance* centred at 1·4 Å with a spread of 0·2 Å.

This recurs in the majority of groups of two atoms A and B in a well-differentiated molecule in its ground state.

One can, therefore, empirically define a *first probable distance* for a pair of given atoms A and B. The distance is generally defined with a spread of 0·2 Å.

Henceforth, two nuclei A and B of a molecule will be said to be neighbours if they are separated by a distance inside the interval of definition of the first probable distance relative to these two atoms.

A pair of neighbouring atoms will be called a strong chemical bond.

The neighbourhood of an atom in a molecule is defined as the ensemble of neighbouring atoms or the ensemble of strong bonds which include it.

The number of atoms neighbouring a given atom in a molecule normally varies from 1 to 8. The angles which for different strong bonds containing an atom varies from molecule to molecule.

Using methods analogous to those used for distances, one can find how the number of angles between bonds varies with the angle. The experimental techniques which give the distances also give the angles with an accuracy varying from 1 to 5°. In some cases the accuracy is better, in others much worse.

(a) We shall first look at the case of an atom with two neighbours which can be called a *second order neighbourhood* or a *digonal neighbourhood*.

We find one angle of 90° in H_2Se [72]
Angle $C\hat{S}C$ is 91° in thiophene [72]
An angle of 92° is found in H_2S [73]
An angle of 95° is found in $PbCl_2$, $PbBr_2$, and PbI_2 [74]
An angle of 98° is found in Br_2Te [75]
An angle of 100° is found in F_2O [76]

The eight angles $S\hat{S}S$ of the molecule of sulphur S_8 are 100° in the vapour phase [77].

An angle of 103° is found in Cl_2S [76]
Two angles of 101° are found in hydrogen peroxide [78]
An angle of 105° is found in water [79]
The angle FÔN of fluorine nitrate is 105° [80]
The angle CÔC of furan is 107° [81]
The angle CŜS of $CH_3-S-S-CH_3$ is 107° [82]
The angle CÔC of methyl oxide is 111° [76]
The angle CÔC of methyl formate is 112° [83]
In the strange molecule FN_2F, two angles of 115° are found. [84]

An angle of 115° is found in Cl_2O [76].

In methyl nitride the angle NÑC measures 120° [85]
An angle of 121° is found in SO_2 [86]
An angle of 130° is found in NO_2 [87]
An angle of 125° is found in CÑCl and ON̂Br [88]

Finally in many molecules, angles of 180° are found. These include the angles HĈC in acetylene [89], the angle NÑO in N_2O, the angle NĈH in hydrocyanic acid, the angle NÑN in methyl nitride [90], the angle OĈO in carbonic anhydride, the angle SĈS in sulphide of carbon [91], the angle CĈO of ketones [92].

We have thus found:

two angles between 88° and 91°
four angles between 92° and 95°
one angle between 96° and 99°
eleven angles between 100° and 103°
four angles between 104° and 107°
one angle between 108° and 111°
four angles between 112° and 115°
zero angles between 116° and 119°
three angles between 120° and 123°
two angles between 124° and 127°
zero angles between 128° and 177°
eight angles between 178° and 181°

The histogram of Fig. 20 summarises these results. Three groups of angles can be seen. The first extends from 88° to 115° and has a maximum at around 102°.

The second extends from 120° to 128°.

The last corresponds to straight angles.

Digonal neighbourhoods can therefore be reasonably divided into three classes:
- quasi-right digonal neighbourhoods (from 88° to 115°)
- obtuse digonal neighbourhoods (from 120° to 128°)
- straight digonal neighbourhoods.

(b) We will now study the case of the atom with three neighbours which consequently correspond to *third order neighbourhoods* or *trigonal neighbourhoods*.

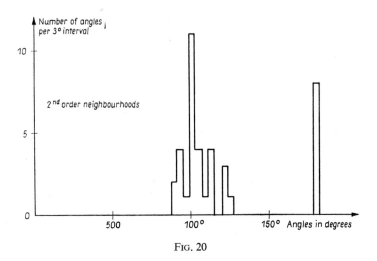

FIG. 20

The nuclei may or may not be in the plane of the three neighbouring atoms. In the first case, the neighbourhood is called *plane*, otherwise *pyramidal*.

The following atoms have plane trigonal neighbourhoods:
- carbon in vinyl bromide [93] ($C\hat{C}Br = 121°$)
- carbon in transdichloro-didoethylene [94] ($C\hat{C}I = 123.5°$)
- carbon in tetracloroethylene [95] ($C\hat{C}Cl = 123.7°$)
- some carbons in perylene [96] ($C\hat{C}H_2 = 125°$)
- carbon in formaldehyde [98] ($O\hat{C}H = 120°$)
- the carbons of naphthalene [97] (angles of 120°)
- carbon in carboxylic group of acetaldehyde [99] ($O\hat{C}H = 121°$)
- those of formic acid [100] ($O\hat{C}O = 120°$)
- carbon of the carboxylic group of methyl format [101] ($O\hat{C}O = 124°$)

— carbons of oxalic chloride[102] ($\hat{OCCl} = 123°$, $\hat{OCC} = 123°$)
— the carbons of phosgene[5] ($\hat{ClCCl} = 117°$)
— and those of thiophosgene[5] ($\hat{ClCCl} = 116°$)
— The majority of carbons of cyclopentadene[103], those of furan[104], of thiophene[103] and of pyrrole[10]
— the atom boron of difluoride of methyl boron[104] ($\hat{CBF} = 121°$)
— boron trichloride[105] ($\hat{ClBCl} = 120°$)
— boron trifluoride[105] ($\hat{BrBBr} = 120°$)
— the boron atoms of trimethyl oxide of boron[106] ($\hat{OBO} = 112°$)
— the nitrogen in the dimer of nitrogen peroxide[107] ($\hat{ONO} = 127°$)
— the nitrogen in nitromethane[95]
— nitric acid[108] (Fig.21) and tetranitromethane[109] ($\hat{ONO} = 127°$)
— sulphur in SO_2[110] ($\hat{OSO} = 120°$).

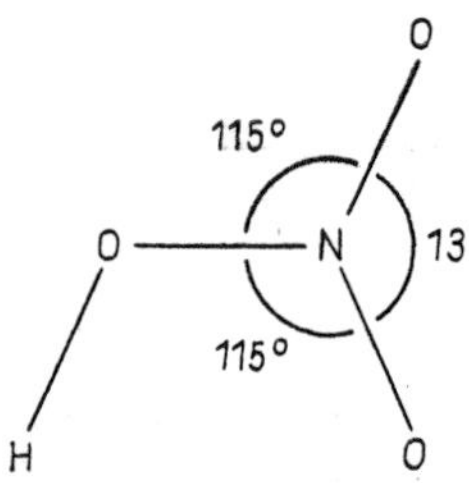

FIG. 21. Nitric acid.

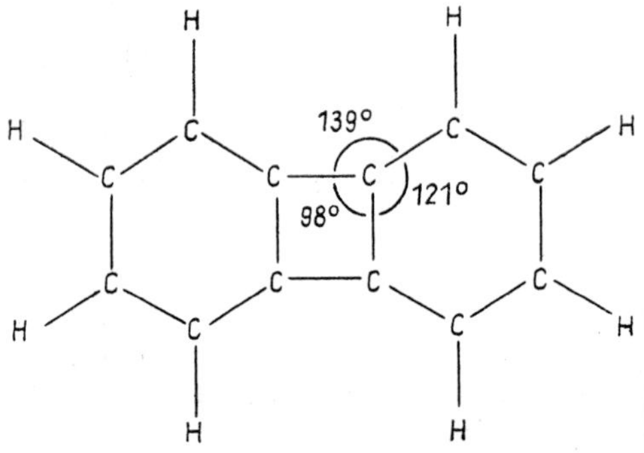

FIG. 22. Biphenylene.

To end, we must mention the case of biphenylene[111] (Fig.22) where some very peculiar angles appear and also the case of methylene cyclobutane[112] (Fig.23).

Figure 24 summarises these results. The essential fact is the appearance of a group of angles extending from 107° to 130°. The most frequent angles are approximately 120°.

Hence, in the case of plane trigonal neighbourhoods, the experimental data shows a predominance towards a regular disposition of bonds. In certain cases, this regularity disappears and the angles oscillate between 107° and 130°.

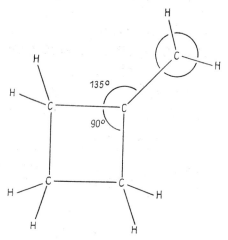

FIG. 23. Methylene cyclobutane.

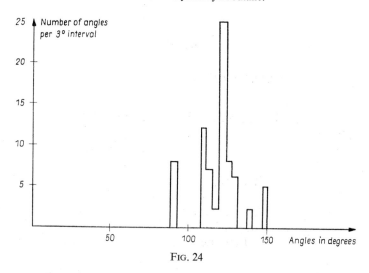

FIG. 24

In the exceptional cases, the existence of rings accompany the appearance of angles in the isolated regions of the histogram of Fig. 24 around 90°, 135°, and 150° (then called *distorted plane trigonal neighbourhoods*).

ESM 5

The following are examples of pyramidal trigonal neighbourhoods. The nitrogen of $\hat{N}H_3$[76] (HNH = 108°); the nitrogen of trimethylamine[113] (C$\hat{N}$C = 113°); the nitrogen in nitrogen fluoride NF_3[115] (F$\hat{N}$F = 102·5°); phosphorus in its trihalides[116] (F$\hat{P}$F = 104°, Cl$\hat{P}$Cl = 101°, Br$\hat{P}$Br = 100°, I$\hat{P}$I = 98°) and in trimethyl phosphine[116] (C$\hat{P}$C = 100°); arsenic in $AsBr_3$ (Br$\hat{As}$Br = 100°), in AsI_3[116] (I$\hat{As}$I = 100°), in $AsCl_3$ (Cl$\hat{As}$Cl = 103°) and in iododimethyl arsenide (I$\hat{As}$C = 98°)[117]; antimony in $SbCl_3$[116] (Cl$\hat{Sb}$Cl = 104°), $SbBr_3$[116] (Br$\hat{Sb}$Br = 96°), SbI_3[116] (I$\hat{Sb}$I = 98°) and sulphur in dimethyl sulphide[118] $(CH_3)_2SO$(O$\hat{S}$C = 107°, C$\hat{S}$C = 100°); and in the chlorides and bromides of thionyle[119] (Br$\hat{S}$Br = 96°, Cl$\hat{S}$Cl = 114°, O$\hat{S}$Cl = 106°).

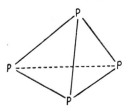

FIG. 25. The molecule P_4 of phosphorus.

In the molecules As_4 and P_4[120] the nuclei are situated at the vertices of a regular tetrahedron. The angles are 60° (Fig. 25).

Figure 26 shows that the situation is very simple.
The angles of a normal pyramidal trigonal neighbourhood vary between 96° and 115°. They are most frequently about 100°. The 60° angles appear in an entirely isolated fashion. They only appear in cyclic compounds. The corresponding neighbourhoods are called *distorted pyramidal trigonal neighbourhoods*.

(c) The case of *tetragonal neighbourhoods* (4 neighbours) is relatively simple.

Except for some cases of regular plane neighbourhoods where the angles are 90° and some distorted plane neighbourhoods (Fig. 27), the majority of neighbourhoods *of order 4* are tetrahedral, the tetrahedra formed by the four neighbouring nuclei being more or less regular.

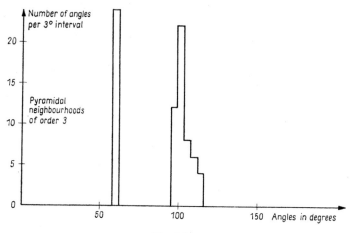

FIG. 26

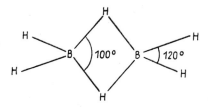

FIG. 27. A hydride of boron showing a distorted tetragonal neighbour-hood of order 4 about the boron.

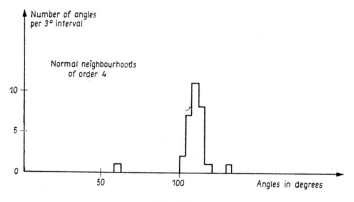

FIG. 28

Usually, the angles vary from 100° to 120°, the most frequent being 110° (Table 15.2, Fig. 28).

TABLE 15.2

Molecule		Nature of angle	Value (degrees)
Perchlorothiophosgene	CCl_4S	ClCS	109[121]
Bromoform	$CHBr_3$	BrCBr	111[122]
Chloroform	$CHCl_3$	ClCCl	112[122]
Fluoroform	CHF_3	FCF	108 or 109[122]
Iodoform	CHI_3	ICI	113[122]
Methylene bromide	Br_2CH_2	BrCBr	112[122]
Methylene iodide	I_2CH_2	ICI	114[122]
	CH_3Br_3Sn	BrSnBr	109[123]
Monobromoethane	$BrCH_2CH_3$	BrCC	109[124]
Trimethylaminoxide	$(CH_3)_3NO$	CNO	104[125]
		CNC	114
Oxychloride of molybdene	MoO_2Cl_2	OMoO	109[126]
		OMoCl	108
		ClMoCl	113
Chromyl chloride	CrO_2Cl_2	OCrO	105[126]
		OCrCl	109
		ClCrCl	113
Sulfuryl chloride	SO_2Cl_2	OSO	120[126]
		OSCl	106
		ClSCl	111
Sulfuryl fluoride	SO_2F_2	OSO	130[126]
		OSF	105
		FSF	100
Vanadyl chloride	Cl_3VO	ClVCl	111[126]
		ClVO	108
Phosphoric anhydride	P_4O_{10}	OPO	116[127]
			101 (s. Fig. 29)
	POF_3	FPF	107[128]
	$POFCl_2$	FPCl	106
		ClPCl	106

In these cases we will speak of tetrahedral neighbourhoods, reserving the term distorted tetrahedral for the very rare cases where the angles deviate greatly from 110° as in cyclopropane[129] and spiropentane[130] (Figs. 30 and 31).

The following table summarises the results obtained and introduces a notation for each type of neighbourhood.

Order	Angles (degrees)		Characteristic	Notation
	Value of maximum	Domain of variation		
1				1
2	100	(88–115)	quasi-right	2d
	120	(120–128)	obtuse	2o
	180		straight	2p
3	100	(96–115)	pyramidal	3y
	120	(107–130)	plane	3p
	60		pyramidal distorted	3yd
	95–135–150		plane distorted	3pd
4	90		plane	4p
	110	(100–120)	tetrahedral	4t
	100–120		plane distorted	4pd
	60–120		tetrahedral distorted	4td

This study can be extended to cover neighbourhoods of order 5, 6, 7 and 8.

The most interesting ones encountered are those derived from a triangular bipyramid, e.g. in PCl_3, and those derived from the octohedron which characterises the sulphur in SF_6 [131].

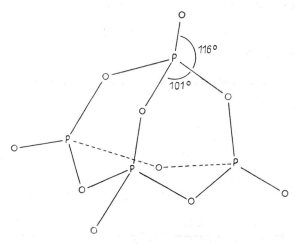

116°
101°

FIG. 29. Molecule of phosphoric anhydrid.

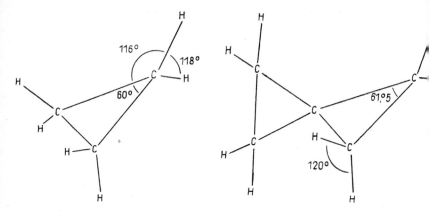

FIG. 30. Cyclopropane.   FIG. 31. Spiropentane.

C. *Valence Angles and the Most Probable Configuration*

Consider a bielectron system and let $\phi(M_1, \omega_1, M_2, \omega_2)$ be the wave function which characterises it. The probability of simultaneously finding electron 1 with spin ω_1 in volume dv_1 at M_1 and electron 2 with spin ω_2 in volume dv_2 at M_2 is

$$dP(M_1, M_2) = |\phi(M_1, \omega_1, M_2, \omega_2)|^2 \, dv_1 \, dv_2.$$

In the case where $M_1 = M_2 = M$ and $\omega_1 = \omega_2 = \omega$,

$$dP(M, M) = |\phi(M, \omega, M, \omega)|^2 \, dv_1 \, dv_2.$$

But, applying Pauli's principle

$$\phi(M_1, \omega_1, M_2, \omega_2) = -\phi(M_2, \omega_2, M_1, \omega_1)$$

In particular

$$\phi(M, \omega, M, \omega) = -\phi(M, \omega, M, \omega),$$

whence

$$\phi(M, \omega, M, \omega) = 0.$$

We can then conclude

$$dP(M, M) = 0.$$

Hence, we cannot encounter two electrons with the same spin in the neighbourhood of the same point. By continuity, it follows that two electrons of the same spin are never neighbours in probable configurations. In accordance with this, we have found (first book, p.116) that in its most probable configuration, atomic carbon (state ^5S) has a pair of electrons of opposite spin on the nucleus and four electrons of the same spin with angles between them of 109° 28'. Similarly (Linnet and Poe, *loc. cit.* first book, p.116) the most probable configuration of beryllium (state ^3P) corresponds to a pair on the nucleus and two electrons of the same spin 2·7 a.u. apart.

Finally, boron (state ^4P) has the same configuration with a pair of electrons on the nucleus and three coplanar electrons at 2·45 a.u. from the nucleus separated by angles of 120° (Fig.32).

We have mentioned (first book, Chapter 8) that in a simple bond two electrons of opposite spin are often found near the line of the nuclei. If, therefore, a number of simple bonds are considered to start from a core of an atom, one can extrapolate that they are organised so that electrons of the same spin gravitate about the core forming angles of 180°, 120° or 109° 28' between them depending on whether there are two, three or four bonds.

This explains why these angles are frequently encountered and how the valence angles of the following molecules are interpreted (Fig. 33a).

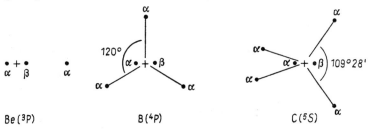

Be (^3P)   B (^4P)   C (^5S)

FIG. 32. The most probable configuration of some atoms.

Unshared electrons must be accounted for in the case of electrons about a core. The following formulae (Fig.33b): show why the valence angles are approximately 109° (108° and 105°) for ammonia and water and not those expected if the molecules had been considered to have only three or two bonds respectively.

Ta You Wu[132] has observed that this method of interpreting valence angles can be criticised.

It will be necessary, in fact, to introduce all the electrons of the atoms concerned into the calculations and it will be preferable to introduce variational parameters for each molecule and use the configuration method rather than a single determinant as was done by Linnet and Poe. One might add that the most probable configuration can only have a small probability in absolute value since

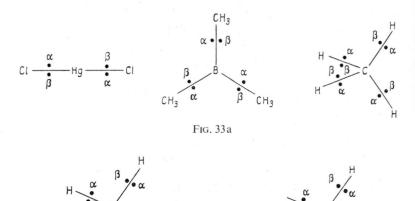

FIG. 33a

FIG. 33b

there is a large number of possible configurations and that it is perhaps dangerous to extend these general conclusions. The analysis given in Sections 15 and 16 of the first book shows that there are other more profound reasons behind the results reached here which gives this method a measure of validity.

D. Hybridation and Valence Angles

We have seen on various occasions that the orbitals in a determinant can be replaced by orthonormal linear combinations of the same functions, without changing the value of the determinant.

We have, for example, in the case of an atom:

$$\Psi = \begin{vmatrix} 2s(1) & 2p(1) \\ 2s(2) & 2p(2) \end{vmatrix} = \begin{vmatrix} \dfrac{1}{\sqrt{2}}\,[2s(1) + 2p(1)] & \dfrac{1}{\sqrt{2}}\,[2s(1) - 2p(1)] \\ \dfrac{1}{\sqrt{2}}\,[2s(2) + 2p(2)] & \dfrac{1}{\sqrt{2}}\,[2s(2) - 2p(2)] \end{vmatrix}$$

Without changing Ψ, we have altered an expression containing delocalised orbitals to one containing more localised hybrids (first book, p. 98).

Let us now consider a molecule formed by an atom A and two hydrogen atoms. Suppose that A contains a core $(1s)^2$, let us try to represent the bonds AH. Generalising the case of diatomic molecules, one can attempt to represent each bond by the introduction of a bonding orbital, a linear combination of atomic orbitals of the atoms forming the bond.

If h_1 and h_2 denote the orbitals $1s$ of the hydrogen atoms and if atom A has a core $(1s)^2$, one might be tempted to introduce the orbitals

$$2s + h_1 \quad \text{and} \quad 2p + h_2.$$

The second expression for Ψ, however, suggests

$$\frac{1}{\sqrt{2}}(2s + 2p) + h_1 \quad \text{and} \quad \frac{1}{\sqrt{2}}(2s - 2p) + h_2.$$

The following functions correspond to these two choices,

$$\phi = N \det 1s(1) \,\overline{1s(2)}\, [2s + h_1](3) \left[\overline{2s + h_1}\right](4) \times$$
$$\times [2p + h_2](5) \left[\overline{2p + h_2}\right](6)$$

$$\phi' = N \det 1s(1) \,\overline{1s(1)}\left[\frac{1}{\sqrt{2}}(2s + 2p) + h_1\right](3) \times$$
$$\times \left[\overline{\frac{1}{\sqrt{2}}(2s + 2p) + h_1}\right](4) \left[\frac{1}{\sqrt{2}}(2s - 2p) + h_2\right](5) \times$$
$$\times \left[\overline{\frac{1}{\sqrt{2}}(2s - 2p) + h_2}\right](6),$$

where N and N' are normalising constants. These two functions are different and one might ask which is the best. Generalising, we must find the best coefficients a, b, c, a', b', c' of the function

$$F = \det 1s(1) \, 1s(2) \, [a2s + b2p + ch_1](3) \left[\overline{a2s + b2p + ch_1}\right](4) \times$$
$$\times [a'2s + b'2p + c'h_2](5) \left[\overline{a'2s + b'2p + c'h_2}\right](6).$$

The most natural procedure is to determine by variation, the parameters which minimise the energy. Since this leads, however, to long computations, we have to look for quicker methods.

Pauling[133] has introduced the concept of the force of a hybrid. In a given direction this is simply its angular component in the approximation where the same radial component is used for the different elements of the hybrid.

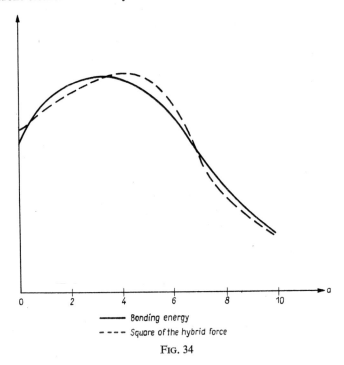

——— Bonding energy

- - - - Square of the hybrid force

FIG. 34

Pauling and Sherman[134] have shown for a one electron bond that its energy varies considerably with the force of the hybrid in the direction of the bond. Figure 34 shows how, in the example chosen, the bonding energy and the square of the force of the hybrid varies with parameter a, the hybrid being

$$as + (10 - a)p.$$

By perhaps rather a premature extrapolation, Pauling concludes that:

1. One is interested in hybrids possessing the greatest force (in absolute value) in any direction.

2. The second nucleus of a bond must be situated in the direction of maximum force of the hybrid associated with the other nucleus.

The second point is in accordance with work done by Coulson [13]. Coulson has, in effect, represented the bonds OH of the water molecule by means of orbitals h_1 and h_2 of the hydrogen atoms and orbitals p_x and p_y. The hydrogen atoms are assumed to be in the Oxy plane, and at a fixed distance from the oxygen nucleus at O, but forming angles α and $-\alpha$ with the bisector of xOy. The angle HÔH is therefore 2α. Coulson found that the energy of the system is a minimum for $\alpha = 45°$, i.e. one hydrogen atom on the x-axis, the other on the y-axis.

In some cases, these remarks can be used to anticipate valence angles.

Consider a molecule of the type AR_n where the bonds AR are simple and the atom A does not have any unshared peripheral electrons. A set of orbitals of A must first be chosen to be introduced into a function like F. A simple procedure consists of noting that in computing the interaction between electrons, a p orbital corresponds to a higher energy than an s orbital. Therefore, as few as possible p orbitals are introduced. As an example, suppose that there is an s orbital and 1, 2 or $3p$ orbitals depending on whether there are 2, 3 or 4 pairs of electrons about the core of A. This is sp, sp^2 or sp^3 hybridation respectively.

Since the different bonds to A are of the same type it is normally assumed that they have, if possible, equal energies. They must then be described by equivalent orbitals.

Now, we have previously met these orbitals (first book, p. 105) and we see that the directions of the maxima of the hybrid forces form angles of 180°, 120°, 109° 28′ for sp, sp^2 or sp^3 hybridation respectively.

The tetrahedral structure of methane is thus explained in yet another way. In this molecule, eight electrons gravitate about the carbon core and we use sp^3 hybridation, bringing with it angles of 109° 28′.

It is easy to show that the equivalent sp^3 hybrids have, in a certain direction, a maximum force which can be obtained by a linear combination of an s orbital and p orbitals.

Since the radial components are supposed common, the angular component of a hybrid can be written

$$T(\theta, \varphi) = \sum_k a_k \Theta_k(\theta, \varphi),$$

where the a_k are the coefficients of hybridation and Θ_k the angular components of the atomic orbitals of the hybrid.

Let us maximise this function in the direction θ_0, φ_0. Normalisation implies

$$\sum_k a_k^2 = 1.$$

Consequently, $T(\theta_0, \varphi_0)$ can be replaced by

$$\Lambda = T(\theta_0, \varphi_0) - \frac{\lambda}{2}\left(\sum_k a_k^2 - 1\right),$$

where λ is a variable factor.

Since T has continuous derivatives, for maximum Λ we must have

$$\frac{\partial \Lambda}{\partial a_k} = 0$$

for each k and hence

$$\Theta_k(\theta_0, \varphi_0) = \lambda a_k.$$

Normalisation allows λ to be fixed:

$$\sum_k a_k^2 = 1 = \frac{\Sigma \Theta_k^2(\theta_0, \varphi_0)}{\lambda},$$

hence

$$\lambda = \sqrt{\{\Sigma \Theta_k^2(\theta_0, \varphi_0)\}}$$

and therefore

$$a_k = \frac{\Theta_k(\theta_0, \varphi_0)}{\sqrt{\{\Sigma \Theta_k^2(\theta_0, \varphi_0)\}}}.$$

These are the coefficients which maximise T in the direction $T(\theta_0, \varphi_0)$.

A hybrid sp^3 is written

$$\varphi = as + bp_x + cp_y + dp_z.$$

The angular component is proportional to

$$T(\theta, \varphi) = a + b\sqrt{3}\sin\theta\cos\varphi + c\sqrt{3}\sin\theta\sin\varphi + d\sqrt{3}\cos\theta.$$

Let us maximise the function in the direction

$$\theta_0 = 54°58' \qquad \varphi_0 = 45°.$$

We have:

$$\cos \theta_0 = 1/\sqrt{3} \quad \sin \theta_0 = \sqrt{2}/\sqrt{3} \quad \cos \varphi_0 = \sin \varphi_0 = 1/\sqrt{2}$$

and

$$\Theta_1(\theta_0, \varphi_0) = \Theta_2(\theta_0, \varphi_0) = \Theta_3(\theta_0, \varphi_0) = \Theta_4(\theta_0, \varphi_0) = 1.$$

Hence

$$a_1 = a_2 = a_3 = a_4 = \tfrac{1}{2}$$

and

$$\varphi = \tfrac{1}{2}(s + p_x + p_y + p_z),$$

which is the first of the equivalent orbitals Te_1, derived from sp^3 hybridation (first book, p. 107).

These hybrids, therefore, should form strong bonds if Pauling's ideas are correct. The sp^3 hybridation must, therefore, be favourable to the formation of stable molecules which explains for example, the importance of the 4 valence of carbon in organic chemistry.

Many objections can be raised to Pauling's theory. In the first place, it can be asked at which point is it reasonable to use the same radial component for different orbitals? When the parameters Z_{eff} are the same, Slater's radial functions are identical; but if a hybridation between s, p and d orbitals is used, it is easy to see that Slater's rules lead to very different Z_{eff}.

Consider the case of phosphorus pentachloride. Five pairs of electrons gravitate about core p. The hybridation sp^3d is then imposed. Now for a phosphorus atom the configuration is found to be

$$(1s)^2 \ (2s)^2 \ (2p)^3 \ (3s) \ (3p)^6 \ (3d)$$

and by Slater's rules

$$(Z_{eff})_{M_{s\,p}} \simeq 5$$

$$(Z_{eff})_{M_d} \simeq 1.$$

The radial components of functions d differ considerably from those of functions s or p.

Craig[136] has shown that the effective parameters which have to be introduced in the molecular orbitals are very different from the preceding values. If, for orbitals s and p, the value 5 remains acceptable, the value 3 has to be chosen for the d orbitals.

Under those conditions, the radial components become very close and this objection loses most of its force.

A second question which can be put is: is the force of a hybrid a good measure of the bonding force? As has been seen before, this conclusion of Pauling's is an extrapolation based on a small number of calculations. Maccoll[137] has observed that the force of a hybrid and the "bonding force" are not always matched. Table 15.3 shows for systems CH, CH_4, C_2H_4 and C_2H_2, the dissociation energy and length of bond of CH, with the force of the hybrid chosen to represent it.

TABLE 15.3

System	Type of hybrid	Force of hybrid	Energy of dissociation (in kcal/mol)	Length of the CH bond (in Å)
CH	p	1·732	80	1·120
CH_4	sp^3	2	104	1·094
C_2H_4	sp^2	1·991	106	1·087
C_2H_2	sp	1·932	121	1·059

The increase in force from orbital p to hybrid sp^3 is accompanied, as hoped, by an increase of energy and a decrease of length. The decrease of force, however, as one passes from sp^3 through sp^2 to sp, is accompanied by an increase of energy and a decrease of length, contrary to what is expected from Pauling's theory.

This is why Maccoll has looked for a different criterion for the force which characterises a hybrid; he has proposed the use of the overlap integral between it and the orbital characterising the other atom of the bond. Figure 35 shows how the overlap integrals S_{CH} for the bonds CH vary as a function of

$$\varrho = \frac{a^2}{a^2 + b^2}$$

characterising the hybrid.

We see that these integrals, contrary to the force of the hybrid, increase from sp^3 to sp^2 and from sp^2 to sp and, in consequence, the bonding energy and the overlap integrals vary in the same sense.

Coulson[13] has given arguments showing that this result will not hold in general. Mulliken[139] has examined this problem in some depth. In Table 15.4 he compares force and integral of overlap.

TABLE 15.4

Bond	Value of overlap integral for different types of hybrid				
	s	p	sp	sp^2	sp^3
Li—Li	0·59	0·05			
C—C	0·34	0·33			0·65
C=C				0·77	
C≡C			0·88		
Force	1	1·732	1·932	1·991	2

We see that both force and overlap increase from an s or p orbital, but in accordance with Maccoll's results they vary in opposite senses in the series sp, sp^2, sp^3. Mulliken has drawn attention to the fact

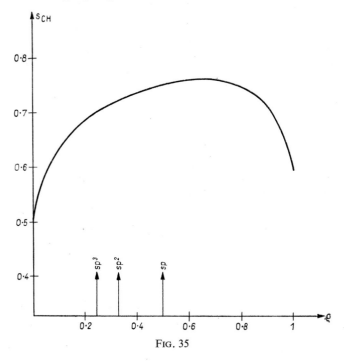

FIG. 35

that the value of this integral depends strongly on the particular form of explicit function used to represent an orbital and that, for example, a function of Slater and a self-consistent field function lead to different results. The relationship between energy and overlap integral merits a deeper analysis. Mulliken[140] has made an important step in this direction by establishing what he somewhat whimsically calls magic formulae. By examining simple cases, he established approximate formulae connecting the bonding energy and the overlap integrals between the orbitals which arise in these bonds. The formulae contain different quantities which are determined empirically and coefficients v which are allowed to vary. As before, the overlap integrals can be expressed as a function of ratios ϱ characterising the hybridation of orbitals introduced. These functions then express the energy as a function of ϱ and v. The values of ϱ and v which give the strongest bond can then be found by variation.

This method has brought us back in a semi-empiric fashion to a point very close to the direct method from which we started.

E. *Walsh's Method*

In Section 15D, the methods essentially depended on the structure of the atomic orbitals used in the representation of the bond. Walsh's method[141] gives prominence to the symmetry orbitals.

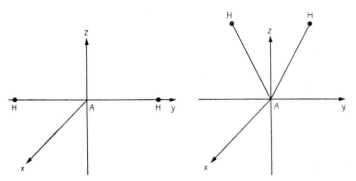

FIG. 36. The molecule AH_2 with angle HAH straight and acute.

Consider a molecule AH_2. Let h_1 and h_2 be the $1s$ orbitals of the hydrogen atoms and suppose that A introduces orbitals $2s$, $2p_x$, $2p_y$ and $2p_z$ into the bonds. The type of symmetry characterising the molecule depends on whether or not angle HÂH equals 180°. If it is, then letting the A nucleus lie on the y-axis, the symmetry is the same as that for a homonuclear diatomic molecule.

We can easily find the symmetry orbitals shown below together with their characteristic symbols:

$$h_1 + h_2; \quad 2s \quad \sigma_g$$

$$h_1 - h_2; \quad p_y \quad \sigma_u$$

$$p_x; \quad\quad p_z \quad \pi_u.$$

If the angle does not equal 180° and if the H nuclei are placed on plane yz such that the z-axis is bisector of HÂH (Fig. 36) then, among the symmetry operators, we can consider $c_2(z)$ a rotation of 180° about the z-axis, and $\sigma_v(y)$ the reflection in plane xz. We can then distinguish the representations of Table 15.5.

TABLE 15.5

	$c_2(z)$	$\sigma_v(y)$
a_1	$+$	$+$
a_2	$+$	$-$
b_1	$-$	$+$
b_2	$-$	$-$

It is immediately obvious that $h_1 + h_2$, $2s$ and $2p_z$ are symmetry orbitals pertaining to representation a_1, p_x to b_1, and that orbitals $h_1 - h_2$ and p_y behave like b_2. The molecular orbitals can be constructed by combining symmetry orbitals of the same representation. This leads naturally to the construction of a correlation diagram of the energies of molecular orbitals against HÂH. Figure 37 shows such a diagram.

Its behaviour can be justified by means of general arguments such as the following. A $2p$ level is higher in energy than a state $2s$; the energy, therefore, increases rapidly between a_1 and π_u. On the other hand, from b_2 to σ_u the energy decreases since $h_1 - h_2$ is by nature anti-bonding. The fine detail of this diagram requires more delicate study.

For instance, the point of intersection of the lines, b_2, σ_u and $2s$, π_u at approximately 110° has been fixed by a method based on the examination of the Rydberg series for the water molecule.

Consider now a molecule containing four electrons about the core of A, e.g. BeH_2. They must occupy the two orbitals of lowest energy. The diagram shows that the sum of the corresponding energies will be less for an angle of $180°$ than for an angle of $90°$.

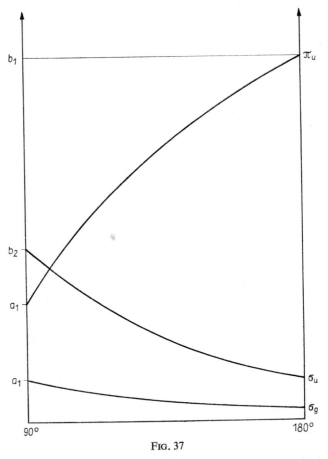

FIG. 37

BeH_2 will, therefore, be linear. If, as in H_2O, H_2S, H_2Se, H_2Te, there are eight electrons about core A, the four orbitals of the diagram will be occupied, in particular orbital $a_1\pi_u$ which is much more advantageous for $90°$.

This is Walsh's interpretation of molecules which have the angle $H\hat{A}H$ almost a right angle.

Although it is easy to find weaknesses in Walsh's reasoning, his method is interesting in the sense that it gives evidence of a connection between the valence angles and the number of electrons contained in a molecule. Table 15.6, taken from Walsh's articles, shows that the connection is very real.

TABLE 15.6

Molecule of type AB_2	Number of electrons about the cores	(Angle in degrees)
NO_2	17	or 132, 154 depending on the authors
NOCl	18	116
SO_2	18	119
ClO_2	19	116
F_2O	20	101
Cl_2O	20	110
I_3	22	180
$(CHBr)^-$	22	180

In the series of molecules of type AB_2, the angle is wide for 17 electrons, falls to about 120° for 18 or 19 electrons, closes a little for 20 electrons then becomes 180° for 22 electrons.

Wheatley[142] has studied, in a similar fashion, molecules of the types

showing that they are plane if they contain (around the cores A) 10, 22, 34, 12, 24 or 36 electrons, and not plane if they have 14, 26 or 38 electrons.

For example, ethylene is plane and contains 12 electrons about carbon cores and hydrazine is not plane and contains 14 electrons about nitrogen cores.

16. SOME REMARKS ON THE STRUCTURE OF POLYATOMIC MOLECULES

A. Localised and Non-localised Bonds

We shall now reintroduce, from a more physical point of view, the distinction made in the first book between localised and non-localised bonds. We shall first recall some of the principal facts characterising the structure of atoms and molecules which we have previously discussed.

The principal phenomena which determine the structure of an atom are the following: (a) a positive nucleus attracting the electrons according to Coulomb's law, while the electrons repel one another. (b) The electrons possess a spin whose value, for a given axis, is either $+\frac{1}{2}h/2\pi$ or $-\frac{1}{2}h/2\pi$.

Two electrons of opposite spins can exist in the same small region of space, while two electrons of the same spin tend to be far apart. Under the influence of these different factors, *the electrons tend to occupy a certain mean position.* Thus, there exists around the nucleus a sphere (corresponding to the K-shell) where there are "holes" for two electrons of opposite spin. Around this sphere there is a spherical shell (corresponding to the L-shell) where there is room for eight electrons (4 of one spin and 4 of the other).

These results can be expressed more rigorously. For instance, in the case of ion F⁻ in its ground state, it has been shown[143] that there is a probability of 80 per cent of encountering two and only two electrons within a sphere with centre the nucleus and radius 0·35 a.u., the other eight electrons being outside this sphere.

In general, two types of regions can be distinguished in a molecule: cores situated near the nuclei, whose electron organisation is nearly the same as in free atoms and the superficial zones which are much more disturbed by the bond. Nevertheless, certain characteristics of the free atom are found in this zone. If the molecule results from the union of the two atoms in the first period, the bond arises from the fusion of the K-shells and the cores reduce to the nuclei themselves. In the neighbourhood of each nucleus there is only room for a maximum of two electrons of opposite spin. If the molecule consists of the union of an atom of the first period and one of the second period, the bond results from the fusion of the K-shell of the first and the L-shell of the second. A K-core of two electrons is found at the nucleus of the latter. In the neighbourhood of this core, there is room for four pairs of electrons of opposite spin and near the nucleus of the first element, one pair can gravitate.

Finally, if the molecule results from the union of two electrons of the second period, the bond comes from the fusion of the two L-shells. Two K-cores, about which four pairs of electrons can gravitate, are then found.

Between two cores (and similarly if they reduce to simple nuclei) there exists a zone relatively near to both nuclei. An electron entering this region, is attracted strongly to both nuclei at the same time. *This is, therefore, a zone of low potential which the electrons occupy in a privileged manner.* It can contain a pair of electrons which, near both the cores, can be considered to gravitate about the two cores simultaneously.

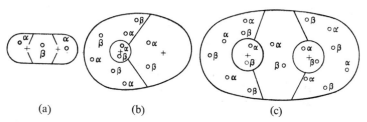

(a) (b) (c)

FIG. 38 (a) Two elements of the first period, e.g. H_2^-, He_2^+; the central zone is then a one electron bond; (b) An element of the first period and an element of the second period, e.g. FH; here, the bond brings in two electrons. (c) Two elements of the second period, e.g. F_2; the central zone corresponds to a two electron bond.

Figure 38 symbolises the structure of systems containing the maximum possible number of electrons. Consider a hydrocarbon such as normal butane. The superficial zone results from the superposition of L-shells of four atoms of carbon and the K-shells of ten atoms of hydrogen. Each carbon introduces into this zone four electrons and each hydrogen one electron. In all, the zone is populated by twenty-six electrons. Now, in the molecule there are thirteen intervals between neighbouring cores. Each of these intervals constitute a position of low potential for two electrons and the twenty-six superficial electrons go in pairs in these intervals making, therefore, thirteen bonds of two electrons. This verifies that eight electrons gravitate about each core. *When all the positions are occupied the molecule is called saturated. Each of its individual bonds between each pair of cores is called localised.*

Let us replace one of the extreme carbons by a very electronegative substitute X, e.g. fluorine. In the bond FC, the mean position of the electrons tends to be nearer the F core than the C core. The carbon loses a fraction of its electrons.

In fact, it needs more electrons than the neighbouring carbon. In the CC bond neighbouring the CF bond the electrons are displaced slightly towards the carbon of the CF bond, moderating its lack of electrons and inducing a further position change to its neighbouring carbon.

Thus, by induction, this transfer of charge is transmitted along the chain, becoming, however, very rapidly attenuated as the electrons under consideration are deviated in zones of low potential where they are not easily deflected: *they are only slightly polarisable.* The hydrogen atoms, being less electronegative than the carbon atoms, allow the electrons of the CH bonds to come a little closer to the carbon cores and also contribute to the nullification of the charges in the carbon atoms. Figure 39 shows the essentials of this phenomenon. The transmission is, therefore, non-alternating and rapidly nullifies the effect of the substitution.

Now consider benzene; this molecule is planar and the superficial zone results from the fusion of the *L*-shells of six carbon atoms and the *K*-shells of six hydrogen atoms; it contains, therefore,

$$6 \times 4 + 6 = 30 \text{ electrons.}$$

There are twelve intervals between neighbouring cores, i.e. places for twenty-four electrons to form two-electron localised bonds CC and CH.

By only considering these twenty-four electrons, it can be seen that six electrons gravitate about each carbon core.

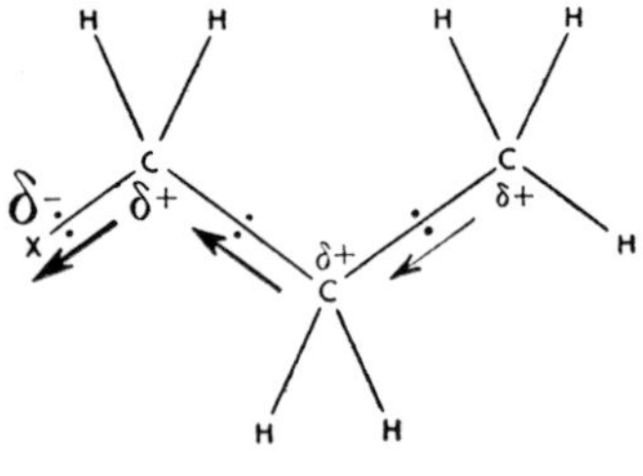

FIG. 39 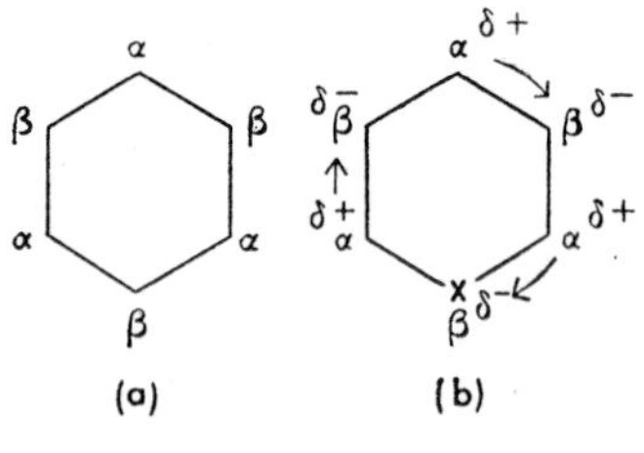   FIG. 40

About each of them, therefore, there are places for two other electrons, *a total of twelve places for six electrons.* Obviously various arrangements are possible for these six electrons and the presence of a substitute can favour one or other arrangement, inducing a wholesale reorganisation of the electron distribution.

Also, the available positions are found both above and below the molecular structure formed of the cores and the localised bonds and, consequently, correspond to zones of higher potential than the intervals between the cores. *Polarisable and easily reorganised, this six electron system is not an entity formed of parts localised between pairs of cores but rather a single bond diffused over the set of six carbon cores of the molecule and is called a de-localised bond of six electrons.*

A very probable configuration of the six electrons is given in Fig. 40a as the electrons of the same spin are then as far away from one another as possible.

Let us replace one of the CH groups by an atom X, supposed more electronegative, such that the number of electrons in the non-localised bonds remains unchanged (as in the case of nitrogen). One of the α electrons will tend to approach the nitrogen. This induces a movement represented by the arrows of Fig. 40b and consequently the appearance of alternating positive and negative charges. Since it is made up of very polarisable electrons dispersed over a large area, this has an important effect on the ensemble of the non-localised bond.

The non-alternating and rapidly decaying effect found for the paraffin series corresponds here to an alternating and slowly decaying effect. In other words, a de-localised bond is capable of transmitting the effect of a perturbator over its entire extent.

Experiment confirms these conclusions. N-butylamine is formed by the replacement of a terminal hydrogen by a methyl in propylamine. This substitution changes the dissociation constant of the amine by only 10 per cent. In water at 25° we have [144]

$$\text{for propylamine} \qquad K_a = 2 \cdot 63 \times 10^{-11}$$
$$\text{for } n\text{-butylamine} \qquad K_a = 2 \cdot 45 \times 10^{-11}$$

10-methyl acridine is produced from acridine by a similar substitution of a methyl.

In a 50 per cent mixture of alcohol and water at 20°, we have [145]

$$\text{for acridine} \qquad K_a = 7 \cdot 7 \times 10^{-5}$$
$$\text{for methyl derivative} \quad K_a = 2 \cdot 0 \times 10^{-5}.$$

The variation here is therefore forty times as much (in relative value) as that in the preceding case. Now, the reasoning made for the benzene nucleus generalises easily for the case of the anthracene nucleus, showing that it contains a non-localised bond extending over all the rings. *This is a property belonging to all hydrocarbons called completely conjugated.*

B. *Note on the Representation of Bonds*
in Polyatomic Molecules by the Self-consistent Field Method:
Localised and De-localised Orbitals

Let us take an approximate wave function ϕ on doubly occupied orbitals:

$$\phi = \det \varphi_1(1)\,\alpha(1)\,\varphi_1(2)\,\beta(2) \ldots \varphi_p(2p-1)\,\alpha(2p-1)\,\varphi_p(2p)\,\beta(2p).$$

The self-consistent field equations can be written

$$\mathfrak{H}^{C.A.C.}\varphi_n = \sum_m E_{mn}\varphi_m$$

by setting

$$\mathfrak{H}^{C.A.C.} = \mathfrak{K} + \mathfrak{B} + \mathfrak{A}$$

(by an obvious extension of equation (21) of first book, p. 80). We have already seen that the orbitals φ in the determinant can be replaced by orthonormal linear combinations

$$\chi_j = \sum_i T_{ji}\varphi_i$$

without changing ϕ.

The self-consistent field equation can then be written

$$\mathfrak{H}^{'C.A.C.}\chi_j = \sum_l e_{jl}\chi_l.$$

Operator $\mathfrak{H}'$ can be written as a function of χ in exactly the same manner as $\mathfrak{H}$ is written as a function of φ. Moreover

$$e_{jl} = \sum T_{mj}^{-1}E_{mn}T_{ln}.$$

There exists a transformation T which diagonalises the matrix E_{mn}. Using the corresponding χ which will be denoted by χ^s, the self-consistent field equations are now written

$$\mathfrak{H}^{s.C.A.C.}\chi_j^s = e_{jj}\chi_j^s.$$

Once the orbitals χ^s are known and fixed this equation can be considered as an eigenvalue equation. Moreover it can be shown that the symmetry operator commutes with $\mathfrak{H}^{s.C.A.C.}$. The functions χ^s, relative to a non-degenerate level of this operator are, therefore, eigenfunctions of the symmetry operators of the molecule. The χ^s are, therefore, symmetry orbitals. Consequently, they have equal absolute values for symmetric points of the molecule. If an orbital χ^s has an important region in a small domain of the molecule then it will have important regions in all symmetric domains.

These symmetric domains are often distant from one another. For example, the four carbon atoms situated in β of naphthalene are of this type. The orbital extends over most of the molecule: *this is why we often call these orbitals de-localised.*

As a further example, consider after Coulson[146] the case of methane in an L.C.A.O. approximation. The carbon nucleus is placed at the origin of rectangular axes $Oxyz$ and the four hydrogen atoms are placed at tetrahedral points of a cube centred on O with faces parallel to the axial planes (points Te_1, Te_2, Te_3, Te_4 of Fig. 15 of the first book). The two electrons of the K-shell of carbon correspond to a core which can be represented by a $1s$ orbital used twice. The other symmetry orbitals may, therefore, be formed by means of orbitals $2s$, $2p_x$, $2p_y$, $2p_z$ of carbon and the $1s$ orbitals of the four hydrogen atoms a, b, c and d respectively.

They have the form

$$s = 2s + \lambda(a + b + c + d)$$

$$t_x = 2p_x + \mu(a + b - c - d)$$

$$t_y = 2p_y + \mu(-a + b + c - d)$$

$$t_z = 2p_z + \mu(-a + b - c + d),$$

where λ and μ can be determined using the self-consistent field method.

By introducing some other approximations, Coulson has found:[147]

$$\lambda = 0.122$$

$$\mu = 0.588.$$

The function representing methane can then be written

$$\phi = N \det 1s(1)\,\overline{1s(2)}\,s(3)\,\overline{s(4)}\,t_x(5)\,\overline{t_x(6)}\,t_y(7)\,\overline{t_y(8)}\,t_z(9)\,\overline{t_z(10)}$$

N being a normalising constant.

Without changing ϕ, the s and t can be replaced by the orthogonal combinations

$$A = s + t_x - t_y - t_z$$

$$B = s + t_x + t_y + t_z$$

$$C = s - t_x + t_y - t_z$$

$$D = s - t_x - t_y + t_z.$$

Then,

$$\phi = N' \det 1s(1)\ \overline{1s(2)}\ A(3)\ \overline{A(4)}\ B(5)\ \overline{B(6)}\ C(7)\ \overline{C(8)}\ D(9)\ \overline{D(10)}$$

N' being another normalising constant.

Let us look more closely at the function B. We have:

$$B = 2s + 2p_x + 2p_y + 2p_z + (\lambda + 3\mu)\, b + (\lambda - \mu)\, (a + c + d)$$

$$= Te_1 + 1 \cdot 886b - 0 \cdot 446(a + c + d).$$

This is principally a combination of tetrahedral hybrid Te_1 (first book, p. 107) and the $1s$ orbital of the hydrogen towards which it points.

Considering the electron density arising from the B orbital alone, we find that, near this hydrogen nucleus, the density is ϱ times greater than that at comparable points near the other nuclei, where

$$\varrho = \frac{(1 \cdot 886)^2}{(0 \cdot 446)^2} \simeq 16.$$

The B orbital is therefore almost "localised" about one of the CH bonds of methane.

It is obvious that the other functions A, B and C are derived by a displacement of B and are each localised along one of the CH bonds. They are, therefore, equivalent orbitals.

In conclusion, a molecule like methane formed by localised bonds can be represented by either localised or non-localised orbitals: the difference between them is a change in notation which does not alter the total wave function.

There is, therefore, no correspondence between localisation for bonds and localisation for orbitals.

With this remark, we end this chapter preparatory to a detailed examination of the electronic structure of polyatomic molecules.

CHAPTER V

Molecules Containing only Cores and Simple Bonds

WE WILL start the detailed examination of the properties of poly-atomic molecules by considering molecules containing only cores and simple bonds and, consequently, containing no unshared electrons.

This type of molecule is, without doubt, the easiest to study. The saturated hydrocarbons C_nH_{2n+2} such as methane and the cyclo-paraffins give good examples of molecules of this type.

17. METHANE

A. *The Method of Self-consistent Field L.C.A.O.*

The simplest molecule of this type is methane CH_4 which was discussed in the last chapter.

We have already said that, using a procedure based on the L.C.A.O. self-consistent field method but continuing some other important approximations, Coulson has produced the orbitals

$$s = 2s + 0 \cdot 122(a + b + c + d)$$

$$t_x = 2p_x + 0 \cdot 588(a + b - c - d)$$

$$t_y = 2p_y + 0 \cdot 588(-a + b + c - d)$$

$$t_z = 2p_z + 0 \cdot 588(-a + b - c + d).$$

In the course of this calculation, he obtained 1·974 and 2·966 a. u. for the two first ionisation energies of this molecule, while experiment[148] gives: 0·4793 and 0·7351.

There is obviously little agreement. A calculation of the same type but containing fewer approximations, has recently been carried out[149]. In this procedure Roothaan's method has been rigorously applied. The only extra approximations have been made in the calculation of some of the molecular integrals appearing in the calculation. Obviously in certain elements of the matrix necessary to the calculation, an integral such as

$$\int 2s(1)\, a(1)\, \frac{1}{r_{12}}\, b(2)\, c(2)\, dv_1\, dv_2$$

arises. This integral is called tetracentric, as it is comprised of four functions centred on different points. The calculation of such an integral, as well as tricentric integrals which also arise, is extremely laborious.

These integrals have had to be estimated by a method due to Mulliken[150] which will be considered later.

A value of 40·15 a. u. is obtained for the total energy of methane, the experimental result being 40·71[151].

The ionisation energies are found to be 1·330 and 1·560. Although better than Coulson's results, these values are still far from the experimental values. It would be interesting to repeat this calculation using the exact values of all the integrals.

B. *Method of Localised Orbitals and the Method of Semi-localised Orbitals*

We have shown in Section 16 that the wave function of methane formed by a determinant made up of the symmetry orbitals is equivalent to one formed by another determinant made up of orbitals almost localised along each bond CH. We have seen, for example, that one of these orbitals can be written

$$B = Te_1 + (\lambda + 3\mu)\, b + (\lambda - \mu)\, [a + c + d].$$

A small "localisation flaw" exists by reason of the presence of a combination of atomic orbitals a, c and d in this orbital directed towards the hydrogen atom b.

It is clear that this "flaw" disappears when

$$\lambda = \mu.$$

The method of *localised orbitals* consists of imposing this equality. Each CH bond is then "represented" in the determinant by a doubly occupied orbital of the type

$$Te + kh,$$

where h is one of the $1s$ orbitals of the hydrogen atoms and Te one of the tetrahedral orbitals of carbon.

The method of "semi-localised" orbitals, already encountered, (Section 6) consists here of associating with each CH bond two simply occupied orbitals $Te + kh$ and $k'Te + h$.

Mueller[152] has used both these methods. He has shown that the method of semi-localised orbitals gives a better result for the bonding energy of methane than the method of localised orbitals. This is not surprising as the latter method introduces an extra variational parameter. Unfortunately, here again it is necesary to make many approximations in the calculation of molecular integrals.

C. Method of the United Atom and Allied Methods

The method of the united atom has also been applied in the case of methane[153]. The complete Hamiltonian is used but the trial function is chosen as if we were considering a neon atom. We, therefore, let

$$\phi = \det 1s(1)\,\alpha(1)\ 1s(2)\,\beta(2)\ 2s(3)\,\alpha(3)\ 2s(4)\,\beta(4)\ 2p_x(5)\,\alpha(5) \times$$

$$\times 2p_x(6)\,\beta(6)\ 2p_y(7)\,\alpha(7)\ 2p_y(8)\,\beta(8)\ 2p_z(9)\,\alpha(9)\ 2p_z(10)\,\beta(10),$$

where the s and p are hydrogen-like functions and determine by variation the effective atomic numbers.

The total energy is only 38·75 a.u. but the ionisation energies are calculated at 11·21 and 18·02 eV, comparing well with the experimental values (13·04 and 20 eV).

A number of variants on this method has been proposed.

Buckingham, Massey and Tibbs[154], for example, have represented methane by a set of ten electrons gravitating in the potential of a carbon nucleus surrounded by a uniformly charged sphere replacing the four protons. The total charge in this sphere is made equal to $4e$ and its radius is interpreted as distance CH.

The best product function of the type

$$(1s)^2\ (2s)^2\ (2p)^6$$

is then found using the self-consistent field method of Hartree. The authors found an excellent value for the energy (40·37 a.u.).

Banyard and March[155] have calculated by means of the wave function, so obtained, the diffraction factor of X-rays for methane. It agrees well with the experimental results of Thomer[156].

Bernal[157] has tackled the problem by finding a function formed by a determinant of analogous orbitals in which the radial parts have the following analytic forms:

$$R(1s) = 2\alpha^{3/2} e^{-\alpha r}$$

$$R(2s) = \left\{ \frac{12\beta^5}{\alpha^2 - \alpha\beta + \beta^2} \right\}^{1/2} [1 - 1/3(\alpha + \beta) r] e^{-\beta r}$$

$$R(2p) = \left(\frac{4\gamma^5}{3} \right)^{1/2} r e^{-\gamma r},$$

where α, β and γ are variational parameters. In fact, to simplify the calculation, Bernal fixed parameter α at the value which it has for nitrogen but, on the other hand, allowed the radius r_0 of the uniformly charged sphere to vary.

The parameters corresponding to minimum energy are

$$\beta = 1\cdot75 \quad \gamma = 1\cdot3 \quad r_0 = 1\cdot975 \pm 0.025 \text{ a. u.}$$

It is interesting to note that this value for r_0 coincides exactly with the length of the bond CH of methane†. The minimum energy obtained is 39·33 a.u. Bernal surmised that this value is not so good as in the previous case because he did not allow α to vary.

Mills[158] has perfected Bernal's calculation, finding the best function

$$(1s)^2 (2s)^2 (2p)^6$$

in the Hartree–Fock sense. He obtained an energy of $-39\cdot38$ a.u., i.e. a gain of 0·05 on Bernal's figure.

Carter[159] has taken a slightly different viewpoint. Keeping the form of the potential, he finds the best product function but instead of using in this product, orbitals of the type 1s, 2s, 2p, etc., he uses functions having the same symmetry properties but of a more general type.

† This is 2·05 a.u. (T. FELDMAN, J. ROMANKO and H. L. WALSH, *Canad. J. Phys.*, **33** (1955), 138).

For example, $2p_x$ is replaced by

$$2T_{2x} = a2p_x + b3d_{yz}.$$

The total energy so obtained is 39·68 a.u.

Koide et al.[160] have modified Carter's method, principally by using a determinant function. They obtained an energy of 39·64 a.u.

When these last results are compared with Buckingham's (40·37 a.u.) one is rather surprised to find that the first calculation gives the best value for the energy. The explanation is very simple. There is a numerical error in Buckingham's work. Koide corrects this, the corresponding energy being only 39·47 a.u.

The following table summarises the calculations using spherically symmetric potentials.

Type of function	Authors	Energy (a.u.)
Product of numerical functions: type $(1s)^2 (2s)^2 (2p)^6$	Buckingham et al.	39·47
Analytic determinant: type $(1s)^2 (2s)^2 (2p)^6$	Bernal	39·33
Numerical determinant: type $(1s)^2 (2s)^2 (2p)^6$	Mills	39·38
Product of analytic functions: type $(1s)^2 (2s)^2 (T_2)^6$	Carter	39·68
Determinant of analytic functions	Koide et al.	39·64

For completeness, we mention a paper by E. Kapuy[161] in which a wave function derived from the mesomeric method is used with the same potential.

Methane has also been studied using the method of Thomas and Fermi[162] and Karplus and Anderson[163] have discussed in this case the problem of interaction between the electron pairs and the spins of nuclei; however, this problem is outside the scope of this book.

18. THE ALICYCLIC PARAFFINS
AND THE IDEA OF A SIMPLE BOND

A. *Individuality of a Simple Bond*

For a molecule as simple as methane, we cannot do a complete self-consistent L.C.A.O. calculation.

Therefore, this method is, for the moment, not applicable to higher homologues of methane. Methods based on the use of a spherically symmetrical wave function are not very satisfying from a physical point of view since they do not describe the CH bonds in the molecule. Hence, we look for a method less difficult than the self-consistent field L.C.A.O. method but at the same time retaining the individuality of the CC and CH bonds in the paraffins. The method of linear combinations of bonding orbitals fulfills these requirements. Before describing this method, we will lay stress on the individuality of simple bonds.

This individuality may be illustrated by looking at, for example, the length and bonding energy of the CC and CH bonds of the paraffins.

Table 18.1 contains the experimental values for the length of these bonds.

TABLE 18.1

Molecule	Length of bonds in Å	
	CC	CH
Methane		$1 \cdot 091^{[164]}$
Ethane	$1 \cdot 543$	$1 \cdot 102^{[165]}$
Propane	$1 \cdot 54 \pm 0 \cdot 02^{[166]}$	
Iso-butane	$1 \cdot 54 \pm 0 \cdot 02^{[167]}$	
Cyclohexane	$1 \cdot 54 \pm 0 \cdot 015^{[168]}$	

This shows that the length of the CC or CH bond in this series is constant to within experimental error.

The idea of the bonding energy of a particular bond of a molecule is not so straightforward as that of the length of the bond[169]. In the present case, the bonding energies of bonds CC and CH can be defined if there exists numbers E_{CC} and E_{CH} such that the formula

$$N_{CC}E_{CC} + N_{CH}E_{CH}$$

gives a good approximation of the atomisation energy of the hydro-carbon where N_{CC} and N_{CH} are the number of CC and CH bonds respectively (first book, p. 183).

Table 18.2 gives[170] the difference between the energy calculated from this formula and the experimental values for several molecules using

$$E_{CH} = 98 \cdot 75 \text{ kcal/mol}$$

$$E_{CC} = 83 \cdot 6 \text{ kcal/mol}$$

the sublimation energy of graphite being fixed at 171·7 kcal/mol.

TABLE 18.2

Molecule	Difference in kcal/mol
Methane	− 3·8
Ethane	− 0·5
Propane	0
n-Butane	0
Isopentane	0
Neopentane	− 0·5
Cyclopentane	− 0·9
Cyclohexane	0

These differences are small, and it is, therefore, possible to assign meaningfully a bonding energy to CC and CH bonds in the paraffin series. This is another proof of the individuality of these bonds in the molecules being considered.

B. *The Method of Linear Combinations of Bonding Orbitals*

The presence in paraffins of bonds having strong individuality suggests their association with orbitals. To represent a paraffin, molecular orbitals φ_j can be defined by analogy with the L.C.A.O. method, as linear combinations of different bonding orbitals Y_i of the bonds CC and CH. Hence,

$$\varphi_j = \sum_i c_{ij} Y_i.$$

Note that this only describes the bonding zone of the paraffin. The description is, consequently, generally adopted in a model where the $1s$ orbitals of carbon are regarded as cores.

Following the view which leads to Roothaan's equations, one obtains formally identical equations which can be solved if the Y_i are known explicitly.

One can also use a semi-empiric method analogous to Hückel's method (first book, Section 28). If $\mathfrak{C}$ denotes the self-consistent field operator, the secular system allowing the calculation of c_{ip} is

$$\sum_i c_{ip} \left[\int Y_p \mathfrak{C} Y_i \, dv - \varepsilon \int Y_p Y_i \, dv \right] = 0.$$

Since we have seen that the paraffin bonds are rather well individualised, it is reasonable to assume that to a first approximation the overlap integrals are zero, i.e.

$$\int Y_p Y_i \, dv = 0 \quad \text{for} \quad i \neq p.$$

In the case of methane, the integral

$$\int Y_p \mathfrak{C} Y_p \, dv$$

is independent of p and the integral

$$\int Y_p \mathfrak{C} Y_i \, dv$$

(with $p \neq i$) does not depend on the indices, by symmetry considerations.

Hence we can then set

$$\alpha_{\mathrm{CH}} = \int Y_p \mathfrak{C} Y_p \, dv$$

$$\beta_{\mathrm{CH,CH'}} = \int Y_p \mathfrak{C} Y_i \, dv.$$

Putting

$$\alpha = \alpha_{\mathrm{CH}} \quad \text{and} \quad \beta = \beta_{\mathrm{CH,CH'}}$$

we find from the secular equation that

$$\begin{vmatrix} \alpha - \varepsilon & \beta & \beta & \beta \\ \beta & \alpha - \varepsilon & \beta & \beta \\ \beta & \beta & \alpha - \varepsilon & \beta \\ \beta & \beta & \beta & \alpha - \varepsilon \end{vmatrix} = 0.$$

The roots of this equation are

$$\varepsilon_1 = \alpha + 3\beta$$

and

$$\varepsilon_2 = \alpha - \beta$$

which is a triple root. Following the Koopmans' theorem, these roots are approximations to the ionisation energies of methane. As β is considered negative, ε_1 corresponds to the first ionisation energy. Honig[148] has found this to be $13 \cdot 04 \pm 0 \cdot 02$ eV.

Hall *(loc. cit.)* found the second ionisation energy to be 20eV†. Hence,

$$\alpha = -14 \cdot 75 \text{ eV} \qquad \beta = -1 \cdot 75 \text{ eV}.$$

Now let us consider the paraffins in general. If the interactions between non-adjacent bonds are neglected, the three following parameters are introduced:

$$c = \int Y_{CC'} \mathfrak{S} Y_{CC'} \, dv \qquad d = \int Y_{CC'} \mathfrak{S} Y_{CH} \, dv$$

$$e = \int Y_{CC'} \mathfrak{S} Y_{C'C''} \, dv.$$

In principle, therefore, the parameters necessary to study the paraffins can be calculated from three new experimental results. In fact Hall preferred to find the values of five parameters giving the best fit over a set of eight molecules. Table 18.3 compares these results with experimental data[148].

TABLE 18.3

Hydrocarbon	First ionisation energy in eV	
	Calculated	Measured
Propane	11·214	11·21
Butane	10·795	10·80
Pentane	10·554	10·55
Hexane	10·412	10·43
Heptane	10·323	10·35
Octane	10·265	10·24
Nonane	10·224	10·21
Decane	10·194	10·19

† M. Lorquet has pointed out that, after the work of Hall, the ionisation energies of methane have been re-evaluated at $13 \cdot 16 \pm 0 \cdot 02$ eV and $19 \cdot 42 \pm 0 \cdot 08$ eV (D. C. FROST and C. A. McDOWELL, *Proc. Roy. Soc.* **A 241** (1957), 194). The resulting modification in the values of α and β is, however, unimportant. They then become: $\alpha = -14 \cdot 72$ and $\beta = 1 \cdot 565$.

We can conclude from the good agreement between theory and experiment† that the method used is well adapted to the study of saturated hydrocarbons. Hence we shall go on to exhibit some of the results obtained using this method. Brown[172] has used this method to determine the atomisation energies of saturated hydrocarbons. He takes account of the overlap integrals and sets

$$S = \int Y_{CH} Y_{CH'} \, dv \quad \alpha = \int Y_{CH} \mathscr{C} Y_{CH} \, dv \quad \alpha + h\gamma = \int Y_{CC'} \mathscr{C} Y_{CC'} \, dv$$

$$\beta = \int Y_{CH} \mathscr{C} Y_{CH'} \, dv \quad \text{and} \quad \gamma = \beta - S\alpha$$

$$\theta\beta = \int Y_{CH} \mathscr{C} Y_{CC'} \, dv \quad \theta S = \int Y_{CH} Y_{CC'} \, dv$$

$$\eta\beta = \int Y_{CC'} \mathscr{C} Y_{C'C''} \, dv \quad \eta S = \int Y_{CC'} Y_{C'C''} \, dv,$$

i.e. he assumes a proportionality between the overlap integrals and the resonance integrals.

He assumes also that the atomisation energy is the sum of energies associated with each occupied orbital, an energy being counted twice for a doubly occupied orbital. This is a gross approximation. It is clear from the self-consistent field formulae (first book, p. 156) that the energy is not equal to the sum of energies ε as the repulsion between electrons is counted twice. Table 18.4 gives the results.

TABLE 18.4

Molecule	Atomisation energy
Methane	$8\alpha - 24S\gamma$
Ethane	$14\alpha + 2h\gamma - (24 + 24\theta^2) \, S\gamma$
Propane	$20\alpha + 4h\gamma - (28 + 40\theta^2 + 4\eta^2) \, S\gamma$
Butane	$26\alpha + 6h\gamma - (32 + 56\theta^2 + 8\eta^2) \, S\gamma$
Isobutane	$26\alpha + 6h\gamma - (36 + 48\theta^2 + 12\eta^2) \, S\gamma$
Pentane	$32\alpha + 8h\gamma - (36 + 72\theta^2 + 12\eta^2) \, S\gamma$
Isopentane	$32\alpha + 8h\gamma - (40 + 64\theta^2 + 16\eta^2) \, S\gamma$
Neopentane	$32\alpha + 8h\gamma - (48 + 48\theta^2 + 24\eta^2) \, S\gamma$
Hexane	$38\alpha + 10h\gamma - (40 + 88\theta^2 + 16\eta^2) \, S\gamma$
2-Methylpentane	$38\alpha + 10h\gamma - (44 + 80\theta^2 + 20\eta^2) \, S\gamma$
3-Methylpentane	$38\alpha + 10h\gamma - (44 + 80\theta^2 + 20\eta^2) \, S\gamma$
2,3-Dimethylbutane	$38\alpha + 10h\gamma - (48 + 72\theta^2 + 24\eta^2) \, S\gamma$
2,2-Dimethylbutane	$38\alpha + 10h\gamma - (52 + 64\theta^2 + 28\eta^2) \, S\gamma$

† M. Lorquet (personal communication). The experimental energies are not known to an accuracy of better than 0·2 eV. The difference between theory and experiment is therefore less than the experimental error.

One sees immediately that if S is neglected the atomisation energy can be written

$$N_{CH}(2\alpha) + N_{CC}(2\alpha + 2h\gamma).$$

With this approximation, there exist theoretical bonding energies 2α and $2d + 2h\gamma$ giving the atomisation energy exactly. Hence, the idea of bonding energy introduced experimentally is justified when the overlap integrals are neglected.

When they are introduced, the small differences between the atomisation energies can be regarded as being isomeric.

It is known that the difference between the atomisation energies of two hydrocarbons is equal to the difference between their formation energies.

Table 18.5 contains some of these [172].

TABLE 18.5

Hydrocarbon	Energy of formation in kcal/mol
Pentane	−35
2,2-Dimethylpropane	−39·7
Hexane	−40
2,2-Dimethylbutane	−44·4

From this table it is obvious that the difference between the formation energies of normal pentane and 2,2-dimethylpropane is 4·7 kcal/mol. This is almost equal to the corresponding difference between hexane and 2,2-dimethylbutane (4·4). This agrees fairly well with the theory as in the two cases in question, the differences (from Table 18.4) have the same value:

$$\Delta E = (12 - 24\theta^2 + 12\eta^2)\, S\gamma.$$

Also, experiment shows that for the following pairs of isomers: butane, isobutane; pentane, isopentane; hexane and isohexane, the differences between atomisation energies are 1·7, 1·9 and 1·7 respectively.

They are almost equal to one another and to a third of the preceding difference. Now Table 18.4 shows that these three differences have the same value,

$$\Delta E' = (4 - 8\theta^2 + 4\eta^2)\, S\gamma$$

which is a third of ΔE.

Brown has used the same method to calculate dissociation energies. The dissociation energy of ethane into two methyl radicals is the difference between the atomisation energy of ethane and twice the atomisation energy of methyl.

By using empirical values for the parameters, Brown obtained the values given in brackets in Table 18.6 which also contains the experimental results. These values are in kcal/mol and are placed on the row and column corresponding to the radicals formed in the course of the dissociation.

TABLE 18.6

Radicals	Methyl	Ethyl	Isopropyl	Tertiobutyl
Methyle	84·5 (84·4)	82·4 (81·7)	80·2 (80·8)	78·1 (78·3)
Ethyl		80·2 (79·4)	78·1 (78·9)	76·0 (75·7)
Isopropyl			76·0 (76·9)	73·8 (72·7)
Tertiobutyl				71·7 (67·0)

Dewar and Petitt[173] have discussed these same problems by means of a perturbation method. We shall not analyse their results which are rather similar to the preceding.

Lennard-Jones and Hall[174] have studied the distribution of electric charge in positive paraffin ions using essentially the method of linear combinations of bonding orbitals.

Analogous to what was done in the L.C.A.O. method, the quantity c_{ij}^2 in the expansion

$$\varphi_j = \sum_i c_{ij} Y_i$$

can be regarded as the contribution of orbital φ_j to the electron population of bond i, provided the overlap integrals are neglected.

Now, considering a positive ion of a paraffin resulting from this by the "loss of an electron" from orbital φ_j, this ionisation produces a hole in the electron population in bond i equal to c_{ij}^2. Such a hole corresponds to a positive charge of

$$ec_{ij}^2.$$

The calculations of coefficients c_{ij} have been carried out by Lennard-Jones and Hall. Numbering the CC bonds from one end, the ionisation of the highest level produces the following holes:

$$0\cdot035 \text{ in bond } 1$$
$$0\cdot115 \text{ in bond } 2$$
$$0\cdot200 \text{ in bond } 3$$
$$0\cdot234 \text{ in bond } 4.$$

The effect of ionisation is much more marked in the centre of the molecule than at its ends.

The quantity

$$n_i = \sum_j \eta_j c_{ij}^2,$$

where η_j is 0, 1 or 2 depending on whether orbital φ_j is unoccupied or singly or doubly occupied, represents the electron population associated with bond i. Since the overlap is neglected, the Y_i for N bonds can be considered as an orthonormal basis over an N-dimensional subspace of the function space. These Y_i allow the construction of N molecular orbitals φ_j. Assuming that the non-ionised hydrocarbon contains $2N$ electrons, each of these orbitals must be used twice. For each c_{ij}, $\eta_j = 2$. Hence,

$$n_i = 2 \sum_j c_{ij}^2.$$

In the Y space, coefficient c_{ij} represents the projection of φ_j on Y_i, or, alternatively, the projection of Y_i on φ_j.

The quantity $\sum_j c_{ij}^2$ is, therefore, equal to the sum of the squares of the projections of Y_i on the set of φ_j. Since Y_i is normalised, this quantity is equal to unity. Hence,

$$\sum_j c_{ij}^2 = 1$$
$$n_i = 2.$$

The electron population of each of the bonds of a paraffin is therefore evaluated at two by the method of linear combinations of bonding orbitals. It is important to note that this result stands if one of the CH bonds is replaced by another two-electron and CX of any electronegativity since the result is independent of the parameters used. Hence, the method of linear combinations of bonding orbitals as it has been presented does not allow one to describe the transfers of charge which are induced in paraffins by the substitution for a hydrogen atom by another atom. To study this effect, Sandorfy and Daudel[175] have used the method of linear combinations of atomic orbitals.

C. The Method of Linear Combinations of Atomic Orbitals

Starting from the method of localised orbitals (p.92) the orbitals Y_i may be represented as a linear combination of two atomic orbitals (in general, hybrids) ψ_{iP} and ψ_{iQ} associated with atoms P and Q making up the bond. The molecular orbitals are then expanded in terms of these atomic orbitals, i.e.

$$\varphi_J = \sum_i \sum_P s_{iPj}\psi_{iP}.$$

Obviously, the calculation of s_{iPj} requires knowledge of parameters

$$\alpha_{iP} = \int \psi_{iP}\mathfrak{S}\psi_{iP}\,dv$$

$$\beta_{lmPQ} = \int \psi_{lP}\mathfrak{S}\psi_{mQ}\,dv$$

and, if the overlaps are neglected, the quantity s_{iPj}^2 represents the electron population furnished by orbital j to atom P and also to bond i. Hence, we can speak of an electron population of a bond and an atomic electron population.

Sandorfy and Daudel have calculated the value of these populations in paraffin derivatives resulting from the replacement of a hydrogen by some other atom X.

They did not consider the CH bonds explicitly and called α_C the coulomb integral characterising a carbon atom, β_{CC} the resonance integral between two hybrids forming a CC bond, and β' the resonance integral between the two hybrids coming from the same carbon. The other resonance integrals are neglected. One can always set

$$\beta' = m\beta_{CC}$$

but the value of m is unknown a priori.

Sandorfy and Daudel have studied the example where the electronegativity of X is such that its coulomb integral α_x can be given by the relation

$$\alpha_X = \alpha_C + \beta_{CC}$$

and have determined the population diagrams for ten arbitrary values of m.

Figure 41 gives the bonds' population distribution obtained thus for a propane derivative and also for propane itself and for $m = \pm 0.25$. Clearly, the effect of the substitute X (considered more electronegative than carbon)

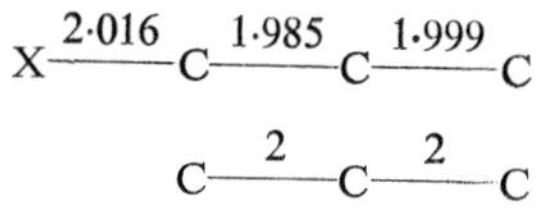

$$X \overset{2\cdot016}{\rule{1cm}{0.4pt}} C \overset{1\cdot985}{\rule{1cm}{0.4pt}} C \overset{1\cdot999}{\rule{1cm}{0.4pt}} C$$

$$C \overset{2}{\rule{1cm}{0.4pt}} C \overset{2}{\rule{1cm}{0.4pt}} C$$

FIG. 41

is to reduce the populations of the CC bonds. *This effect is not oscillatory and dies away rapidly.*

Sandorfy[176] has extended and improved this procedure by calculating the CH bonds explicitly.

Yoshizumi[177] has determined m empirically by using experimental values of polar moments of CH_3Cl, and $C_2H_5 Cl$. He found

$$m = \pm 0.34.$$

D. *Julg's Method of Perturbation*

Julg's method[178] consists of expressing the characteristic function ϕ of a paraffin derivative by configuration interaction formed of bonding orbitals Y of the paraffin. The coefficient of the expression are then calculated by perturbation.

We start by associating with each bond i a bonding orbital Y_i and an antibonding orbital Y_i^*. The function representing the fundamental state of the paraffin can then be written

$$\Upsilon_0 = \det Y_1(1) \, \bar{Y}_1(2) \, Y_2(3) \, \bar{Y}_2(4)....$$

To represent the excited states, it is sufficient to replace one or more of the functions Y_i by the corresponding Y_i^*.

For instance one would set

$$\Upsilon_1 = \det Y_1^*(1)\ \bar{Y}_1(2)\ Y_2(3)\ \bar{Y}_2(4)\ \cdots$$
$$+ \det Y_1(1)\ \bar{Y}_1^*(2)\ Y_2(3)\ \bar{Y}_2(4)\ \cdots$$
$$\Upsilon_2 = \det Y_1(1)\ \bar{Y}_1(2)\ Y_2^*(3)\ \bar{Y}_2(4)\ \cdots$$
$$+ \det Y_1(1)\ \bar{Y}_1(2)\ Y_2(3)\ \bar{Y}_2^*(4)\ \cdots.$$

If a hydrogen in a paraffin chain is replaced by a substitute X, it is natural to express the function ϕ of the derivative obtained on the basis Υ_j according to the formula

$$\phi = \sum_j c_j \Upsilon_j.$$

If $\Re$ represents the perturbation due to the substitution of X for H and if E_j represents the energy associated with γ_j, we have, by the formula of perturbations†,

$$c_j = - \frac{\int Y_j \Re Y_0\ dv}{E_j - E_0}.$$

If the paraffin is not branched and if the CC bonds are numbered from the perturbation, Julg showed that

$$c_j = \frac{K}{1+\alpha} \left(\frac{\alpha}{1+\alpha} \right)^{j-1}.$$

To obtain this formula, small integrals are neglected and

$$K = - \frac{\sqrt{2}}{\varepsilon} \int Y_0 \Re Y_1\ dv$$

$$\alpha = - \frac{4\sqrt{2}}{\varepsilon} \int Y_1(1)\ Y_1^*(1)\ \frac{1}{r_{12}}\ Y_2(2)\ Y_2^*(2)\ dv_1\ dv_2$$

$$a = \frac{4\sqrt{2}}{\varepsilon} \int Y_1(1)\ Y_1^*(1)\ \frac{1}{r_{12}}\ Y_1(2)\ Y_1^*(2)\ dv_1\ dv_2.$$

Y_0 represents the bond CX and $\varepsilon = E_j - E_0$.

By expressing the bonding orbitals in terms of atomic orbitals, Julg has shown that α is small and positive.

† First book, p. 12.

Hence, the absolute value of c_j decreases very rapidly with j. Given that Y_j introduces the effect of the perturbation on bond j, the effect of the perturbation *rapidly decays*. Moreover Julg showed that the population of the CC bonds are either all increased or all decreased. Hence, the effect is not oscillatory.

These results generalise those of Sandorfy and Daudel.

E. *A Method Based on the Use of Atomic Polarisability*

Pitzer and Catalano [179] have studied the energy of formation of paraffins by a method which is a little outside the scope of this book but which we shall mention briefly.

It consists of attributing the majority of differences between heats of formation of isomers to the existence of interaction between non-bonded atoms of the paraffins.

Following Slater and Kirkwood, these interactions produce between two atoms A and B the energy

$$\Delta E_{AB} = -\frac{3e\hbar}{2m^{1/2}R^6} \frac{\alpha_A \alpha_B}{[(\alpha_A/N_A)^{1/2} + (\alpha_A/N_B)^{1/2}]}.$$

Besides the usual universal constants, this formula contains the polarisabilities α_i of the atoms involved, the numbers N_i of "their polarisable electrons" and the distance R which separate these atoms.

Using Ketelaar's values for the polarisability of H and C, i.e.

$$\alpha_H = 0\cdot42 \quad \text{and} \quad \alpha_C = 0\cdot93$$

with

$$N_H = 1 \quad \text{and} \quad N_C = 4$$

the energy of interaction ΔE_C between the non-bonded atoms of a paraffin is found to be

$$\Delta E_C = -[22\cdot6 \, \Sigma \, R_{CC}^{-6} + 8\cdot68 \, \Sigma \, R_{CH}^{-6} + 3\cdot42 \, \Sigma \, R_{HH}^{-6}] \times 10^{-60} \text{ ergs.}$$

The energy of formation ΔH_f of the hydrocarbon at $0°K$ is expressed by the formula

$$\Delta H_f = -11\cdot34n - 21\cdot69 + \Delta E_C + \tfrac{1}{2}h \sum_i \nu_i + \Delta E_s,$$

where n is the number of carbon atoms.

ΔE_s represents the energy due to steric hindrance. The authors assume that it is zero in the molecules which they studied. The term in ν_i represents the energy of vibrations at the temperature of $0\,^\circ$K. It was evaluated by means of a semi-empiric formula.

Table 18.7 compares the calculated values of ΔH_f with experimental results. All the energies are expressed in kcal/mol.

TABLE 18.7

Molecule	$-\Delta E_C$	$-\Delta H_f$ calculated	$-\Delta H_f$ observed
Methane	8·80	14·31	15·99
Ethane	17·35	16·50	16·52
Propane	27·24	20·03	19·48
n-Butane (trans)	37·20	23·63	23·67
Isobutane	38·48	24·91	25·30
n-Pentane ($t - t$)	47·16	27·23	27·23
Isopentane	50·46	28·03	28·81

There is a fairly good agreement between theory and experiment.

F. *The Valence Bond*

Heitler[180] has determined the dissociation energy of the first CH bond in the molecules of methane and ethane, i.e. the energies corresponding to the reactions

$$CH_4 \rightarrow CH_3 + H,$$
$$C_2H_6 \rightarrow C_2H_3 + H.$$

He uses the valence bond method (first book, Section 25) and expresses the energies of the systems CH_4, C_2H_6, CH_3, C_2H_5 as functions of coulomb integrals and exchange integrals which he evaluates empirically.

He obtained 4·55 eV for the first energy (experimental value 4·45 eV) and 4·20 for the second (4·25).

19. THE CYCLIC PARAFFINS AND STRAINED BONDS

Following Pauling, we have seen that, in forming a chemical bond AB, it is advantageous to choose hybrids having maximum possible force in any direction, the nucleus B being placed in the direction where the hybrid coming from A has this maximum force.

We have also seen that the hybrids sp^3 which point towards the vertices of a regular tetrahedron are the most "directional" in this sense. In a molecule like methane, therefore, bonds can be described according to Pauling's theory: the most directional hybrids coming from carbon, the hydrogen nuclei in the direction of greatest force.

For cycloparaffins, however, the situation is somewhat less favourable.

Consider the case of cyclopropane. The angles $C\hat{C}C$ are 60°.

Hence, if the most directional hybrids of carbon are chosen, they do not point towards the other carbons. If hybrids of a carbon are chosen pointing towards the others (assuming this is possible) they are not the most directional.

Since both of Pauling's criteria cannot be satisfactory, one is led to look for a compromise.

This is why Kilpatrick and Pitzer[181] have investigated the nature of hybrids about a carbon which have the maximum possible force in the direction of another carbon.

Consider a carbon atom of cyclopropane; it is natural to form both the CC bonds which start from this carbon atom by using equivalent hybrids t_1 and t_2. Similarly, the two CH bonds may be represented with the aid of equivalent hybrids t_3 and t_4. Without loss of generality we can set

$$t_1 = as + bp_z + 1/\sqrt{2}p_x$$
$$t_2 = as + bp_z - 1/\sqrt{2}\,p_x$$
$$t_3 = bs - ap_z + 1/\sqrt{2}\,p_y$$
$$t_4 = bs - ap_z - 1/\sqrt{2}\,p_y$$
$$b = \sqrt{(\tfrac{1}{2} - a^2)}$$

Obviously, t_1 and t_2 have their maximum in the xy-plane and t_3 and t_4 in the yz-plane. These directions are shown in Fig. 42.

Let f_1 be the force of hybrid t_1. Then,

$$f_1 = a + \sqrt{(\tfrac{1}{2} - a^2)}\,\sqrt{3}\cos\theta + \sqrt{(\tfrac{3}{2})}\sin\theta.$$

Following Pauling's ideas, this force is maximised in the direction of the bond which makes an angle $\theta_0 = 30°$ with the z-axis in the case given by Fig. 42. For df_1/da to be zero,

$$a = \frac{1}{\sqrt{(2 + 6\cos^2\theta_0)}} \qquad b = \sqrt{\left(\frac{3\cos^2\theta_0}{2 + 6\cos^2\theta_0}\right)}$$

and, consequently, the function f_1 possessing the maximum possible value in direction θ_0 can be written

$$f_1 = \frac{1}{\sqrt{(2 + 6\cos^2\theta_0)}} + \sqrt{\left(\frac{3\cos^2\theta_0}{2 + 6\cos^2\theta_0}\right)}\sqrt{3}\cos\theta + \sqrt{(\tfrac{3}{2})}\sin\theta.$$

The maximum of this function is not, in general, at $\theta = \theta_0$. In the present case where $\theta_0 = 30°$, the maximum is at $\theta = 50°$. The

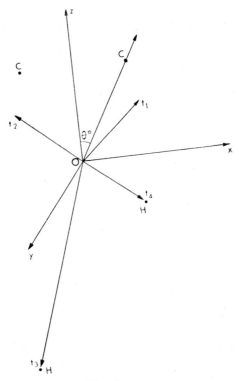

FIG. 42

values obtained for a and b give at the same time the expressions for t_3 and t_4. One easily finds that the directions of their maximum force form an angle of 122°. Hence, we deduce that the angle HĈH in cyclopropane must be 122°. Experiment [182] gives 118 ± 2°. The agreement is very satisfying and confirms the existence in this molecule of an appreciable difference between the directions of the

CC bonds and the direction of maximum force of hybrids associated with them.

This difference may be considered as a measure of tension which was introduced by Baeyer in organic chemistry.

We say that a *bond is strained* or constitutes a *banana-bond* when the angles formed by the line of the nuclei and the direction of the corresponding hybrid maxima are not zero.

Mashima [183] has reconsidered the problem by maximising the greatest projection of a point of polarogram of the hybrid onto the line of the nuclei CC. The angle HĈH obtained is 118°12' which agrees well with the experimental value. The tension angle remains at the same order of magnitude (21°18').

Simonetta *et al.*[184] have extended this discussion to include energy considerations. The preceding studies have assumed implicitly that the energy of a bond is of the form

$$\frac{f_i f_j E^0_{ij}}{(f_i f_j)_{max}},$$

where f_i and f_j are the associated hybrid forces in the direction of the bond and E^0_{ij} the energy of the bond when the product of the forces attain its maximum value $(f_i f_j)_{max}$, i.e. in the absence of tension[185]. The Italian authors prefer to use a formula of this type,

$$\frac{S_{ij} E^0_{ij}}{(\overline{S}_{ij})},$$

where S_{ij} is the overlap integral between the hybrids and $\overline{S}_{ij}$ is what it would be for energy E^0_{ij}. This is certainly a very reasonable formula by reason of the arguments developed in Section 15D.

The total energy of cyclopropane can then be written in the form

$$E = 3 \left(2 \frac{S_{CH}}{\overline{S}_{CH}} E^0_{CH} + \frac{S_{CC}}{\overline{S}_{CC}} E^0_{CC} \right).$$

By using the experimental values for E^0_{OH} and E^0_{CC} and by calculating the variation of the length of bond CH with the structure of the carbon hybrid used for its representation, the authors have calculated the variation of E with the tension angle. They found that the minimum total energy occurs when this angle is 22·5°.

The energy E can equally well be expressed as a function of angle HĈH and there is a relation between this angle and the tension angle. Near the energy minimum, the variation of E with angle HĈH is given by the approximate formula

$$E = k \, (\text{HĈH})^2$$

where $k = 0.0725$ kcal/mol.

It is interesting to compare this theoretic value with that deduced from infrared spectra which is 0.0364 kcal/mol[186].

Coulson and Moffitt[187], in an earlier paper, carried out a more elaborate calculation of the energy as a function of the tension angle. They found that minimum energy corresponds to a tension angle of 23° and angle HĈH of 113°.

Cyclobutane also contains strained bonds, as the angle formed by the line of nuclei CC is 90° and thus stays lower than the tetrahedric angle. For cyclopentane the angle rises to 108° and so there is no tension in this hydrocarbon. For bigger rings, the angle of a plane regular polygon becomes greater than the tetrahedric angle. One might think that "inverse" tensions would appear. In fact, this is not so as the carbon atoms cease to be coplanar and allow tetrahedric angles to form. This is the basis on which, for example, the stereochemistry of cyclohexane may be explained[189].

Finally, certain polycyclic paraffin hydrocarbons such as spiropentane contain strained bonds. Simonetta *et al.* have studied this case in the article mentioned.

CHAPTER VI

Small Molecules Formed by Simple Bonds and Unshared Electrons

20. ROLE OF UNSHARED ELECTRONS

We have already mentioned the importance of unshared electrons in the determination of the structure of molecules.

For example, we have seen that the unshared electron pair of the ammonia molecule play almost as big a role as an NH bond in the determination of valence angles. This is the explanation why these angles are very near those of methane.

It is only recently, however, that the importance of such electrons has been fully recognised.

Van Vleck and Sherman[190], for instance, minimised the role of the free pair in NH_3 by representing it with the aid of a $2s$ orbital. They represented a nitrogen atom by

$$(1s)^2 (2s)^2 (2p_x) (2p_y) (2p_z)$$

and formed the bonding orbitals by means of p orbitals and associated the free pair with $2s$ spin orbitals.

Moffitt[191] has suggested the "representation" of the free pairs of carbon monoxide by hybrid orbitals between $2s$ and $2p$. Similarly, Robinson[192] has shown that the best calculation of the polar moment of hydrochloric acid is made when the free pairs are represented by hybrids. Finally, Lennard-Jones and Pople[193] have specified the nature of orbitals which can be associated with unshared electrons and Pople[194] has treated the particular case of water.

From these studies, it appears that unshared electrons play a first order role in the determination of polar moments of a molecule.

Furthermore, it is evident that since they are less bound to the molecule, this group of unshared electrons contribute most to the first ionisations and excitations of the molecule.

We will discuss the two molecules NH_3 and H_2O, the molecule-ion NH_3^+, and the radical CH_3.

21. THE MOLECULES OF AMMONIA
AND WATER IN THEIR EQUILIBRIUM CONFIGURATIONS

A. *The Method of Localised Orbitals*

Duncan and Pople[195] used the method of localised orbitals to study ammonia, water and hydrofluoric acid. We will summarise their treatment of H_2O.

The bonding orbitals can be written

$$\chi(b_1) = \lambda \left\{ \cos \varepsilon_b \cdot 2s + \sin \varepsilon_b \cdot 2p(b_1) \right\} + \mu a$$

$$\chi(b_2) = \lambda \left\{ \cos \varepsilon_b \cdot 2s + \sin \varepsilon_b \cdot 2p(b_2) \right\} + \mu b,$$

where a and b correspond to $1s$ functions of the hydrogen atoms and $2p(b_z)$ are combinations of p functions "pointing" towards these hydrogen atoms. The equivalent orbitals characterising the two pairs of unshared electrons are

$$\chi(l_1) = \cos \varepsilon_j \cdot 2s + \sin \varepsilon_j \cdot 2p(l_1)$$

$$\chi(l_2) = \cos \varepsilon_j \cdot 2s + \sin \varepsilon_j \cdot 2p(l_2).$$

Obviously, if the ratio λ/μ and the angle $\hat{HOH}$ are fixed, all the parameters of the problem are fixed by the orthonormality conditions.

The angle was fixed at the experimental value and λ/μ chosen to give the correct value of the dipolar moment, i.e.

$$\frac{\lambda}{\mu} = 1 \cdot 06.$$

If M_S, M_L and M_P are the electric moments associated with the free pairs, the bonding electrons and the nuclei respectively, then

$$M_S = \quad 3 \cdot 03 \times 10^{-18} \quad (C.G.S.K)$$

$$M_L = -6 \cdot 82 \times 10^{-18}$$

$$M_P = \quad 5 \cdot 63 \times 10^{-18}.$$

One sees that if the moment due to the unshared electrons is neglected, the sense of the polar moment is reversed. The importance of these electrons in the polar moment is obvious. The angle between the directions of maximum force of orbitals $\chi(l_1)$ and $\chi(l_2)$ is 120·2°.

Similar conclusions are reached in the case of NH_3.

B. *Self-consistent Field and Configuration Interaction Methods*

The ammonia molecule has been studied by three different authors using the self-consistent field method. We will state Kaplan's results[196] which seem to be the best as in this case all the integrals (tri- and tetracentric) are evaluated directly and the atomic orbitals used are those of Hartree–Fock. In Higuchi's[197] paper, most of the integrals are only estimated by various approximations. Duncan's[198] paper is based on the use of Slater's orbitals.

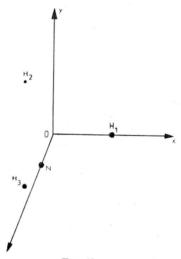

FIG. 43

The axes (Fig. 43) are chosen so that the nuclei H_1, H_2 and H_3 lie in plane xOy, H_1 being on Ox. The nitrogen nucleus is placed on the z-axis. Let a, b and c be the $1s$ orbitals of these hydrogen atoms, and $1s$, $2s$, $2px$, $2py$ and $2pz$ the nitrogen orbitals. The symmetry of the molecule suggests the combinations

$$h_0 = n_0(a + b + c)$$
$$h_x = n_x[a - \tfrac{1}{2}(b + c)]$$
$$h_y = n_y(b - c)$$

and we have to introduce the three following three types of molecular orbitals:

$$\lambda\, 1s + \mu\, 2s + \nu\, 2p_z + \varrho h_0$$
$$\nu'\, 2p_x + \varrho' h_x$$
$$\nu'\, 2p_y + \varrho' h_y.$$

The problem has been treated by introducing all the electrons. The molecular integrals were evaluated by means of the methods of Barnett and Coulson[199] and of Lundqvist and Löwdin[200]. The solution of Roothaan's equations were carried out in an electronic computer using a programme by Nesbet[201].

The molecular orbitals representing the ground state together with the corresponding energies ε (in atomic units) are given below.

$$\varepsilon_1 = -15 \cdot 5682$$

$$\varphi_1 = 1 \cdot 0001\,(1s) - 0 \cdot 0033\,(2s) - 0 \cdot 0020\,(2p_z) - 0 \cdot 0013\,(h_0)$$

$$\varepsilon_2 = -1 \cdot 1482$$

$$\varphi_2 = 0 \cdot 0286\,(1s) + 0 \cdot 7591\,(2s) + 0 \cdot 1616\,(2p_z) - 0 \cdot 2711\,(h_0)$$

$$\varepsilon_3 = \varepsilon_4 = -0 \cdot 6625$$

$$\varphi_3 = 0 \cdot 6195\,(2p_x) + 0 \cdot 4860\,(h_x)$$

$$\varphi_4 = 0 \cdot 6195\,(2p_y) + 0 \cdot 4860\,(h_y)$$

$$\varepsilon_5 = -0 \cdot 4646$$

$$\varphi_5 = 0 \cdot 0257\,(1s) - 0 \cdot 4418\,(2s) + 0 \cdot 8956\,(2p_z) - 0 \cdot 2582\,(h_0).$$

Orbital φ_5 can be considered to correspond roughly to the unshared pair and in this sense the pair contributes greatly to the first ionisation of the molecule.

By the Koopmans, theorem, the first ionisation energy is approximately $-\varepsilon_5$, i.e. 14 eV. Experiment[202] gives $11 \cdot 0 \pm 0 \cdot 2$ eV. The total energy was calculated at $-56 \cdot 266$ a.u. Experiment gives $-56 \cdot 596$. The bonding energy was evaluated at $0 \cdot 364$ a.u. which is approximately 80 per cent of the experimental value ($0 \cdot 459$). Finally, the calculation gives $1 \cdot 82$ for the polar moment (experimental value $1 \cdot 46$).

Hence, there is a good agreement between theory and experiment.

Kaplan has increased the accuracy of the energy evaluation by doing a configuration interaction calculation.

The self-consistent field method and configuration interaction method have also been used in the case of the water molecule. This work, due to Ellison and Shull[203], resembles the preceding calculation. We shall not analyse this in detail. The total molecular energy was calculated for various values of angle HÔH, but the polycentric integrals were not evaluated exactly.

As in the case of methane, one can pass from the model using symmetry orbitals to one based on equivalent orbitals.

One can ask, for example, if the equivalent orbitals give electric moments for the bonds and unshared electrons analogous to those of the method of localised orbitals.

Unfortunately, in a case like that of water, the problem is not uniquely defined. One can ask, for example, whether one chooses bonding orbitals whose hybrid points towards the hydrogen or, on the other hand, whether the electric moment corresponding to the orbital is to be colinear with the axis of the bond. Hamilton[204] has discussed this problem, but has not obtained very satisfactory results.

C. *The United Atom Method*

Using this method, Funabashi and Magee[205] have studied the water molecule and at the same time the methane molecule (cf. Section 17C). The results are comparable. They have been improved by Banyard and March[206].

The same authors, in another article,[207] evaluated the coefficients f of diffraction of X-rays in the water and ammonia molecule by developing functions of the same type as Bernal's as in the case of methane. Here again, there is a reasonable agreement with experiment.

22. RELATIONSHIP BETWEEN ELECTRONIC STRUCTURE AND THE POSITION OF NUCLEI, ORBITALS FOLLOWING AND POTENTIAL BARRIER

A. *The Water Molecule*

As has already been mentioned (Section 15 A), the energy of the water molecule has been calculated [208] as a function of angle HÔH and the distance OH by means of a configuration interaction method. All the electrons were introduced. The wave function is a linear combination of thirty determinants. The energy is minimised at an angle of 96° (experimental value, 105°) and a distance OH of 1·95 Å (experimental value, 1·85). We also stated that Ellison and Shull have calculated the energy of the water molecule for different angles.

B. *Ammonia and Associated Compounds*

Kaplan's calculation has been carried out for both the equilibrium position of the nuclei of NH_3 and the plane configuration. In his calculation of configuration interaction, Kaplan finds $-56·280$ and $-56·133$ a.u. respectively. The potential barrier that the nuclei must overcome for an inversion of NH_3 is then $0·147$ a.u., i.e. $3·97$ eV, while the experimental value is $0·25$ eV.

Obviously, the non-empiric methods of calculation are at present more elaborate and give rather bad results for the variation of the energy of a polyatomic molecule with the position of its nuclei. Semi-empiric methods, however, yield some interesting results.

Kolos [209] studied the variation of the energy of NH_3 and PH_3 with the angles (assumed equal to one another). He used the same wave function as Duncan and Pople, but instead of determining the ratio λ/μ from the polar moment, he assumes that the square of this ratio varies as the ratio of the electronegativities of the atoms making up the bond (see Section 39 B) which leads to

$$\lambda/\mu = 1·2 \quad \text{for} \quad NH_3$$

$$\lambda/\mu = 1 \quad \text{for} \quad PH_3.$$

Then, by evaluating the energy by making approximations for the polycentric integrals and introducing a curious normalisation condition, he finds that this energy passes through a minimum for 102° for NH_3 and 98° for PH_3. The experimental values are 106° 47′ [210] and 93°50′ [211] respectively. Without being outstanding, this theory nevertheless interprets the fact that the valence is higher for NH_3.

Wheland and Chen [212] have also evaluated the energy of molecule NH_3 as a function of valence angle in a semi-empiric manner. The energy is expressed as a function of parameters such as

$$\alpha_{xx} = \int p_x \mathfrak{H} p_x \, dv$$

$$\gamma_{ax} = \int a \mathfrak{H} p_x \, dv, \quad \text{etc.} \ldots$$

The parameters are chosen to give a value for the potential barrier agreeing with the experimental value. This work is only of interest because the same parameters serve to calculate the potential barrier of the transition *cis* → *trans* of the molecule HN = NH. An energy of 33 kcal/mol is obtained while in the case of ammonia this barrier is only about 6 kcal/mol. This explains why one cannot separate the entiomorphic forms of amines NRR′R″ when they are known to be *cis* and *trans* isomers of nitrogen derivatives. Simonetta and Vaciago [213] have extended this discussion to the case of PH_3.

To end the section, we shall make some remarks on a problem raised by Linett *et al.*[214] and discussed by Cohan and Coulson [215] for NH_3. We have previously given arguments which assume that, in the equilibrium state, the protons of a molecule like NH_3 are placed in the directions of maximum force of the hybrids associated with the nitrogen. We know nothing, however, of what happens in a non-equilibrium position. According to the Born–Oppenheimer theorem we know only that *the orbitals must be adjusted to follow the movement of the nuclei,* but one can assume that, away from the equilibrium position, the line of the nuclei NH makes a certain angle with the "directions" of the associated hybrids. This led Coulson and Cohan to represent the potential surface of ammonia by the relation

$$U = \tfrac{1}{2}k_1 \sum (\Delta l_i)^2 + \tfrac{1}{2}k_f \sum (\delta_i)^2 + \tfrac{1}{2}k_h \sum_{i<j} (\delta_{ij})^2 + \tfrac{1}{2}k_l \sum (\delta_{pi})^2,$$

where Δl_i represents the elongation of the NH bond, δ_i the angle between the line of the nuclei NH_i and the direction of the associated hybrid, δ_{ij} the difference of the angle between the directions of the hybrids associated with NH_i and NH_j and the corresponding angle in the equilibrium position and δ_{pi} the difference of the angle between the hybrid associated with bond NH_i and the direction of the hybrid associated with the free pair and the corresponding angle in the equilibrium position.

The constants k_1, k_f, k_h and k_l were chosen so that the experimental frequencies of oscillation and the variation of polar moment of the molecule with position of its nuclei are reproduced as closely as possible. These measurements are given by study of the infrared spectrum of the molecule. For a non-infinite value of k_f, corresponding to a non-equilibrium position, we find that there can be a difference between the direction of the bond and that of the hybrid.

The agreement between the form of the potential surface obtained above and that determined by Duchesne and Ottelet[216] from a different point of view is an argument in favour of Cohan and Coulson's work.

23. The Ion Molecule NH_3^+
and the Methyl Radical

NH_3^+ has been studied by the method of configuration interactions by Lorquet and Lefebvre-Brion[217]. The method followed is that of Kaplan.

The values of energies obtained are compared with experiment in the following table.

	Energy calculated in a.u.		Experimental values
	Pyramid form	Plane form	
$N^+ + 3H$	$-55\cdot3288$	$-55\cdot3288$	$-55\cdot592$
NH_3^+ (S.C.F.)	$-55\cdot8148$	$-55\cdot7326$	$-56\cdot213$
NH_3^+ (C.I.)	$-55\cdot8348$	$-55\cdot7551$	$-56\cdot213$

S.C.F. — Self-consistent field
C.I. — configuration interaction

Once again, the agreement between experiment and theory for total energies is very good. The atomisation energy found ($0\cdot506$ a.u. in C.I. method) represents a good proportion of the experimental value which is $0\cdot621$ a.u.

The calculation assumes that the stable form of the ion is pyramidal but we have seen in the example of ammonia that a prediction of this type must be taken with reserve.

The orbitals of the pyramidal ground state and corresponding energies are given below:

$$\varphi_1 = 1 \cdot 0000 \, (1s) - 0 \cdot 0018 \, (2s) - 0 \cdot 0010 \, (2p_z) - 0 \cdot 0003 \, (h_0)$$

$$\varepsilon_1 = -16 \cdot 2268$$

$$\varphi_2 = 0 \cdot 0197 \, (1s) + 0 \cdot 8207 \, (2s) + 0 \cdot 2165 \, (2p_z) - 0 \cdot 1864 \, (h_0)$$

$$\varepsilon_2 = -1 \cdot 6378$$

$$\varphi_3 = 0 \cdot 7211 \, (2p_x) + 0 \cdot 3738 \, (h_x)$$

$$\varepsilon_3 = \varepsilon_4 = -1 \cdot 1383$$

$$\varphi_4 = 0 \cdot 7211 \, (2p_y) + 0 \cdot 3738 \, (h_y)$$

$$\varphi_5 = 0 \cdot 0208 \, (1s) - 0 \cdot 4302 \, (2s) + 0 \cdot 9044 \, (2p_z) - 0 \cdot 2118 \, (h_0).$$

Note that orbital φ_2 is somewhat different from that already found by Kaplan. The "loss of an electron from the lone pair" is interpreted by an important redistribution of electrons in the NH bonds.

This is also shown by the calculation of electron populations. In ammonia, the nitrogen carries 7·76 electrons and each hydrogen 0·75 electrons. For the ion NH_3^+, the population of the nitrogen falls only to 7·43 but that of the hydrogen atoms is lowered to 0·52.

Hence, the ionisation, which might be intuitively thought of as affecting only the free pair, has in fact strong repercussions on the hydrogen atoms, and after ionisation the nitrogen remains negative.

Finally, note that whereas applying the Koopmans, theorem, the ionisation energy of NH_3 is 14 eV, it falls to 12·1 eV if it is calculated directly from the difference between the energies of NH_3^+ and NH_3 by the S.C.F. method. The latter calculation is therefore more satisfactory as the experimental value is 10·2 eV.

We end this chapter by mentioning that Beltrame and Simonetta [218] have studied the methyl radical using Mulliken's magic formula. They found that contrary to what has been said for the isoelectronic system NH_3^+, the plane form of CH_3 is more stable than its pyramidal form.

Experiment seems to confirm this result.

CHAPTER VII

The Ethylene Molecule

24. ETHYLENE TREATED AS A TWO ELECTRON PROBLEM. THE π APPROXIMATION. MORE ON THE IDEA OF A CORE

Ethylene C_2H_4 is considered as a plane molecule. Angles $H\hat{C}H$ and $C\hat{C}H$ are approximately $120°$[(219)]. Using the self-consistent field method, the molecular orbitals φ are naturally expressed in terms of the $1s$ orbitals of the four hydrogen atoms h_1, h_2, h_3 and h_4 and the orbitals $1s_1$, $2s_1$, $2p_{1x}$, $2p_{1y}$ and $2p_{1z}$ associated with carbon C_1 (Fig. 44) and $1s_2$, $2s_2$, $2p_{2x}$ and $2p_{2y}$ and $2p_{2z}$ associated with C_2.

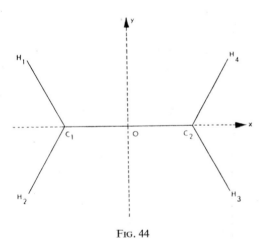

FIG. 44

As the molecule contains sixteen electrons, the representation of the ground state requires eight molecular orbitals. Instead of expressing the φ directly as functions of atomic orbitals, they can be expressed by means of linear combinations of atomic orbitals, e.g.

as functions of equivalent orbitals. The geometry of the molecule forces us to form these equivalent orbitals by means of trigonal hybrids.

Let σ_1, t_1, t_2 be the hybrids associated with C_1 pointing towards C_2, H_1 and H_2 respectively and σ_2, t_3 and t_4 hybrids associated with C_2 pointing towards C_1, H_3 and H_4.

We introduce the following equivalent orbitals:

$$1s_1, \quad 1s_2,$$

$$\chi_1 = \lambda h_1 + \mu t_1, \qquad \chi_1' = \lambda' h_1 - \mu' t_1$$

$$\chi_2 = \lambda h_2 + \mu t_2, \qquad \chi_2' = \lambda' h_2 - \mu' t_2$$

$$\chi_3 = \lambda h_3 + \mu t_3, \qquad \chi_3' = \lambda' h_3 - \mu' t_3$$

$$\chi_4 = \lambda h_4 + \mu t_4, \qquad \chi_4' = \lambda' h_4 - \mu' t_4$$

$$\sigma = N_\sigma(\sigma_1 + \sigma_2), \qquad \sigma^* = N_{\sigma*}(\sigma_1 - \sigma_2)$$

$$\pi = N_\pi(2p_{1z} + 2p_{2z}), \qquad \pi^* = N_{\pi*}(2p_{1z} - 2p_{2z})$$

and, from them, derive the following symmetry orbitals:

$$\phi_1 = K(1s_1 + 1s_2)$$

$$\phi_2 = K'(1s_1 - 1s_2)$$

$$\phi_3 = a(\chi_1 + \chi_2 + \chi_3 + \chi_4)$$

$$\phi_4 = b(\chi_1 + \chi_2 - \chi_3 - \chi_4)$$

$$\phi_5 = c(\chi_1 - \chi_2 - \chi_3 + \chi_4)$$

$$\phi_6 = d(\chi_1 - \chi_2 + \chi_3 - \chi_4)$$

$$\phi_{11} = a'(\chi_1' + \chi_2' + \chi_3' + \chi_4')$$

$$\phi_{12} = b'(\chi_1' + \chi_2' - \chi_3' - \chi_4')$$

$$\phi_{13} = c'(\chi_1' - \chi_2' - \chi_3' + \chi_4')$$

$$\phi_{14} = d'(\chi_1' - \chi_2' + \chi_3' - \chi_4')$$

$$\phi_7 = \sigma$$

$$\phi_{10} = \sigma^*$$

$$\phi_8 = \pi$$

$$\phi_9 = \pi^*$$

Obviously, in all these expressions, λ, μ, λ', μ', N_σ, $N_{\sigma*}$, N_π, $N_{\pi*}$, K, K', a, b, c, d, a', b', c', d' are normalising coefficients, considered positive.

Let us characterise by S_x, S_y, S_p, A_x, A_y, A_p, the orbitals which are symmetric or antisymmetric with respect to axis Ox, Oy or the plane of the molecule respectively.

The orbitals

ϕ_1, ϕ_3, ϕ_7, ϕ_{11} are characterised by S_x, S_y, S_p

ϕ_2, ϕ_4, ϕ_{10}, ϕ_{12} are characterised by S_x, A_y, S_p

ϕ_5, ϕ_{13} are characterised by A_x, S_y, S_p

ϕ_6, ϕ_{14} are characterised by A_x, A_y, S_p

ϕ_8 is characterised by S_x, S_y, A_p

ϕ_9 is characterised by S_x, A_y, A_p

and we know that the self-consistent field functions can be calculated so that the molecular orbitals φ are linear combinations of symmetry orbitals belonging to the same symmetry class as defined above. Unfortunately, this calculation has not yet been carried out and the presence of polycentric integrals will make it very laborious. Previous experience in this field, however, allows us to predict the qualitative behaviour of the results which can be expected.

Indeed, orbitals of very different energies do not "mix" much, and the energy of a bonding orbital differs from that of the corresponding antibonding orbital by as much as the overlap of the functions which form them. From the class ϕ_1, ϕ_3, ϕ_7, ϕ_{11}, four orbitals will be obtained of which one, φ_1, will be almost entirely made up of ϕ_1, as this last orbital is formed by $1s$ functions, corresponding to a much lower energy than that associated with orbitals ϕ_3, ϕ_7 and ϕ_{11}. Two other orbitals φ_3 and φ_7 will contain appreciable quantities of ϕ_3 and ϕ_7 and little of ϕ_{11} while the fourth φ_{11} will be rich in ϕ_{11}, formed by "antibonding" orbitals.

Similarly, the class ϕ_2, ϕ_4, ϕ_{10} and ϕ_{12} gives φ_2 made up mainly of ϕ_2, φ_4 of ϕ_4 and φ_{10} and φ_{12} mixtures of ϕ_{10} and ϕ_{12}.

Both ϕ_5, ϕ_{13} and ϕ_6, ϕ_{14} mix very little since one orbital is formed of bonding orbitals and the other of antibonding orbitals. φ_5, φ_{13}, φ_6 and φ_{14} denote the corresponding molecular orbitals.

As both ϕ_8 and ϕ_9 are alone in their class, they are molecular orbitals. Hence,

$$\varphi_8 = \phi_8 \quad \varphi_9 = \phi_9.$$

Of all these molecular orbitals, φ_1 and φ_2 correspond to the lowest levels as they are rich in $1s$ functions. The overlap between $1s_1$ and $1s_2$ being very small, these two orbitals have approximately the same energy. Then comes the orbitals φ_3, φ_4, φ_5, φ_6, φ_7, combinations of orbitals χ and σ, and after that φ_8 as the overlap between orbitals $2p_z$ is smaller than that between t orbitals or between a t orbital and an h orbital.

The other molecular orbitals φ_9, φ_{10}, φ_{11}, φ_{12}, φ_{13}, φ_{14} correspond to higher energies since they are formed of antibonding elements. The energy of φ_9 will be rather close to that of φ_8 as the overlap between $2p_{z1}$ and $2p_{z2}$ is small.

In conclusion *the orbital*

$$\varphi_8 = \pi$$

and *the orbital*

$$\varphi_9 = \pi^*$$

are the last occupied orbital and the first unoccupied orbital respectively for the ground state of ethylene.

We might therefore expect that the first ionisations and excitations will be mainly concerned with the orbitals π and π^* which will be called simply the "π orbitals".

The self-consistent field operator can be written in the form:

$$\mathfrak{H}^{\text{C.A.C.}} = \mathfrak{H}^N + \Sigma\, J_j - \Sigma'\, K_j,$$

where J_{ij} is the coulomb operator associated with orbital φ_j such that

$$J_j \varphi_i(1) = \left(\int \varphi_j^2(2)\, \frac{e^2}{r_{21}}\, dv_2 \right) \varphi_i(1)$$

and K_j the exchange operator such that

$$K_j \varphi_i(1) = \left(\int \varphi_j(2)\, \varphi_i(2)\, \frac{e^2}{r_{21}}\, dv_2 \right) \varphi_j(1).$$

The sum Σ' extends over all the spin orbitals, whereas the sum Σ' only extends over those spin orbitals associated with the same spin function on which the operator acts.

If we are interested in the ground state of ethylene described by the function

$$\phi = \det \varphi_1 \overline{\varphi}_1 \varphi_2 \overline{\varphi}_2 \varphi_3 \overline{\varphi}_3 \varphi_4 \overline{\varphi}_4 \varphi_5 \overline{\varphi}_5 \varphi_6 \overline{\varphi}_6 \varphi_7 \overline{\varphi}_7 \varphi_8 \overline{\varphi}_8$$

then

$$\mathfrak{H}^{\text{C.A.C.}} = \mathfrak{H}^N + \sum_{j=1}^{7} (2J_j - K_j) + 2J_8 - K_8.$$

Now if we consider a slightly excited or ionised state and if we assume that only the π orbitals are perturbed, the following quantity is unchanged in the operator

$$\mathfrak{H}^C = \mathfrak{H}^N + \sum_{j=1}^{7} (2J_j - K_j).$$

This invariant operator is called the *core operator*. This type of reasoning is called a π *approximation* where ethylene is considered as formed of two electrons in the field of this operator and being repulsed from one another by Coulomb's law. The total operator of the problem can then be written

$$\mathfrak{H} = \mathfrak{H}^C(1) + \mathfrak{H}^C(2) + e^2/r_{12}.$$

The ground state of ethylene is then simply

$$\phi_{\text{I}} = \det \pi\overline{\pi}$$

the first triplet

$$\phi_{\text{II}} = \begin{cases} \det \pi\pi^* \\ \text{or} \\ \det \overline{\pi}\overline{\pi}^* \\ \text{or} \\ \dfrac{1}{\sqrt{2}} [\det \pi\overline{\pi}^* + \det \overline{\pi}\pi^*] \end{cases}$$

and the first singly excited states

$$\phi_{\text{III}} = \frac{1}{\sqrt{2}} [\det \pi\overline{\pi}^* - \det \overline{\pi}\pi^*]$$

$$\phi_{\text{IV}} = \det \overline{\pi}^*\overline{\pi}^*.$$

These functions can be used to construct a configuration interaction function. The problem is formally the same as that of the hydrogen molecule. The rules already established (first book, p. 167) for the calculation of the matrix elements apply here, replacing

$$\mathfrak{T}_k + \mathfrak{h}_A(k) + \cdots \mathfrak{h}_J(k) + \cdots$$

by

$$\mathfrak{H}^c(k).$$

We find, for example,

$$\mathfrak{H}_{\mathrm{I\,I}} = 2\varepsilon_\pi^C + J_{\pi\pi}$$

$$\mathfrak{H}_{\mathrm{II\,II}} = \varepsilon_\pi^C + \varepsilon_{\pi*}^C + J_{\pi\pi*} - K_{\pi\pi*}$$

$$\mathfrak{H}_{\mathrm{III\,III}} = \varepsilon_\pi^C + \varepsilon_{\pi*}^C + J_{\pi\pi*} + K_{\pi\pi*}$$

$$\mathfrak{H}_{\mathrm{IV\,IV}} = 2\varepsilon_{\pi*}^C + J_{\pi*\pi*},$$

where

$$\varepsilon_i^C = \int \varphi_i \mathfrak{H}^C \varphi_i \, dv$$

$$J_{ij} = \int \varphi_i J_j \varphi_i \, dv = (ii, jj)$$

$$K_{ij} = \int \varphi_i K_j \varphi_i \, dv = (ij, ij).$$

The integrals J_{ij} and K_{ij} are easily evaluated and the calculation of energy levels and hence first ionisation energies is reduced to finding the ε_i^C.

25. THE CORE POTENTIAL OF GOEPPERT-MAYER AND SKLAR

The rigorous calculation of these quantities requires once again knowledge of polycentric integrals. To avoid this difficulty Parr and Crawford [220] have used an approximation proposed by Goeppert-Mayer and Sklar [221]. In the present case this approximation reduces to neglecting the effect of hydrogen atoms and making allowance for the rest of the core by assuming that it reduces to a coulomb field produced by a charge distribution equal to the difference between that of two carbons in the ^5S state and that of orbitals $2p_{z1}$, and $2p_{z2}$. The core operator then reduces to

$$\mathfrak{H}^c = -\frac{h^2 \Delta}{8\pi^2 m} + u_1^+ + u_2^+,$$

where

$$u_i^+ = u_i - \int [2p_{zi}(2)]^2 \frac{e^2}{r_{21}} \, dv_2$$

and u_i represents the coulomb potential of a carbon at i in a ^5S state. The density of such an atom is then spherically symmetric, and hence the calculations are eased.

The only term which appears and which remains rather difficult to evaluate is then

$$-\frac{h^2}{8\pi^2 m} \Delta(2p_{zi}),$$

but one can consider to a first approximation that $2p_{zi}$ represents the movement of an electron in the field u_i^+. Hence,

$$\left(-\frac{h^2\Delta}{8\pi^2 m} + u_i^+\right) 2p_{zi} = W_{2p} \cdot 2p_{zi},$$

where W_{2p} is a constant representing an ionisation energy of carbon which Mulliken[222] estimated at $-11\cdot28$ eV. Using Slater's orbitals with $Z = 3\cdot18$ for the L shell of carbon we find (in eV)

$$J_{\pi\pi} = 13\cdot0758 \qquad K_{\pi\pi*} = 4\cdot1597$$

$$J_{\pi\pi*} = 13\cdot0109 \qquad \varepsilon_\pi^C = W_{2p} - 12\cdot4399$$

$$J_{\pi*\pi*} = 13\cdot4391 \qquad \varepsilon_{\pi*}^C = W_{2p} - 6\cdot3757.$$

The different excitation energies of ethylene can then be calculated easily.

For example, the transition $\phi_{\mathrm{I}} \to \phi_{\mathrm{II}}$ corresponds to the energy

$$E_{\mathrm{III}} = \mathfrak{H}_{\mathrm{IIII}} - \mathfrak{H}_{\mathrm{II}} = \varepsilon_{\pi*}^C - \varepsilon_\pi^C + J_{\pi\pi*} - J_{\pi\pi} - K_{\pi\pi*} = 1\cdot8 \text{ eV}.$$

Similarly, the energy of transition $\phi_{\mathrm{I}} \to \phi_{\mathrm{III}}$ is given as $10\cdot2$ eV. Finally, the first ionisation energy is found at $10\cdot64$ eV.

The absorption spectrum[223] shows a feeble band diffused between $6\cdot35$ and $6\cdot6$ eV which is interpreted as due to a singlet–triplet transition and then a band at $7\cdot6$ eV. Obviously, the preceding theory considerably exaggerates the difference between the triplet state described by ϕ_{II} and the single state corresponding to ϕ_{III}. The position of the centre of gravity of states II and III, given by experiment as about 7 eV, is, on the other hand, better represented by the theory ($\{1.8 + 10.2\}/2 = 6$). The experimental value for the ionisation energy is 10.45 eV [224]. This agrees well with the value found by calculation.

Sponer and Löwdin [225] have used Hartree–Fock atomic orbitals in the same manner. Their results differ little from those of Parr and Crawford.

The introduction of configuration interactions limited to π and π^* does not improve the situation.

26. THE INTERACTION $\pi - \sigma$

This is why it has been suggested that the basis of the configuration interaction be extended by treating the problem of ethylene as a four electron problem using orbitals π, π^*, σ and σ^*. Moser [226], however, has shown that this does not modify the preceding results appreciably. "The interaction π–σ" is not important.

27. THE SEMI-EMPIRIC METHOD OF PARISER AND PARR

The preceding results indicate that the approximation of potential of Goeppert-Mayer and Sklar is not very satisfactory. As any attempt to improve them by non-empiric methods is made difficult by the polycentric integrals, some semi-empiric method must be found.

The method of Pariser and Parr [227] consists of neglecting both the overlap between orbitals $2p_{z1}$ and $2p_{z2}$ and *all the bielectronic integrals* containing a product of the form $2p_{z1}(i)/2p_{z2}(i)$. The expression for ε, J, K are then considerably simplified.

For example, letting

$$\pi_1 = 2p_{z1} \quad \text{and} \quad \pi_2 = 2p_{z2}$$

we have

$$\varepsilon_\pi^C = \int \pi_1 \mathfrak{H}^C \pi_1 \, dv - \int \pi_1 \mathfrak{H}^C \pi_2 \, dv.$$

Let

$$\alpha_i^C = \int \pi_i \mathfrak{H}^C \pi_i \, dv \qquad \beta_{12} = \int \pi_1 \mathfrak{H}^C \pi_2 \, dv.$$

β_{12} is then treated as an empirical parameter which can be chosen as well to agree with either the results of the previous calculation or those of experiment.

The expression for α_1^C, for example, becomes

$$\alpha_1^C = W_{2p} - [(\pi_1\pi_1/\pi_2\pi_2) + (\pi_1\pi_1/u_2)],$$

where

$$(\pi_1\pi_1/\pi_2\pi_2) = \int \pi_1(1)\,\pi_1(1)\,\frac{e^2}{r_{12}}\,\pi_2(2)\,\pi_2(2)\,dv_{12}$$

$$(\pi_1\pi_1/u_2) = \int \pi_1(1)\,u_2\pi_1(1)\,dv_1$$

using the same type of approximation as Goeppert-Mayer and Sklar. This calculation can be improved by adding the quantity $\Sigma(\pi_1\,\pi_1/u_{H_k})$ to account for the potential u_{H_k} centred on each hydrogen atom. The terms which then appear are called penetration integrals. The calculation of integrals $(\pi_1\pi_1/\pi_2\pi_2)$ is easy, but Parr[228] has proposed that they be estimated on a procedure based on the replacement of the π_i orbitals by uniformly charged spheres tangential to the plane of the molecule.

In most of the integrals already encountered $(\pi_1\pi_1/\pi_1\pi_1)$ must be used to calculate the J and K. It can be given either a theoretical or an empirical value.

It may seem strange to introduce these empirical values for quantities which are known theoretically, but this may be thought of as compensating for the terms neglected in the method of Pariser and Parr.

Various authors[229] have shown that the neglect of these terms can be justified if the orbitals π_1 and π_2 are assumed to be the orthogonal orbitals defined by Löwdin[230] rather than the actual atomic orbitals.

Be this as it may, we can obtain, in the case of ethylene, values of molecular quantities agreeing with experiment by using the semi-empiric method of Pariser and Parr, but this is not very significant as it introduces empirical quantities. The interest in the method lies in the possibility of applying it to entire classes of molecules as we shall see presently.

Concluding this chapter, the π approximation seems to be based on reasonable theoretical considerations, but the impossibility of calculating the polycentric integrals require the use of unsatisfactory approximations when working from a non-empiric point of view. One is then obliged to use more or less empiric methods, the value of which can only be judged on results given when they are applied to entire classes of molecules. The analysis of these results will be the object of the following chapters.

CHAPTER VIII

Purely Conjugated Hydrocarbons Treated by "Naïve" Methods

28. PURELY CONJUGATED HYDROCARBONS AND "NAÏVE" METHODS

Purely conjugated hydrocarbons are defined as those hydrocarbons whose formulae can be written with alternate simple and double bonds over all the molecule. Butadiene, benzene, fulvene and azulene fall into this category.

butadiene   benzene   fulvene   azulene

A hydrocarbon such as the following

will be considered in the limit as purely conjugated since the alternation of bonds cannot be entirely respected.

On the other hand, toluene, ethylbenzene, carriers of methyl or ethyl substituents, will be considered as substituted conjugated hydrocarbons but not purely conjugated.

Purely conjugated hydrocarbons are plane or nearly plane whenever angles of about 120° can form between the bonds starting from a carbon. For instance, naphthalene is plane [231] and 3, 4–5, 6-dibenzophenanthrene is nearly plane [232].

3,4–5, 6-dibenzophenanthrene

On the other hand, when angles of 120° are impossible, the molecule cannot be plane. We can contrast the case of plane cyclo-octo-decanonane [234] with the case of non-plane cyclo-octatetrene [235].

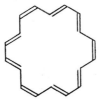

cyclo-octodecanonane   cycló-octatetrene

Our study will be limited to plane or nearly plane hydrocarbons. For a plane molecule we can generalise the reasoning applied in the case of ethylene and form a series of π orbitals as linear combinations of $2p_z$ orbitals associated with each carbon atom, i.e.

$$\pi_j = \sum_i c_{ij}\, 2p_{zi}.$$

It is easy to show that these orbitals behave like molecular orbitals and that the electron re-organisations produced, by small perturbations, are concerned almost completely with these orbitals. The next step is therefore to study the properties of plane hydrocarbons using the π approximation which may be assumed to be also suitable for nearly plane molecules.

The calculation of c_{ij} can be carried out in principle by the self-consistent field method which requires knowledge of elements of the form

$$\alpha_i = \int 2p_{zi} \mathfrak{S} \, 2p_{zi} \, dv$$

$$\beta_{1m} = \int 2p_{zi} \mathfrak{S} \, 2p_{zm} \, dv.$$

As these calculations are very laborious, we can apply, as a first step, some simple procedure such as Hückel's approximation (first book, p.157) or Whelland's approximation (first book, p.160). Such methods are sometimes called "naïve" methods as they are not very elaborate. We will now try them in a particular case suitable to their application. They produce quite satisfactory results on the whole.

29. ENERGY MEASUREMENTS IN HÜCKEL'S APPROXIMATION

In Hückel's approximation, the α_i are assumed equal:

$$\alpha_1 = \alpha_2 = \cdots \alpha_i = \alpha.$$

This is a reasonable hypothesis, as all the carbons of a conjugated hydrocarbon have three neighbours. However, these neighbours may consist of either one, two or three carbon atoms together with two, one, or zero hydrogen atoms respectively. The atom will be called an atom of type one, two or three respectively and the integral α assigned accordingly. We shall return to this point later.

It is also assumed that the β_{ij} between neighbouring atoms are equal:

$$\beta_{12} = \beta_{23} = \cdots \beta_{ij} \cdots = \beta$$

and that the β_{ij} between non-neighbouring atoms are negligible. We shall see how the β_{ij} varies with interatomic distance which gives the order of magnitude of the neglected terms. The biggest approximation is the neglect of the overlap integrals. These can be accounted for by using Wheland's procedure.

The secular system is written

$$\sum c_{ij}[C_{ij} - \varepsilon_j \delta_{ij}] = 0$$

with

$$C_{ij} = \beta \text{ or } 0 \qquad \text{for } i \neq j$$

$$C_{ii} = \alpha$$

δ_{ij} being the Kronecker symbol and ε_j the energy associated with the jth orbital. These energies are then of the form

$$\varepsilon_j = \alpha - m_j\beta,$$

where the m_j are solutions of the secular equation.

A. *Ionisation Energy*

By Koopmans' theorem, these ε_j are approximations to the ionisation energies of hydrocarbons. As in the case of ethylene, each carbon introduces a π electron into the system. For a molecule containing $2n$ carbons, the n first orbitals are doubly occupied in the ground state. The first ionisation energy corresponds to the nth

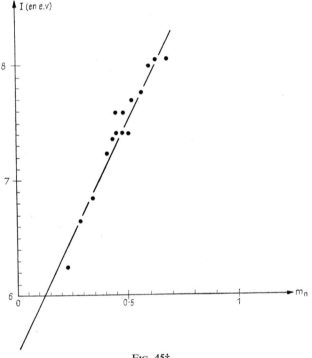

FIG. 45†

† This graph is taken from R. DAUDEL, R. LEFEBVRE and C. MOSER, *Quantum Chemistry, Methods and Applications*, Interscience (1939), p. 180.

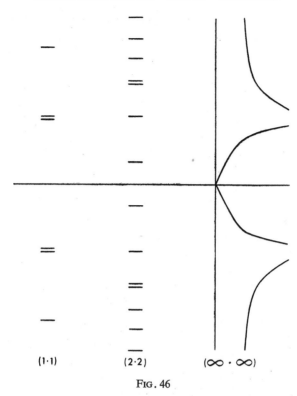

(1·1)   (2·2)   (∞ · ∞)

FIG. 46

root of the secular equation. Figure 45 shows how the experimental value of the ionisation energy I† varies with this root m_n. A linear relation of the form

$$I = 5·5 + 4m_n$$

fits the experimental points. Hence we conclude that, from the ionisation energy

$$\alpha = -5·5 \text{ eV} \qquad \beta = -4 \text{ eV}.$$

Coulson, Schaad and Burnelle [236] have studied how the ε_j of purely conjugate hydrocarbons vary in various series of molecules tending towards graphite.

Figure 46 shows the results they obtained in the case of the "rectangular" family. The case (∞, ∞) corresponds to graphite and

† For a more precise discussion, see Chapter IX.

as, in this case, the spectrum of ε_j becomes continuous, the figure represents the variation of the density of states $N(\varepsilon)$ such that

$$dN = N(\varepsilon)\, d\varepsilon$$

represents the number of energy states in the interval $d\varepsilon$ at ε.

One sees that the order of degeneracy of the levels $\varepsilon = \alpha \pm \beta$ increases proportionately with the size of the molecules. Moreover, the levels occur more frequently about this value. This allows us to understand the behaviour of function $N(\varepsilon)$ and in particular its infinite value for $\varepsilon = \alpha \pm \beta$. Note also that the energy ε_n tends towards α as n tends to infinity. We can deduce from this that the first ionisation energy of graphite is 5·5 eV. Experiment gives 4·39 eV. Coulson and his collaborators have, in the same paper, studied levels of the same series of molecules using the method of linear combinations of bond orbitals.

B. Alternant and Non-alternant Hydrocarbons. Radicals and Biradicals

It is useful to classify completely conjugated hydrocarbons into *alternant hydrocarbons* and *non-alternant hydrocarbons*. The former are those for which the carbon atoms can be marked with a plus and minus sign alternately such that only plus signs are encountered next to minus signs and vice versa. Hydrocarbons for which this is impossible are called non-alternant.

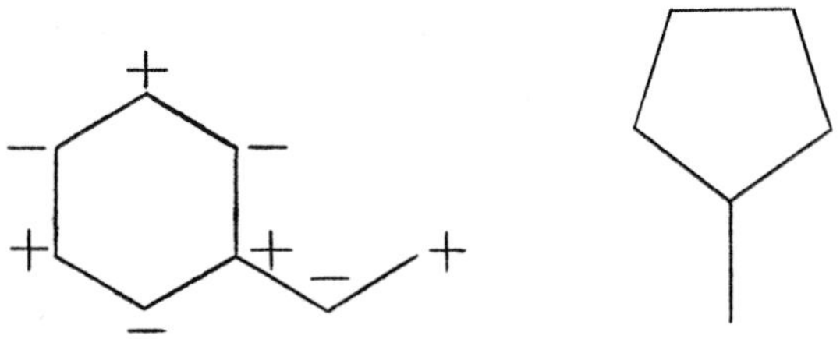

Fig. 47

Only the presence of an odd cycle stops a hydrocarbon from being alternant (see Fig. 47). It has been shown [237] that the ε_j of alternant hydrocarbons occur in pairs. For each orbital energy

$$\varepsilon_j = \alpha + m_j\beta$$

there corresponds

$$\varepsilon_{j'} = \alpha - m_j\beta.$$

In the case where there are an even number, $2n$, of carbon atoms, these are n orbitals with positive coefficients (called *bonding*, as β is negative) and n orbitals with negative coefficients (called *antibonding*). In the ground states, only the bonding orbitals are used in the wave function; each used twice.

In the case where there are an odd number of carbon atoms, the molecule is called a *free radical*, e.g. triphenylmethyl. The number of orbitals is then odd. They must be symmetrical about the value $\varepsilon = \alpha$. For this root

$$\varepsilon_j = \alpha + m_j\beta = \varepsilon_{j'} = \alpha - m_j\beta,$$

i.e. $m_j = 0$. Secular equations of all free radicals must have at least one root $m = 0$. The corresponding orbital is called *non-bonding*. In the ground state of the radical, it is singly occupied if it corresponds to a simple root. This does not mean that the root $m = 0$ does not occur for even numbers of carbon atoms. However, if such a root exists, it must be least a double root, as the value $\varepsilon_j = \alpha$ must correspond to $\varepsilon_{j'} = \alpha$. If $m = 0$ is only double, then two electrons must exist in orbitals of energy $\varepsilon = \alpha$. One can, however, use φ_j twice, $\varphi_{j'}$ twice or φ_j once and $\varphi_{j'}$ once as one pleases. The first two cases result necessarily in a singlet state while the second can represent either a singlet or a triplet state. From Hund's empirical rules, the triplet state will be the most stable [238]. An even alternant hydrocarbon, for which $m = 0$ is a root, will therefore be triplet in its ground state. It is then said to act as a *biradical*. Dewar and Longuet-Higgins [239] have demonstrated that the root $m = 0$ occurs for all hydrocarbons containing no cycles other than benzene cycles, and for which one cannot write a Kékulé formula. *Hence any hydrocarbon containing no cycles other than benzene cycles and for which one cannot write a Kékulé formula, is a biradical.* For example Schlenk's hydrocarbon:

Samuel[240] has shown that this rule can be extended to include hydrocarbons whose only cycles are cycles with $2K$ sides, where K is odd.

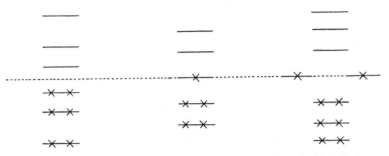

FIG. 48. Diagrammatic representation of the occupation of orbitals in the ground state of alternant hydrocarbons.

Figure 48 summarises what has been said about the utilisation of orbitals in the ground state of alternant hydrocarbons.

C. Atomisation and Resonance Energies

We have seen that for paraffins, one can define energies of simple bonds E_{C-C} and E_{C-H} which allow the atomisation energy of the molecule to be retrieved to within a few kcal/mol. We have found:

$$E_{C-C} = 98 \cdot 75 \qquad E_{C-H} = 83 \cdot 6$$
$$\text{(in kcal/mol.)}$$

If we wish to retrieve the atomisation energy of ethylene, we must assume that the energy of the double bond $C=C$ is

$$E_{C=C} = 148 \cdot 4 \text{ kcal/mol.}$$

If a Kékulian formula is then used to represent benzene, we find for its atomisation energy[241],

$$6 \times 98 \cdot 75 + 3 \times 83 \cdot 6 + 3 \times 148 \cdot 4 = 1288 \cdot 5 \text{ kcal/mol.}$$

while experiment gives 1323·5 kcal/mol, i.e. 35 kcal/mol more. This excess of stability of benzene over the formula of Kékulé is called the *resonance energy*. This quantity is generally important for conjugated hydrocarbons containing cycles of six lines. It can be considered as a measure of their *aromatic character*[242]. The resonance energy is often assumed to come from the π system. In the "naïve" methods, the energy associated with the π orbitals has been calculated by simply taking the sum of the ε_j associated with occupied orbitals; an ε_j being counted the number of times the corresponding orbital is used. In the case of benzene, for example, the ε_j of occupied orbitals are†

$$\varepsilon_1 = \alpha + 2\beta$$

$$\varepsilon_2 = \alpha + \beta$$

the second level being doubly degenerate.

The total energy E_π associated with π system is then

$$E_\pi = 2\varepsilon_1 + 4\varepsilon_2 = 6\alpha + 8\beta.$$

In ethylene, the unique occupied π orbital has a value $\alpha + \beta$ for ε. If benzene contains three ethylene bonds, as is assumed in Kékulé's formula, its energy E_{K_π} will be

$$E_{K_\pi} = 6\alpha + 6\beta.$$

The difference

$$R = E_{K_\pi} - E_\pi = -2\beta$$

is frequently considered to be a measure of the resonance energy of benzene. The existence of this energy shows that the organisation of π systems which occur in benzene is more stable than the ensemble of three double bonds. From this, β is deduced to be $-17{\cdot}5\,\text{kcal/mol}$, i.e. a little less than an electron-volt which is less than a quarter of the value found from the ionisation energy. Be this as it may, Table 29.1 compares[243] experimental results with those found by evaluating R for a number of different molecules.

Obviously, by assuming that β is constant at about $17\,\text{kcal/mol}$, a good approximation is made for the resonance energy.

This type of reasoning, however, runs into a serious difficulty. If benzene has a Kékulian structure, it will have three double CC bonds and three simple CC bonds. The length of a C=C bond is about $1{\cdot}34\,\text{Å}$ and a C—C bond $1{\cdot}54\,\text{Å}$. In fact, experiment shows

† The values of ε_j and of various theoretical quantities characteristic of conjugated molecules in "naïve" methods are summarised in the *Dictionnaire des grandeurs théoriques descriptive des molécules* edited by C. A. COULSON and R. DAUDEL. This publication will be referred to in the text as D.G.T.

that benzene has a regular hexagonal structure of side 1·39 Å. To get from the Kékulian structure to the actual structure, therefore, the double bonds must be elongated and the simple bonds contracted.

TABLE 29.1

Molecule	R in kcal/mol (experimental)	R in β (calculated)	β (in kcal/mol)
Naphthalene	61	3·68	16·6
Anthracene	83·5	5·31	15·7
Phenanthrene	91·6	5·45	16·8
Naphthacene	110	6·93	15·9
Chrysene	116·5	7·19	16·1
Triphenylene	117·7	7·27	16·2

The energy necessary for this transformation is called the compression–extension energy E_{CE}[244].

To take account of this, one must write

$$R = (E_{K_\pi} - E_\pi) - E_{CE}.$$

Now, it can be shown that

$$E_{CE} \simeq 0·8R,$$

which results in

$$R = 0·55(E_{K_\pi} - E_\pi),$$

which leads to the multiplication of the preceding values of β by 1·8. This produces, therefore, values of the integral nearer to that found from the ionisation energies.

D. *Excitation Energies*

Under the assumptions which we are using where the total energy of the π system is obtained by summing energies associated with occupied orbitals, it is clear that the first excited state is obtained by "pushing" an electron of the last occupied orbital (n, say) into the first unoccupied orbital ($n + 1$). For an even hydrocarbon, (which is *not* a biradical), the nth orbital and the ($n + 1$)th orbital will then both be only singly occupied. The representation obtained will fit either a triplet or singlet state. By simply summing the ε, we obviously obtain the same energy for the singlet state and the corresponding triplet state. Hence, using Huckel's approximation, we cannot distinguish between the first triplet state and the first singlet excited state.

The transition energy of the ground state to one of these states is given by

$$\Delta\varepsilon = \varepsilon_{n+1} - \varepsilon_n = (m_{n+1} - m_n)\,\beta.$$

The corresponding singlet–singlet transition has been indentified with Clar's p bands (for reasons which we will clarify later), i.e. the first set of intense bands which are encountered in the electronic spectrum as one goes from long to short wavelength.

Tables 29.2 and 29.3[245] allow comparison to be made between the wavelength λ corresponding to maximum absorption of the preceding bands system and the value of $m_{n+1} - m_n$ found by D.G.T.

TABLE 29.2

Molecule	$m_{n+1} - m_n$	(Å)
Benzene	2	2080
Naphthalene	1·236	2750
Anthracene	0·828	3750
Naphthacene	0·588	4740
Pentacene	0·438	5810

TABLE 29.3

Molecule	$m_{n+1} - m_n$	λ(Å)
Anthracene	0·828	3750
Phenanthrene	1·050	2930
Naphthacene	0·588	4740
1,2-Benzanthracene	0·904	3590

Obviously, it is sufficient to assume that β is constant from one hydrocarbon to another to account for the qualitative effects shown in these tables, i.e. the bathochrome effect induced by the annealation in the acene series (Table 29.2) and the hypsochrome effect observed when one passes from a linear hydrocarbon to the corresponding angular hydrocarbon. However, if β is calculated to obtain a numerical agreement between theory and experiment, it is found to vary considerably from one case to another; nevertheless, its value stays between the values found from resonance energies and from the ionisation energies. H. Koutecky and J. Paldus have pointed out (in a personal communication) that if one assumes a relationship of the form

$$\Delta\varepsilon = (m_{n+1} - m_n)\beta + C,$$

where C is a constant determined empirically, this leads to a reasonably constant value of β. The term C can be interpreted as a repulsion effect between electrons which are badly represented in Hückel's approximation.

30. QUANTITIES DEPENDING ON COEFFICIENTS OF HÜCKEL'S APPROXIMATION

A. *Analysis of the Electron Population and Polar Moment*

Since, in Hückel's approximation, the overlap is neglected, the contribution of a π_j orbital to the electron population of the ith electron is simply c_{ij}^2. The electron charge carried to the ith atom by the ensemble of π orbitals is then

$$q_i = e \sum_j \eta_j c_{ij}^2,$$

where η_j is 0, 1 or 2 depending on whether the jth orbital is unoccupied, singly or doubly occupied. It can be demonstrated [246] that for the ground state of an alternant hydrocarbon

$$q_i = e$$

for all the carbons. This is not so for non-alternant hydrocarbons. Figure 49 gives the distribution of charges q_i (e being taken as unity) for some molecules, after D.G.T.

Note that the $2p_z$ orbitals are such that the symmetry conditions explained at the end of Section 10 are satisfied. The contribution of π orbitals to the dipolar moment of the molecule is then simply

$$\sum_i q_i \vec{r}_i,$$

where $\vec{r}_i$ is the radius vector associated with nuclei i.

As the concept of polar moment applies to a zero charge distribution and each atom introduces an electron into the π system, it is natural to associate with the preceding contribution a term arising from one of the protons of each carbon, i.e.

$$-e \sum_i \vec{r}_i .$$

The dipolar moment of the π system can then be written

$$\vec{\mu}_\pi = \sum_i (q_i - e) \vec{r}_i .$$

The total dipolar moment of the molecule is obtained by adding to this quantity the moment associated with the rest of the molecule, i.e. with the σ orbitals of the CC bonds and with the CH bonds.

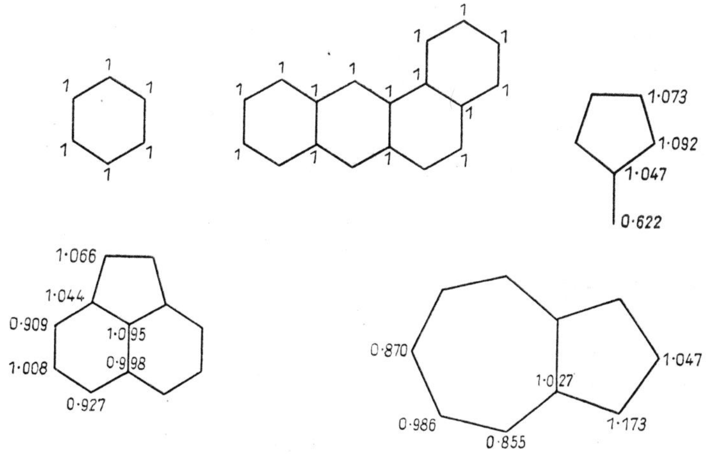

Fig. 49

It is reasonable to assume that the σ bonds between two identical cores will not be polar. It is obvious from the geometry of the molecule that the moments of CH bonds will neutralise one another. Hence, the dipolar moment of the molecule reduces to $\vec{\mu}_\pi$. Now we have seen that for an alternant hydrocarbon $q_i = e$ and hence $\vec{\mu}_\pi = 0$. The dipolar moment of such a molecule must therefore be very small. This has been confirmed experimentally[247].

For a non-alternant hydrocarbon, on the other hand, we might expect to find an appreciable polar moment. This is also confirmed experimentally. Table 30.1 compares $\vec{\mu}_\pi$ with the experimental values of the polar moments of some non-alternant hydrocarbons.

This shows that, in general, Hückel's approximation leads to an overestimation of polar moments.

TABLE 30.1

Molecule	$\vec{\mu}_\pi$(in debyes)	Experimental moment (in debyes)
Fulvene	4·7[248]	1·2[249]
Azulene	6·9[250]	1[250]
Acenaphtylene	2·86[248]	0·3[250]

B. *Intensity and Polarisation of Band Systems of Electron Spectra. Oscillator Strength*

The absorption of light by a substance in low concentration follows the law of Lambert–Bouger–Beer:

$$I_v = I_{0v}\, e^{-\varepsilon_v cd}.$$

In this formula I_{0v} is the incident intensity of the light, assumed monochromatic with frequency v, I_v the transmitted intensity, c the concentration and d the thickness of the substance crossed, and ε_v is defined as the *molecular extinction coefficient* of the substance for frequency v when c is expressed in gramme-molecules per unit volume.

The mean *oscillator strength* f of a band system between frequencies v_1 and v_2 is defined as[252]

$$f = \frac{mc^2}{\pi e^2 N}\int_{v_1}^{v_2}\varepsilon\, dv.$$

In this formula, c is the speed of light and N is Avogadro's number. It can be proved that f can be expressed theoretically by means of the expression

$$f = \frac{8\pi^2 mc}{3h}\, v\lambda_{el}^2$$

when the transition takes place between non-degenerate levels[253]. $\vec{\lambda}_{el}$ here denotes the moment of the electron transition defined by the formula

$$\vec{\lambda}_{el} = \sum_i \int \phi' \vec{r}_i \phi \, dv,$$

where ϕ and ϕ' represent the wave functions associated with the initial and final states (see first book, page 180)†.

Let us then calculate the moment of transition of the ground state of the π system of a hydrocarbon represented by

$$\phi = \varphi_1(1) \overline{\varphi_1(2)} \dots \varphi_n(2n-1) \overline{\varphi_n(2n)}$$

to an excited state represented by

$$\phi' = \varphi_1(1) \overline{\varphi_1(2)} \dots \varphi_n(2n-1) \overline{\varphi_p(2n)}.$$

By adapting the arguments given for dipolar moments, we find that

$$\vec{\lambda}_{el} = \sum_i c_{in}c_{ip}\vec{r}_i.$$

For the transition to the first excited state of butadiene, we find

$$f \simeq 0 \cdot 75 \,(\text{C.G.S.})$$

whereas experiment gives

$$f = 0 \cdot 53(^{253}).$$

If the wave functions are expressed more correctly in the form

$$\phi' = \frac{1}{\sqrt{2}} \left\{ \det \varphi_1(1) \dots \varphi_n(2n-1) \overline{\varphi_p(2n)} \right.$$

$$\left. + \det \varphi_1(1) \dots \overline{\varphi_n(2n-1)} \varphi_p(2n) \right\}$$

we find that $\vec{\lambda}_{el}$ is multiplied by $\sqrt{2}$; f is then $1 \cdot 5$. This is an illustration of a more general fact: the application of Hückel's approximation to find oscillator strengths of singlet–singlet transitions gives values of about three times the experimental values.

The direction of vector $\vec{\lambda}_{el}$ is called the *direction of polarisation* of the transition. It is always found to be in the plane of the hydro-

† Note that the quantity defined here differs by a factor e from the definition given in the first book. Both definitions are found in the literature.

ESM 10

carbon. When the hydrocarbon has symmetry, λ_{el} is often parallel to one of the axes. In the case of naphthalene and anthracene, the p-band is found to be polarised along the small axis of the molecule using Hückel's approximation[254]. It is rather difficult to verify the theory from this point of view as the experimental determination of the direction of polarisation of a band system is a delicate procedure. In the case of the p-bands of naphthalene, for example, Passerini and Ross[255] indicate a polarisation along the small axis while McClure[256] finds a polarisation along the long axis.

C. *Bond Orders and Interatomic Distances*

We have already mentioned that the length of the simple bonds CC and CH of paraffins are constant to about 0·02 Å. This generalises for the majority of simple bonds in most molecules. It also extends to double and triple bonds. In the case of CC bonds, for example, the lengths of simple, double and triple bonds are within 0·02 Å of 1·54, 1·34 and 1·20 respectively.

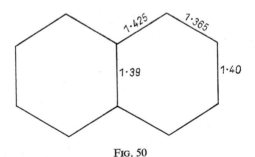

Fig. 50

Figure 50 gives the experimental values of the lengths of the bonds of naphthalene[257]. The error is about 0·01 Å. This shows considerable variation from one bond to another; the maximum difference being 0·06 Å. Moreover, the lengths do not correspond to either simple or double bonds. We conclude, therefore, that the CC bonds of conjugated hydrocarbons are neither simple nor double but are of some intermediate type.

The interpretation of this is simple, as in our π approximation each CC bond has a contribution from the π system, together with a σ bond. This contribution will now be examined more closely.

Consider the expression for the energy associated with an orbital φ_j:

$$\varepsilon_j = \int \varphi_j \mathfrak{C} \varphi_j \, dv.$$

φ_j can be expanded as

$$\varphi_j = \sum_i c_{ij} 2p_{zi}$$

giving

$$\varepsilon_j = \sum_i c_{ij}^2 \alpha_i + \sum_i \sum_{i'} c_{ij} c_{i'j} \beta_{ii'} = \sum_i c_{ij}^2 \alpha_i + 2 \sum_{i<i'} c_{ij} c_{i'j} \beta_{ii'}.$$

In this expression, the quantity $2c_{ij} c_{i'j} \beta_{ii'}$ can be assumed to represent the contribution of φ_j to the energy of bond ii'. The contribution of the entire π system is then

$$2 \sum_i \eta_j c_{ij} c_{i'j} \beta_{ii'}.$$

As $\beta_{ii'}$ is assumed to be independent of the bond, the quantity which characterises this contribution is

$$p_{ii'} = \sum_i \eta_j c_{ij} c_{i'j}$$

which is called the bond order[258]. This can be shown to be zero for a simple bond and one for ethylene. We also introduce the *total bond order* which varies from 1 for a simple CC bond to 2 for a double CC bond.

If this order is a good measure of the bonding energy we would expect it to be a decreasing function of distance between the carbon nuclei. Figure 51 shows that this is generally true[259].

The curve in this figure can then be used to calculate approximate interatomic distances for conjugate hydrocarbons. Note that the dispersion of points about this fitted line is of the order of 0·02 Å. The experimental errors themselves are seldom less. The bond order is therefore a very interesting quantity as it allows one to obtain a good approximation of the lengths of bonds of conjugated hydrocarbons which have not been studied experimentally.

For instance, we might ask whether it is possible to predict the behaviour of lengths of bonds in different series of conjugated hydrocarbons as the number of carbon atoms tends to infinity.

Lennard-Jones[260] has studied linear polyenes of formula $C_{2n}H_{2n+2}$ and has concluded that, as n tends to infinity, the lengths of bonds remote from the extremities of the chain tend to become equal. This conclusion can be reached quickly, as it is possible to show that for such a chain the order of the bond between atoms r and $r + 1$ is

$$p_{r,r+1} = \frac{1}{2n + 1} \left\{ \operatorname{cosec} \frac{\pi}{4n + 2} + (-1)^{r-1} \operatorname{cosec} \frac{(2r + 1)\pi}{4n + 2} \right\}.$$

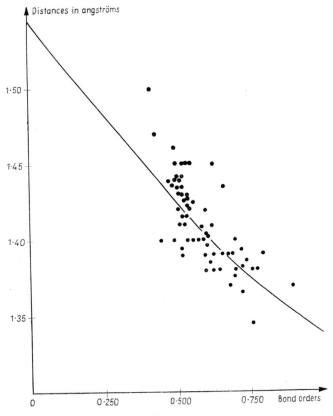

Fig. 51. Bond orders.

As n tends to infinity, the first cosecant tends to infinity. Towards the middle of the chain near $r = n$ the second cosecant is nearly unity and is therefore negligible compared with the first. The order $p_{r,r+1}$ and hence the length of the bond does not vary much with r. Dewar[261], however, has observed that if this situation is real-ised, the frequency corresponding to the first system of spectrum bands will tend to zero whereas in fact it seems to have a finite limit.

This is the reason that Labhard[262], Ooshika[263], Longuet-Higgins and Salem[264] have recently reconsidered this type of problem. We shall say a few words on the latter's work as the method used by these authors fits into this chapter.

They have laid stress on the case of cyclic polyenes of the form $C_{2n}H_{2n}$. For these compounds to be plane with angles of 120°, n must equal $4m + 2$. Hückel's approximation leads to finding that all the bonds have equal lengths independent of n. Longuet-Higgins and Salem expressed the bonding energy $\mathscr{V}$ in the form

$$\mathscr{V} = \mathscr{F} + \mathscr{E}.$$

$\mathscr{F}$ represents the energy of the σ bonds and $\mathscr{E}$ the energy of the π system. We have already seen that the energies of localised bonds are more or less additive. Hence,

$$\mathscr{F} = \sum_i f(r_i),$$

where $f(r_i)$ is the energy associated with the ith bond of length r_i.

We are now in a position to find if, as n tends to infinity, the system formed by equal bonds is as stable as a system formed of bonds of alternating lengths r_1 and r_2.

Deviating a little from Hückel's approximation, therefore, β_1 and β_2 will be defined as the corresponding resonance integrals. The π energy can be easily shown to be

$$\mathscr{E} = -2 \sum_n^{-n} \sqrt{\left(\beta_1^2 + \beta_2^2 + 2\beta_1\beta_2 \cos \frac{2\pi j}{2n+1} \right)}.$$

This formula applies equally well to the system of equal bonds by setting

$$\beta_1 = \beta_2 = \beta_0,$$

where β_0 represents the common value of the resonance integrals. Let

$$\beta_1 = \beta_0 \, e^{-x} \quad \text{and} \quad \beta_2 = \beta_0 \, e^{+x}.$$

Then

$$\left(\frac{\partial^2 \mathscr{V}}{\partial x^2} \right)_{x=0} = \left(\frac{\partial^2 \mathscr{F}}{\partial x^2} \right)_{x=0} + 4\beta_0 \sum_{-n}^n \sec \left(\frac{j\pi}{2n+1} \right).$$

The term on the right is proportional to n by reason of the formula

$$\mathscr{F} = \sum_i f_i.$$

The second diverges as $n \log n$ as n tends to infinity. The sign will therefore have the sign of the second term, i.e. the sign of β_0 which is negative. *The system of equal bonds will therefore be unstable relative to the system of alternating bonds.*

The same type of reasoning applies to linear polyenes and this explains why the frequency of the first system of absorption bands does not tend to zero. Obviously, in the discussion of such problems, we must take with some reserve the conclusions of Huckel's method which assumes *a priori*, that the resonance integrals β are equal and neglects the variation of β with the length of the bonds.

Salem and Longuet-Higgins have also extended this discussion to the case of polyacenes [265].

31. Some Remarks on the Fact that Certain Conjugated Hydrocarbons are not Plane

The results which have just been discussed are based on the separation of π orbitals from other orbitals, which in turn is based on the planeness of the molecule. Now, while numerous hydrocarbons have been found to be very probably plane, there are others which are certainly not so. This is so for 3,4–5,6-dibenzophenanthrene where the distance x in the formula below is about 3 Å [266] while it would only be 1·4 Å if the molecule were plane.

Coulson and Senent [267] have studied this problem. The principle of the method consists of establishing a semi-empirical formula giving the electron energy u as a function of the position of the nuclei.

If, for example, we assume that the molecule is derived from what it would be if the steric hindrance did not exist by simple displacements of the nuclei perpendicular to the plane which it would form, then the energy U is found to be a sum of terms of the form

$$U_i = \tfrac{1}{2}k(z_2 + z_3 + z_4 - 3z_1)^2$$

for each carbon i and

$$U_{ij} = \tfrac{1}{2}k'(z_3 - z_4 + z_5 - z_6)^2$$

for each bond ij.

z_2, z_3 and z_4 are the displacements (measured from the plane) of nuclei which are adjacent nucleus i of distance z_1; z_3, z_4 and z_5 are the displacements of nuclei neighbouring nuclei i and j respectively.

By minimising U, we can then find the probable position of the nuclei in the non-plane hydrocarbon. Using this type of procedure, Senent and Herraez [268] have shown that the increase in energy due to steric hindrance of CH bonds in phenanthrene is:

(a) 0·54 kcal/mol if the molecule is assumed plane, only the angles of the bonds changing.

(b) 43·6 kcal/mol if the molecule is assumed plane only the length of the bonds changing.

(c) 6·61 kcal/mol if the steric hindrance is expressed by vertical displacements of the nuclei.

They conclude that the effect of the steric hindrance is a mixture of effects (a) and (c) but that the interatomic distances are not altered much.

This conclusion is in agreement with experimental work by Lipscomb, Robertson and Rossman which indicated that the non-planeness does not affect the length of the bonds. We might hope, then, that the application of Hückel's approximation in these cases is not unreasonable and that the effect of the distortion does not introduce a significant error, bearing in mind the significance of approximations inherent in the method.

32. WHELAND'S APPROXIMATION

Among these approximations, the neglect of the overlap integral between $2p_z$ orbitals associated with two neighbouring atoms appears to be the most debatable. Now this can be avoided without too much complication by giving them a constant value S. This is Wheland's approximation (first book, p. 160). We have shown that the energies ε_j then become

$$\varepsilon_j = \alpha - m'_j \gamma,$$

where

$$\gamma = \beta - S\alpha \quad \text{and} \quad m'_j = \frac{m_j}{1 - S m_j}.$$

The first important consequence of the introduction of S is that even for an alternant hydrocarbon the levels are not symmetric with respect to α, as the coefficients m_j corresponding to opposite values $+x$ and $-x$ have values

$$\frac{x}{1 + Sx} \quad \text{and} \quad \frac{-x}{1 - Sx} \text{ of } m'_j.$$

As we shall see later, this may not be an improvement.

On the other hand, an advantageous consequence of introducing S is the decrease of the difference observed between the values of parameters obtained from spectra and those obtained from an examination of resonance energies. Pulman[270] has observed that if

$$\gamma = 2 \cdot 218 \text{ eV}$$

the transition energies ΔE between the ground state and the first triplet state for conjugated hydrocarbons are found as shown in Table 32.1.

TABLE 32.1

Molecules	ΔE (eV)	
	Calculated	Observed
Naphthalene	2·81	2·64
Anthracene	1·86	1·82
Phenanthrene	2·75	2·67
Pyrene	2	2·08
Chrysene	2·35	2·45
1,2–5,6-Dibenzanthracene	2·17	2·26
1,2-Benzanthracene	2·03	2·04
Naphthacene	1·31	1·26
Triphenylene	3·13	2·94
Coronene	2·44	2·37

The contribution of orbital φ_j to the electron population of the atom becomes (as shown in Section 10)

$$c_i^2 + \sum_{i'} c_i c_{i'} S.$$

Chirgwin and Coulson have shown[271] that the inclusion of S here does not have any important consequences; in particular, the charge in alternant hydrocarbons remains at e.

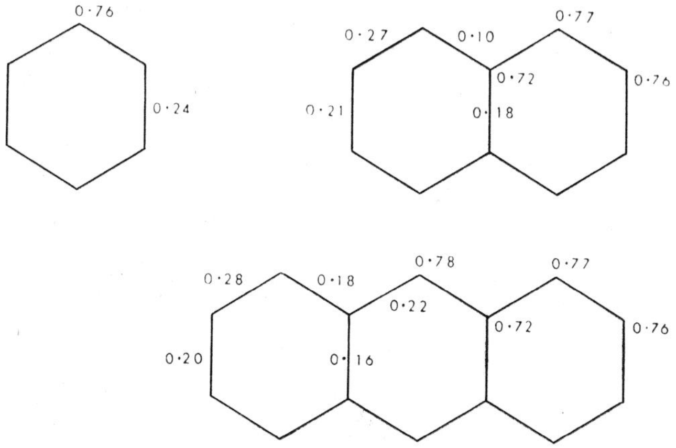

FIG. 52

More recently, Maslen and Coulson[272] have proposed that the c_i^2 terms of this expression be defined as the atomic charge and the $c_i c_{i'} S$ terms as the charge of bond ii' (the overlap population as defined by Mulliken). Figure 52 shows some of the results obtained in this manner by these authors.

A. and B. Pullman have indicated[273] that the inclusion of S is of little importance in the calculation of oscillator strengths. Finally Chirgwin and Coulson[274] have shown that the same applies in the calculation of interatomic distances.

33. OTHER NAÏVE METHODS

A. *Method of Spin States and Mesomerie*

One can apply in a very simple manner the method of spin states for which we have laid the foundations in the first book, p. 139, by assuming that the π electrons of a conjugated hydrocarbon gravitate in the field of the nuclei and of a core formed by the other electrons. The operator $\mathfrak{H}$ will be assumed to represent the Hamiltonian corresponding to this problem. The problem treated on p. 143 of the same book and relative to three electrons in the field of three nuclei, corresponds formally to the study of π orbitals of an allyl radical containing "three π electrons". The only difference comes in the meaning of the Hamiltonian operator and, consequently, in the values of integrals Q and A. Inasmuch as they are not explicit and in keeping with the "naïve" use of this method, the same hypotheses are usually adopted. This implies that we neglect all the overlap integrals as well as all the exchange integrals between non-neighbouring atoms. There are serious theoretical objections to neglecting the overlaps[275]. Be this as it may, this procedure allows us to express in a general fashion the π energies of the first states of a molecule as a function of Q and A. In the case of allyl, we find (cf. first book, p. 143):

$$E_{\pi 1} = U_{ap1} = Q - A(1 + \sqrt{2})$$
$$E_{\pi 2} = U_{ap2} = Q - A$$
$$E_{\pi 3} = U_{ap3} = Q - A(1 - \sqrt{2}).$$

The corresponding wave functions are obtained explicitly as by Hückel's method. For $E_{\pi 2}$, we find (first book, p. 144):

$$\phi_{ap2} = \frac{1}{\sqrt{2}} \{|Y|_1 - |Y|_2\}$$

the $|Y|$ being made up of $2p_z$ orbitals. As in Hückel's approximation, Q and A can be determined empirically, calculated from resonance energy[276] from bond orders[277], etc. This problem can also be treated by the method of mesomerie (first book, p. 144) which is mathematically equivalent to the method of spin states.

These methods give on the whole similar results to the method of molecular orbitals with Hückel's approximation[278]. The principle differences arise from the fact that the neglect of ionic spin states or ionic formulas normally makes the definition of charge rather vague together with quantities which depend on it (such as dipolar moment).

We have already mentioned (first book, p. 151) that certain authors have introduced ionic terms but this makes the calculations much more laborious than Hückel's method.

B. *Dirac Potential Method*

In the naïve methods so far used, the Hamiltonian operator has not been expressed explicitly. On the other hand, there are other types of method in which the Hamiltonian is explicit but in an extremely simple form.

For instance, Frost[279] has proposed that the potential arising from a core be represented by a sum of potentials in the form of Dirac functions arising from each nuclei.

Frost also proposed to further simplify the problem by reducing it to one dimension. Hence, a hydrogen atom is replaced by a straight line passing through the nuclei on which the electron moves.

The wave equation is then simply

$$- \frac{h^2}{8\pi^2 m} \frac{d^2\psi(x)}{dx^2} - g\delta(x)\,\psi(x) = E\psi(x),$$

where x is the distance from the nucleus and g a constant.

For a bonding state ($E < 0$) and away from $x = 0$, the solution of this equation is

$$\psi = A\,e^{-c|x|},$$

with

$$c = \sqrt{\left(-\frac{8\pi^2 mE}{h^2}\right)}.$$

In the neighbourhood of $x = 0$,

$$\frac{h^2}{8\pi^2 m} \int_{-\varepsilon}^{+\varepsilon} \frac{d^2\psi(x)}{dx^2}\,dx - g\int_{-\varepsilon}^{+\varepsilon} \delta(x)\,\psi(x)\,dx = E\int_{-\varepsilon}^{+\varepsilon} \psi(x)\,dx,$$

where ε is a small positive number.

As ε tends to zero, we have

$$-\frac{h^2}{8\pi^2 m}\left[\left(\frac{d\psi(x)}{dx}\right)_{+\varepsilon} - \left(\frac{d\psi(x)}{dx}\right)_{-\varepsilon}\right] = g\psi(0).$$

But for $x > 0$,

$$\frac{d\psi}{dx} = -Ac\,e^{-c|x|}$$

for $x < 0$,

$$\frac{d\psi}{dx} = +Ac\,e^{-c|x|}.$$

Hence

$$g = \frac{h^2 c}{4\pi^2 m}$$

and finally

$$c = \frac{4\pi^2 mg}{h^2}$$

$$E = -\frac{2\pi^2 mg^2}{h^2}.$$

By choosing g such that

$$g = e^2$$

we obtain

$$E = -\frac{2\pi^2 me^4}{h^2}$$

which is the exact value of the energy of the ground state of hydrogen. The corresponding wave function

$$\psi(x) = A\,e^{-\frac{4\pi^2 me^2}{h^2}|x|} = A\,e^{-\frac{|x|}{a_0}}$$

is also the exact value of the wave function of hydrogen along the axis of x.

It is equally interesting to apply this in the case of the ion-molecules of hydrogen. The molecule is then reduced to the line of the nuclei and the origin is taken as the middle of the line of nuclei which are placed at $R/2$ and $-R/2$. The equation is

$$-\frac{h^2}{8\pi^2 m}\frac{d^2\psi}{dx^2} - g\,[\delta(x - R/2) + \delta(x + R/2)]\,\psi = E\psi.$$

A simple method of forming a solution of this equation consists of setting

$$\psi = A\psi_a + B\psi_b$$

with

$$\psi_a = e^{-c|x_a|} \qquad \psi_b = e^{-c|x_b|},$$

where x_a and x_b denote the distances from the two nuclei.

The Dirac potentials impose relationships already seen between right and left derivatives at $x = R/2$ and $x = -R/2$.

This condition for the first nuclei is

$$-\frac{h^2}{8\pi^2 m} 2cA = g(A + B\,e^{-R})$$

and for the second,

$$-\frac{h^2}{8\pi^2 m} 2cB = g(A\,e^{-R} + B).$$

As in Hückel's method, the coefficients A and B are solutions of a secular system. Here, we find

$$A/B = \pm 1$$

and hence

$$\psi_+ = A_+(\psi_a + \psi_b)$$

$$\psi_- = A_-(\psi_a - \psi_b).$$

These orbitals are analogous to those obtained from the usual L.C.A.O. method.

This procedure has been extended to the case of conjugate hydrocarbons[280]. Consider the case of benzene. The study of the π system will be reduced to one of six electrons *without interaction between them* placed in a hexagon under the influence of a potential made up of Dirac function at each vertex of the hexagon.

By denoting the abscissa of the jth nucleus by jR, we have the equation

$$-\frac{h^2}{8\pi^2 m} \frac{d^2\psi}{dx^2} - g\left[\sum_{j=1}^{6} \delta(x - jR)\right]\psi = E\psi$$

with a solution of the form

$$\psi = \sum_{k=1}^{6} a_k \psi_k(x),$$

where the $\psi_j(x)$ are of the form

$$\psi_j(x) = e^{-c|x-jR|} - e^{-2cR}\,e^{+c|x-jR|}$$

between nuclei adjacent to nuclei jR, and zero elsewhere. Obviously, the ψ_j are zero on the nuclei adjacent to j, i.e. for $(j-1)R$ and $(j+1)R$.

The condition

$$-\frac{h^2}{8\pi^2 m}\left[\left(\frac{d\psi(x)}{dx}\right)_{jR+\varepsilon} - \left(\frac{d\psi(x)}{dx}\right)_{jR-\varepsilon}\right] = g\psi(jR)$$

allows the calculation of a_k.

Let

$$p = e^{-cR} \quad \text{and} \quad \left(\Delta\,\frac{d\psi}{dx}\right)_{jR+\varepsilon} = \left(\frac{d\psi(x)}{dx}\right)_{jR+\varepsilon} - \left(\frac{d\psi(x)}{dx}\right)_{jR-\varepsilon}$$

Since, ψ_{j-1} and ψ_{j+1} are zero at jR, then

$$\psi(jR) = a_j(1 - p^2).$$

Only ψ_j, ψ_{j-1} and ψ_{j+1} contribute to $\{\Delta\,(d\psi/dx)\}_{jR+\varepsilon}$ as the other ψ_k are zero near nucleus j.

Then

$$-\left(\Delta\,\frac{d\psi}{dx}\right)_{jR+\varepsilon} = 2ca_{j-1}p + 2ca_j(1 + p^2) + 2ca_{j+1}p.$$

From this,

$$+\frac{h^2}{8\pi^2 m}\,2cpa_{j-1} + \left[\frac{h^2}{8\pi^2 m}\,2c(1 + p^2) - g(1 - p)^2\right]a_j$$

$$+\frac{h^2}{8\pi^2 m}\,2cpa_{j+1} = 0,$$

i.e. by setting

$$y = \frac{(1 + p^2)}{p} - \frac{g(1 - p^2)\,4\pi^2 m}{h^2 cp}$$

$$a_{j-1} + ya_j + a_{j+1} = 0.$$

The coefficients a_j are then solutions of the same secular system as the coefficients c_i of the L.C.A.O. method with Hückel's approximation.

C. *Free Electron Method*

We end this chapter by a discussion of the free electron or metallic model method. This has been developed by various authors[281].

In the simplest form, it is sometimes called the box model and it consists of replacing the molecule by a box (having the same dimensions as the molecule) where the potential is zero except on the edges where it becomes infinite. To study the π system, the "π electrons" are introduced into the box, neglecting their interactions.

In the case of a linear conjugated chain such as butadiene for example, we consider a tube of length L and negligible cross-section. The equation is

$$- \frac{h^2}{8\pi^2 m} \frac{d^2\psi}{dx^2} = E\psi$$

with solutions of the form

$$\psi_n = (2L)^{\frac{1}{2}} \sin \frac{n\pi x}{L}$$

with

$$E_n = \frac{n^2 h^2}{8mL^2} .$$

Figure 53 compares these orbitals with those obtained from Hückel's method. If the nuclei are placed suitably in the tube, the analogy between the two types of orbitals becomes obvious. Walsh has shown that the essential properties of orbitals, i.e. the number of their nodes, do not depend much on the form of potential used. This explains why similar results are obtained from a non-explicit potential as in Hückel's method, a Dirac function potential, and a "box" potential. The length L can be used as an empirical parameter to fit theory to experiment.

Recently, the Chicago group have modified the free electron method to a form nearer to the L.C.A.O. method, (Hückel and Wheland's approximation). The molecular orbitals are formed of linear combinations of sinusoidal atomic orbitals. A conservation condition must be imposed for each nucleus: the sum of the derivatives with respect to the current variable of the orbitals about a nucleus must be zero. This condition is similar to that found for Frost's method. The orbital coefficients are derived from a secular system which resembles closely the one in Hückel's method.

Kuhn[284] has recently modified the continuity condition. This modification has been criticised by Frost[285].

Nevertheless, such a method can find, by integration of the wave function, the length of a bond and the quantities on either side of an atom which replace the bond orders, i.e. the atomic population of Hückel's method.

Fernandez *et al.*[286] have applied this method to various hydrocarbons and compared the results with those obtained by Hückel's method. They found a good overall agreement between the two methods.

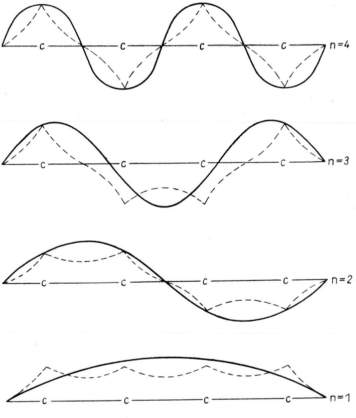

FIG. 53. Unbroken lines: orbital of the free electron model. Broken lines: L.C.A.O. orbital.

Labhart[287] has also improved this method by taking account of the σ structure. Other authors have also included repulsion between the electrons[288].

CHAPTER IX

Purely Conjugated Hydrocarbons Using "Elaborate" Methods

34. The Self-consistent Field Method According to Lefebvre

In contrast to the naïve methods which we have been discussing, the self-consistent field and configuration interaction methods are usually classed as elaborate methods. We shall now discuss their application to conjugated hydrocarbons.

We shall set forth the results of the self-consistent field method first. To do this it will be useful to return once again to the formalism of this method in order to give maximum generality.

In its most general form, this method consists of finding the best configuration representing a state of a molecule.

So far, we have only discussed the case where this configuration reduces to one term and mainly where this term is formed of "complete shells", i.e. of orbitals used twice.

But the configuration can be a linear combination of determinants. In order to establish the equations for this case, four different points of view are available; the first due to Lefebvre[289], the second to McWeeny[290], the third to Roothaan[291] and the fourth to Masse[292]. We have already mentioned the first two in Section 9. We shall now give some details of Lefebvre's method.

Let us consider first the case of a configuration represented by one determinant of the form

$$\phi = \det \varphi_1 \varphi_2 \dots \varphi_n,$$

where the φ are orthonormal.

Case 1 is where we try to find the best orbitals in the most general sense, and case 2 in the L.C.A.O. sense.

We shall start by completing the series of φ by the functions

φ_{n+1}, φ_{n+2}, ..., so as to form a complete basis in case 1 or a basis equivalent to the L.C.A.O. basis of atomic orbitals in case 2.

It remains to express the total variation of the φ on this basis and to annul the first order variation of the energy. An orbital φ_i (with $1 \leqslant i \leqslant n$) becomes

$$\varphi_j' = \varphi_i + \sum_{k \neq i} s_{ik}\varphi_k.$$

In order for the φ_i' to be orthogonal to a first order, we must have

$$s_{ik} = -s_{ki}.$$

Let us assume, for simplicity, that the functions are real. Then, to a first order,

$$\int \varphi_i'\varphi_j'dv = \int \varphi_i\varphi_j \, dv + \sum_{k \neq i} s_{ik} \int \varphi_k\varphi_j \, dv + \sum_{l \neq j} s_{jl} \int \varphi_l\varphi_i \, dv$$

and hence by reason of the orthonormality conditions

$$\int \varphi_i'\varphi_j'dv = 0 = (s_{ij} + s_{ji}).$$

Under this variation, function ϕ becomes, to a first order,

$$\phi' = \phi + \sum_{i,k} s_{ik}\phi^{i,k} \qquad \text{with} \qquad k > n,$$

where $\phi^{i,k}$ denotes the determinant

$$\phi^{i,k} = \det \varphi_1, \varphi_2 \cdots \varphi_{i-1}, \varphi_k, \varphi_{i+1} \cdots \varphi_n.$$

Since the $\phi^{i,k}$ are orthogonal to ϕ, the ϕ' are normal to a first order. In fact, we have

$$\int \phi'^2 \, dv = \int \phi^2 \, dv + 2 \sum_{i,k} s_{ik} \int \phi\phi^{i,k} \, dv = \int \phi^2 \, dv = 1.$$

The total energy U then becomes

$$U' = U + 2 \sum_{i,k} s_{ik} \int \phi \mathfrak{H} \phi^{i,k} \, dv.$$

As the c_{ik} are arbitrary, this leads to

$$\int \phi \mathfrak{H} \phi^{i,k} \, dv = 0$$

for $1 \leqslant i \leqslant n$ and $n < k$.

Obviously, the necessary and sufficient condition for the first variation of the energy to be zero is that all the elements of the matrix between the ϕ space and the $\phi^{i,k}$ space are zero. This is a generalisation to the case of finite bases of Brillouin's theorem.[293]

The matrix elements are easily expressed, by applying the rules given in the first book (p. 167). This gives

$$\int \phi \mathfrak{H} \phi^{i,k} \, dv = \pm \left[(ik) + \sum_j (ik, jj) - \sum_j (ij, kj) \right] = 0,$$

for $1 \leqslant i \leqslant n$, $1 \leqslant j \leqslant n$ and $n < k$.

These are Lefebvre's self-consistent field conditions. They can be used to calculate L.C.A.O. coefficients of self-consistent molecular orbitals. Lefebvre has shown that if one starts with approximate orbitals and tries to improve them, i.e. by decreasing the value of the expressions in brackets, one is lead to a set of non-homogeneous linear equations which gives the value of the improved coefficients which can be used for a new iteration.

The self-consistent conditions lead easily to the classical equations since

$$\int \phi \mathfrak{H} \phi^{i,k} \, dv = \int \varphi_i(\mu) \left[\mathfrak{H}^N(\mu) + \sum_j (J_j - K_j) \right] \varphi_k(\mu) \, dv_\mu = 0,$$

where $\mathfrak{H}^N(\mu)$ is the sum of the kinetic operator associated with the μth electron and the potential energy of the μth electron due to the nuclei.

The self-consistent field operator is then

$$\mathfrak{H}^{\text{C.A.C.}} = \mathfrak{H}^N(\mu) + \sum_j (J_j - K_j).$$

Note that if

$$\int \varphi_i \mathfrak{H}^{\text{C.A.C.}} \varphi_k \, dv = E_{ik},$$

the self-consistent conditions are

$$E_{ik} = 0 \qquad 1 \leqslant i \leqslant n \qquad n < k.$$

In case 1,

$$\mathfrak{H}^{\text{C.A.C.}} \varphi_i = \sum_k E_{ik} \varphi_k$$

as E_{ik} is zero for $n < k$ this series of equations coincides exactly with those of the self-consistent field.

The interest in the self-consistence conditions resides in the fact that their establishment and use are not very much more difficult in the case where the configuration contains many molecular terms, while self-consistent field equations, on the other hand, have a very delicate form in this case.

In case 2, the φ are expressed on the L.C.A.O. basis which contains a certain number, m, of elements assumed orthonormal,

$$\varphi_i = \sum_p c_{ip}\psi_p \quad 1 \leqslant i, p \leqslant m.$$

φ_i is characterised by a vector of components c_{ip} which will be called $\vec{c}_i$.

Let us introduce the matrix

$$\| \mathfrak{H}^{\text{C.A.C.}} \|$$

with elements

$$H_{ip} = \int \psi_i \mathfrak{H}^{\text{C.A.C.}} \psi_p \, dv.$$

The action of this matrix on $\vec{c}_i$ is to transform it into another vector of the ψ space. We then have

$$\| \mathfrak{H}^{\text{C.A.C.}} \| \, \vec{c}_i = \sum_k e_{ik}\vec{c}_k \quad 1 \leqslant k \leqslant m$$

with

$$e_{ik} = \vec{c}_k \| \mathfrak{H}^{\text{C.A.C.}} \| \, \vec{c}_i.$$

Obviously the self-consistence conditions give

$$e_{ik} = 0 \quad 1 \leqslant i \leqslant n \quad n < k \leqslant m.$$

We can then conclude that

$$\| \mathfrak{H}^{\text{C.A.C.}} \| \vec{c}_i = \sum_k e_{ik}\vec{c}_k$$

This is the matrix form of Roothaan's equations.

35. THE SELF-CONSISTENT FIELD METHOD WITH PARISER AND PARR'S APPROXIMATION

To rigorously satisfy the self-consistence conditions, we must evaluate multicentric integrals as well as quantities associated with the wave functions. Because of the difficulty of these evaluations, we use the approximations of Goeppert-Mayer and Sklar or of Pariser and Parr.

We shall look a little closer at the formalism which leads to Pariser and Parr's approximation in the case of conjugated molecules. As this method neglects the overlap integrals, the atomic orbitals form an orthonormal L.C.A.O. basis.

Roothaan's equations then have the form which has already been established and the integrals α and β, which have been used in the case of naïve methods, can be interpreted as elements of the matrix of the self-consistent field operator.

We then have

$$\alpha_i = H_{ii} \quad \beta_{ik} = H_{ik}.$$

If we are studying the ground state of an even hydrocarbon we are in a case of complete shells doubly occupied.

The self-consistent field operator is then

$$\mathfrak{H}^{\text{C.A.C.}} = \mathfrak{H}^C + \sum_j (2J_j - K_j),$$

as we have already indicated, and which can be derived simply by using, for example, Lefebvre's method.

By setting

$$\alpha_i^C = \int \pi_i \mathfrak{H}^C \pi_i \, dv$$

then

$$\alpha_i = \alpha_i^C + \sum_j 2 \int \varphi_j^2(2) \frac{e^2}{r_{21}} \pi_i^2(1) \, dv_2 \, dv_1$$

$$- \sum_j \int \varphi_j(2) \pi_i(2) \frac{e^2}{r_{21}} \varphi_j(1) \pi_i(1) \, dv_1 \, dv_2.$$

The first integral on the right-hand side becomes

$$I = \sum_l \sum_{l'} c_{jl} c_{jl'} \int \pi_l \pi_{l'} \frac{e^2}{r_{21}} \pi_i^2 \, dv_1 \, dv_2$$

remembering the L.C.A.O. expansion of φ_j,

$$\varphi_j = \sum_l c_{jl} \pi_l.$$

In Pariser and Parr's approximation, I reduces to

$$I = \sum_l c_{jl}^2 (l, l/i, i),$$

where

$$(l, l/i, i) = \int \pi^2(2) \frac{e^2}{r_{12}} \pi_i^2(1) \, dv_1 \, dv_2.$$

The second integral becomes

$$I' = \sum_l \sum_{l'} c_{jl} c_{jl'} \int \pi_l \pi_i \frac{e^2}{r_{21}} \pi_{l'} \pi_i \, dv_1 \, dv_2$$

which reduces to

$$I'_i = c_{ji}^2 (ii/ii).$$

In all:

$$\alpha_i = \alpha_i^C + \sum_l q_l(ii/ll) - \tfrac{1}{2} q_i(ii/ii).$$

By setting

$$\beta_{ik}^C = \int \pi_i \mathfrak{H}^C \pi_k \, dv$$

we similarly find

$$\beta_{ik} = \beta_{ik}^C - \tfrac{1}{2} p_{ik}(ii/kk).$$

If we now use the approximation of Goeppert-Mayer and Sklar to evaluate α_i^C, we find

$$\alpha_i^C = W_{2pi} - \sum_{l \neq i} (ii/ll)\dagger$$

by neglecting the small integrals between centres which are neutral (potential in U_i, penetration integrals). We have finally

$$\alpha_i = W_{2pi} + \sum_{l \neq i} (q_l - 1) (ii/ll) + \tfrac{1}{2} q_i(ii/ii)$$

$$\beta_{ik} = \beta_{ik}^C - \tfrac{1}{2} p_{ik}(ii/kk).$$

These are then the matrix elements which determine the coefficients c_{ij}.

It is easy to see that they also occur in the calculation of approximate ionisation energies in the application of the Koopmans theorem. In fact we have

$$e_j = \int \varphi_j \mathfrak{H}^{C.A.C.} \varphi_j \, dv = \sum_l \sum_{l'} c_{lj} c_{l'j} H_{ll'}$$

$$= \sum_i c_{ij}^2 \alpha_i + \sum_{l < l'} 2 c_{lj} c_{l'j} \beta_{ll'}.$$

† As each atom gives only one π electron to the delocalised bond.

On the other hand, the calculation of total electron energy associated with a configuration requires other parameters.

Let us take as an example a state in which each orbital is doubly occupied; if, as in the naïve methods, the total energy is calculated by summing the energies associated with each orbital, we find

$$\sum_j 2e_j = \sum_i q_i \alpha_i + 2 \sum_{l<l'} p_{ll'} \beta_{ll'}.$$

This method counts the interaction between the electrons twice. The α and β must be reduced by half the inter-electron energy, i.e. $(\alpha - \alpha^c)/2$ and $(\beta - \beta^c)/2$. The α and β then become

$$\bar{\alpha} = \alpha - \frac{\alpha - \alpha^c}{2} = \frac{\alpha + \alpha^c}{2}$$

$$\bar{\beta} = \beta - \frac{\beta - \beta^c}{2} = \frac{\beta + \beta^c}{2}$$

and the total energy is

$$W = \sum_i q_i \bar{\alpha}_i + 2 \sum_{l<l'} p_{ll'} \bar{\beta}_{ll'}.$$

This formula can also be derived directly by using the formulae of the first book (p. 167) on the configuration

$$\phi = \det \varphi_1 \bar{\varphi}_1 \varphi_2 \bar{\varphi}_2 \cdots \varphi_n \bar{\varphi}_n.$$

This gives

$$\int \phi \mathfrak{H} \phi \, dv = 2 \sum_j \varepsilon_j^c + \sum_j (jj, jj)$$

$$+ 2 \left[\sum_{\substack{j \ j' \\ j \neq j'}} (jj, j'j') - \tfrac{1}{2} \sum_{\substack{j \ j' \\ j \neq j'}} (jj', jj') \right]$$

$$2 \sum_j \varepsilon_j^c + 2 \sum_j \sum_{j'} [(jj, j'j') - \tfrac{1}{2}(jj', jj')].$$

By expanding the φ_j in terms of the π_j, the preceding expression for W is found.

Note that if it is wished to take account of the repulsion between cores, it is sufficient to add

$$\sum_{i<l} (ii/ll).$$

We obtain[294]

$$W' = \sum_i q_i \left[W_{2pi} - \sum_{l \neq i} (ii/ll) + \tfrac{1}{2} \sum_l q_l(ii/ll) - \tfrac{1}{4}q_i(ii/ii) \right]$$
$$+ 2 \sum_{l < l'} p_{ll'}[\beta^C_{ll'} - \tfrac{1}{4}p_{ll'}(ll/ll')] + \sum_{i < l} \sum (ii/ll)$$
$$= \sum_i q_i[W_{2pi} + \tfrac{1}{4}q_i(ii/ii)] + 2 \sum_{l < l'} \sum p_{ll'}[\beta^C_{ll'} - \tfrac{1}{4}p_{ll'}(ll/l'l')]$$
$$+ \sum_{l < l'} \sum (q_l - 1)(ll/l'l')(q_{l'} - 1).$$

The last term of W' then represents the energy of coulomb repulsion between the apparent charges of different atoms of the conjugated system.

In the case of alternant hydrocarbons, great simplifications can be made.

Indeed, Pople[294] has shown that in the case of Pariser and Parr's approximation, the orbitals of alternant hydrocarbons remain in pairs as in Huckel's method. (Pople and Brickstock[295] have studied this point of view for ions, Lefebvre[296] for radicals and McLachlan[297] has examined the entire problem thoroughly.)

The result of this is that all the charges q are unity as in Huckel's method. The integrals α_i reduce to

$$\alpha_i = W_{2pi} + \tfrac{1}{2}(ii/ii),$$

which are independent of i.

The integrals β_{ik}

$$\beta_{ik} = \beta^C_{ik} - \tfrac{1}{2}p_{ik}(ii/kk)$$

vary little for neighbouring atoms, especially in the case of hydrocarbons formed by joined hexagons where the p_{ik} have nearly constant value. The approximations based on Huckel's method are therefore justified and this is why the coefficients of the orbitals calculated by Pariser and Parr's method resemble closely the coefficients of Huckel's method. Since the energies depend on the coefficients only to a second order, we can determine the energies conveniently by using Pariser and Parr's method with Huckel's coefficients.

36. Energies by the Self-consistent Field Method

A. *Ionisation Energies and Electron Affinities*

Matsen *et al.*[289] have studied ionising energies I, and electron affinities E, of alternant hydrocarbons. These energies were determined by means of the Koopmans theorem which gives here

$$I = \alpha + \sum_{l < l'} 2c_{lj}c_{l'j}\beta_{ll'}$$

$$E = \alpha - \sum_{l < l'} 2c_{lj}c_{l'j}\beta_{ll'}$$

by reason of the α being constant and the symmetry relationship between the orbitals. Note that[299]

$$I + E = 2\alpha.$$

The calculations of I and E have been carried out using the preceding formulae by fixing α empirically at

$$\alpha = -3\cdot87\,\text{eV}$$

and using Pariser's[300] value for β_{ik}^{C} and ii/kk.

The following table shows that theory and experiment are in agreement.

	I calculated	I measured
Benzene	9·37	9·24–9·01
Naphthalene	8·12	8·12
Phenanthrene	7·94	8·06
Anthracene	7·25	7·66
Naphthacene	6·92	7·15
1,2-Benzophenanthrene	7·88	7·84

Unfortunately, only a few ionisation energies have been measured. To increase the possibilities of comparison, Hedges and Matsen have compared the results of their calculations for 24 substances with ionisation energies calculated by assuming a linear relationship between them and the frequencies of p-bands. As this relationship is suggested by Hückel's approximation, the agreement observed by the authors is a measure of the consistency of the theory rather than a good correlation between theory and experiment.

The authors have calculated the electron affinities by the same method. Here again there is not much precise experimental data. The following table compares theory and experiment.

	E (eV) calculated	E (eV) measured [301]
Naphthalene	−0·38	+0·65
Phenanthrene	−0·20	+0·69
Anthracene	+0·49	+1·19
Graphite	+3·87	+4·39

Many polarographic measurements exist but they contain, as well as the electron affinity, the variation of free energy when a dissolved molecule changes to the corresponding ion. This quantity is of the order of a few electron volts and varies with the shape of the molecule, according to a relationship of Born roughly represented by

$$\Delta E \text{ (sol)} = \sum_j \frac{q_j^2}{2r_j} (1 - 1/K),$$

where r_j is the apparent radius of atom j and K the specific inductance of the medium. The following table compares the ΔE calculated by this formula and evaluated from the difference between the polarographic measure $E_{1/2}$ and the calculated electron affinity E.

	$E_{1/2} - E$ (eV)	ΔE (sol) (eV)
Benzene	3·81	1·8
Naphthalene	2·97	1·1
Phenanthrene	2·83	0·8
Anthracene	2·62	0·8

Bearing in mind that Hückel's method gives good results for ionisation energy, one can ask whether Pariser and Parr's method brings a significant improvement. The study of alternant free radicals immediately shows the importance of the explicit introduction of interactions between electrons contained in Pariser and Parr's approximation. In Hückel's all alternating free radicals have the same ionisation energy,

$$I = \alpha.$$

Using the other approximation, however, this energy varies from one molecule to another, as might be expected from experiment. The following table[302] compares experiment with Pariser and Parr's method.

	I (eV) calculated	I (eV) measured
Allyl	8·23	8·16
Benzyl	7·78	7·73
Triphenylmethyl	6·82	6·5

B. *Resonance Energies*

Resonance energies of alternant hydrocarbons have been studied by Pariser and Parr's method. The principal improvement occurs in the case of free radicals and ions[303].

C. *Excitation Energies*

The self-consistent field method is particularly well suited to the calculation of frequencies associated with Clar's *p*-band. It allows us to distinguish between the singlet and triplet state which could not be done by Hückel's method. These two states are represented by the function

$$\phi = \frac{1}{\sqrt{2}} \{ \det \varphi_1 \bar{\varphi}_1 \varphi_2 \bar{\varphi}_2 \cdots \varphi_n \bar{\varphi}_{n+1} \pm \det \varphi_1 \bar{\varphi}_1 \varphi_2 \bar{\varphi}_2 \cdots \bar{\varphi}_n \varphi_{n+1} \}.$$

The state is triplet if the sign is positive and singlet if negative.

The formulae in the first book (p. 107) allow the calculation of energies associated with these two states. By using approximations of the type of Pariser and Parr, but effectively solving the self-consistent field equations for the ground state and using the virtual orbitals, Pople[304] has calculated these energies. The following table compares them with experimental data.

	Band ^1p (cm^{-1})		Band ^3p (cm^{-1})	
	Calculated	Observed	Calculated	Observed
Naphthalene	37,500	34,500	25,000	21,300
Anthracene	30,000	26,500	18,000	14,700

Hall has also studied the triplet state by a self-consistent field method using orbitals of what he calls the standard excited state[305]

Another question is the importance of the error committed by using virtual orbitals. Lefebvre[306] has found that in the case of *trans*-butadiene, the self-consistent orbitals recalculated for the excited states corresponding to *p*-bands differ little from those of the ground state for the singlet state, and differ considerably for the triplet state. It is, therefore, probable that the approximation of virtual orbitals is better for the study of absorption spectrum than phosphorescence.

37. STUDY OF QUANTITIES DEPENDING ON COEFFICIENTS OF ORBITALS IN THE SELF-CONSISTENT FIELD METHOD

We might expect that the self-consistent field method would lead to coefficients rather different from those found by Hückel's method.

It is true, in certain cases, that the explicit introduction of interactions between electrons improves the agreement between theory and experiment. In fact, this improvement is chiefly evident in non-alternant hydrocarbons. This is how Berthier[307] obtained a good value for the dipolar moment of fulvene while Hückel's method gives far too big a value. The charges, the bond orders calculated by the self-consistent field method for the ground state of ions or alternant hydrocarbons, differ little from those obtained by Hückel's method.

This subject has been discussed by Pople[308] for carbonium ions and by Hall[309] on alternant hydrocarbons.

Pritchard and Sumner[310] have discussed in detail the case of naphthalene and anthracene and reviewed a great number of other substances[311]. They conclude that, on the whole, the self-consistent field method does not improve the calculation of interatomic distances. Peacock[312] has proposed a simplified view to calculate the bond orders and charges in this type of method[313]. Finally, here are some references of detailed study of some important molecules including the alternants: benzene[315], butadiene[314], naphthalene[316], diphenyle[317] fulvene [307] and the free radicals allyl[318] and benzene[306].

Other interesting papers include Stuart and Mackor's work[319] on the spectrum of certain carbonium ions as well as a series on the positive and negative ions of alternant hydrocarbons[320]. In these papers, the analogy found experimentally between spectra of ions of opposite charge derived from the same hydrocarbon can be interpreted equally well by Hückel's approximation and the self-consistent field method.

38. THE PRINCIPAL RESULTS OF THE APPLICATION OF THE CONFIGURATION INTERACTION METHOD

Lefebvre's theorem,

$$\int \phi \mathfrak{H} \phi^{i,k} \, dv = 0 \quad \text{for} \quad 1 \leqslant i \leqslant n \quad \text{and} \quad n < k$$

shows that there is no interaction between the ground configuration of the self-consistent field and the mono-excited states. We might expect, therefore, that the configuration interaction method does not appreciably change the description of ground states, particularly the energy measurements.

In fact, it is in the study of excited states represented by means of virtual orbitals that the interaction method yields the most spectacular results. We shall start with the analysis of this problem.

Let us consider an even alternant hydrocarbon. Let n be the number of the last occupied orbital. We know that in both Hückel's method and Pariser and Parr's approximation, the energies associated with the $n-1$ and $n+2$ orbitals, on one hand, and the n and $n+1$ orbitals on the other, are symmetrical about α (Fig. 54). In Hückel's method, the configurations

$$\phi^{n,n+2} \quad \text{and} \quad \phi^{n-1,n+1}$$

have exactly the same energy.

It may be expected that they will interact strongly, leading to levels having no simple relationship with either $\phi^{n,n+2}$ or $\phi^{n-1,n+1}$. This is why Dewar and Longuet-Higgins[321] have proposed that the first excited states of alternant hydrocarbons be described by means of the configuration $\phi^{n,n+1}$, the combination $a\phi^{n,n+2} + b\phi^{n-1,n+1}$ and the configuration $\phi^{n-1,n+2}$. This is the simplest way to introduce

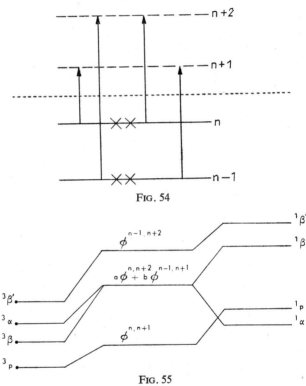

Fig. 54

Fig. 55

configuration interactions into this problem. $\phi^{n,n+1}$ and $\phi^{n-1,n+2}$ each give rise to a singlet and a triplet. The combination $a\phi^{n,n+2} + b\phi^{n-1,n+1}$ gives two singlets and two triplets.

When the calculations are carried out using Pariser and Parr's method, one of the singlets arising from the combination can sometimes have a lower energy than the singlet $\phi^{n,n+1}$. The transition moment between the ground state and the singlet of the combination is found to be zero. We might expect, therefore, that this level corresponds to a system of weak bands. It is assumed that it corresponds to Clar's $^1\alpha$ system. We have already said that $\phi^{n,n+1}$ is considered to correspond to ^1p and ^3p bands. The second singlet arising from the combination will then correspond to $^1\beta$. The triplets of the combination will be denoted by $^3\alpha$ and $^3\beta$ and the configuration $\phi^{n-1,n+2}$ gives rise to $^1\beta'$ and $^3\beta'$. Figure 55 shows the complex levels calculated for naphthalene and the following table compares experiment and theoretical results for naphthalene and phenanthrene.

Notation of band system	Frequencies (cm^{-1})	
	Calculated	Measured
Naphthalene		
1_α	35,500	32,000
1_p	37,500	34,500
1_β	49,500	45,500
$1_{\beta'}$	50,000	60,000
3_p	25,000	21,300
3_β	33,000	
3_α	25,500	
$3_{\beta'}$	39,000	
Anthracene		
1_p	30,000	26,500
1_α	33,500	(28,000)
1_β	45,500	39,000
$1_{\beta'}$	52,000	45,500
3_p	18,000	14,700
3_β	32,000	
3_α	33,500	
$3_{\beta'}$	43,500	

Pariser[323] has studied a large number of alternant hydrocarbons in a similar manner.

In the study of ground states, the improvement introduced by the configuration interaction method makes itself felt mainly for quantities which depend directly on the coefficients. Since at least doubly excited configurations must be introduced, the calculations are rather laborious in these cases and a simplification is often introduced by using the method of *alternant orbitals* of Löwdin[324]. Consider the case of an alternant hydrocarbon which, in the self-consistent field method, will be represented by

$$\phi = \det \varphi_1 \bar{\varphi}_1 \varphi_2 \bar{\varphi}_2 \cdots \varphi_n \bar{\varphi}_n.$$

Let us define φ_1', φ_2', ... φ_n' as the virtual orbitals symmetric to φ_1, φ_2, ... φ_n respectively. Now, each pair $\varphi_j\overline{\varphi}_j$ is replaced in the determinant by the pair

$$(\varphi_j + \lambda\varphi_j')\,\overline{(\varphi_j - \lambda\varphi_j')}.$$

The function ϕ becomes

$$\phi' = \det\,(\varphi_1 + \lambda\varphi_1')\,\overline{(\varphi_1 - \lambda\varphi_1')}\,(\varphi_2 + \lambda\varphi_2')\,\overline{(\varphi_2 - \lambda\varphi_2')}$$

$$... (\varphi_n + \lambda\varphi_n')\,\overline{(\varphi_n - \lambda\varphi_n')}.$$

This substitution is based on a physical idea. Configuration interaction is a means of introducing the correlations between the positions of the electrons. The self-consistent field method does not take account of correlations between electrons of opposite spin (as the same space function is associated with two spin functions α and β). This is why Löwdin has introduced two different space functions depending on whether the spin function is α or β.

As the two image functions φ and φ' differ in sign for all indices of one parity, the combination

$$\varphi_1 + \lambda\varphi_1'$$

with λ small and positive, will have a smaller value than φ_1 near atoms of this parity, while the combination

$$\varphi_1 - \lambda\varphi_1'$$

will have a smaller value near atoms of the opposite parity. The choice of these functions will therefore decrease the probability of finding two electrons of opposite spin in the same small region of space.

However, as ϕ is not an eigenfunction of operator $\mathfrak{S}^2$, it is necessary to transform it with a projection operator. We then obtain a linear combination of determinants of the "configuration interaction" type. The simplification lies in the fact that the coefficients of these determinants are all functions of one parameter λ which can be determined by minimising energy or by optimising the fit between a calculated quantity and its experimental value.

Itoh and Yoshizumi[325] have studied the benzene molecule by this method. They found a value for the energy of the ground state which was 2·35 eV lower than that found by self-consistent calculations. The same method has been applied to a family of alternant hydrocarbons by Pauncz and de Heer[326] using Pariser and Parr's approximation. Finally, Lefebvre, McConnel and Dearman[327] have applied this method to the calculation of spin density in alternant free radicals. Spin density is the difference between the probabilities of encountering an electron of spin $+\frac{1}{2}h/2\pi$ and one with spin $-\frac{1}{2}h/2\pi$.

For an alternant free radical, the self-consistent field method indicates that this quantity is alternately zero or a considerable value near various carbon atoms depending on the parity of the atom. Experiment shows that it is non-zero throughout. The method of alternant orbitals gives a quantitative explanation of this fact.

To end we give some references of works based on methods like configuration interaction, i.e. more elaborate than the self-consistent field method.

They concern allyl[328], triarylmethyls[329], cyclopentadenyl[330], butadiene[331], cyclo-butadiene[332], benzene[333], naphthalene[334], fulvene[335] and azulene[336].

CHAPTER X

Conjugated Molecules

39. CHARACTERISTIC PROPERTIES OF SUBSTITUENTS AND HETERO-ATOMS. GENERAL INDICATIONS ON THESE METHODS USED TO ACCOUNT FOR THEM

A. *The Number of π Electrons Carried by a Substituent or a Hetero-atom, Electronegativity, Free Electrons, Hyperconjugation*

A vast family of conjugated molecules is generated by introducing substituents, hetero-atoms or sets of these two types of perturbations into a conjugated hydrocarbon.

The most common hetero-atoms are boron, nitrogen, phosphorus, arsenic, oxygen and sulphur.

Among the substituents are the halogens, the amine group, the phenol group, the nitro group, the carboxylic and sulphonic acid groups, and the alkyl groups.

These perturbators can be characterised by the number of electrons they introduce into the π system of the molecule, by the number and disposition of their free electrons and finally by the electronegativity of the atoms which are contained in them.

The same hetero-atom can carry different numbers of π electrons depending on the molecule considered and also on its position in the molecule. For example, it is assumed that the nitrogen in pyridine carries one π electron to the conjugate system while it introduces two in the case of pyrrole. This difference is mainly due to the fact that the nitrogen in pyridine is only connected to two carbons and carries a pair of free electrons whereas in pyrrole it is connected to two carbons and a hydrogen. Figure 56 symbolises this situation.

In the case of the substituents F, Cl, Br, I, NH_2 and OH, it is assumed that the halogen, nitrogen or oxygen atoms furnish two π electrons to the conjugate system (see Fig. 57). Figures 56 and 57 show that the preceding hypotheses (which, as we shall see, are confirmed by their consequences) imply that the atoms which carry π electrons are in a state of trigonal hybridisation and that the orbitals corresponding to free electrons are always occupied by two

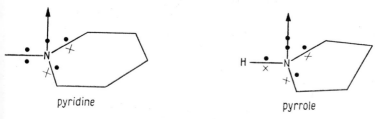

pyridine   pyrrole

FIG. 56. The electrons associated with the nitrogen are denoted by the points, the others by crosses. The electrons carried to the π system are on the arrows.

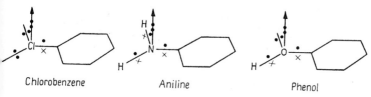

Chlorobenzene   Aniline   Phenol

FIG. 57. (Same notations as in Fig. 56.)

electrons: the remaining electrons associable to the atom (5 for nitrogen, 6 for oxygen, 7 for chlorine) are supplied to the π system.

This state of hybridisation is also suggested by the co-planarity of the nuclei in pyrrole [338] and aniline.

We might expect that the alkyl groups do not introduce any electrons into the π system since these substituents contain only saturated bonds. We shall see, however, that certain authors have assumed that the conjugated system extends over some of these substituents including the methyl. This phenomenon, sometimes disputed, is called hyperconjugation. We shall return to this later.

Figure 56 and 57 show that hetero-atoms and substituents can carry pairs of free electrons. As we have discussed in Chapter VI, these electrons will normally have an important role in ionisation phenomena, spectra, and the polar moment of conjugated electrons. We shall study examples of molecules where the free electrons have primary importance.

B. *Global Methods*

There are essentially two classes of methods for the treatment of hetero-atomic or substituted molecules. One set consists of considering these molecules as being derived by the perturbation of a conjugated hydrocarbon. The other set, called global, consists of treating the molecule without consideration of its analogy with a simpler molecule. The methods described in Chapters VIII and IX are, in general, applicable to conjugated molecules provided that some amendments are made.

In the case of naïve methods, these amendments transform, for example, Hückel's approximation to Pauling and Wheland's approximation[337]. Let us consider the case of pyridine. We still neglect the overlap integrals and the resonance integrals between non-adjacent atoms. It is also assumed that the coulomb integrals relative to carbon atoms are all equal to a certain value α_C and that the resonance integrals between two neighbouring carbon atoms are all equal to β_{CC}. On the other hand, we have to introduce a new coulomb integral α_N to represent the nitrogen and a resonance integral β_{CN} to represent the two CN bonds. Let

$$\alpha_N = \alpha_C + \xi_N \beta_{CC} \quad \text{and} \quad \beta_{CN} = \eta_{CN} \beta_{CC}.$$

The secular equation is then written

$$\begin{vmatrix} \alpha_C + \xi_N \beta_{CC} - e & \eta_{CN}\beta_{CC} & 0 & 0 & 0 & \eta_{CN}\beta_{CC} \\ \eta_{CN}\beta_{CC} & \alpha_C - e & \beta_{CC} & 0 & 0 & 0 \\ 0 & \beta_{CC} & \alpha_C - e & \beta_{CC} & 0 & 0 \\ 0 & 0 & \beta_{CC} & \alpha_C - e & \beta_{CC} & 0 \\ 0 & 0 & 0 & \beta_{CC} & \alpha_C - e & \beta_{CC} \\ \eta_{CN}\beta_{CC} & 0 & 0 & 0 & \beta_{CC} & \alpha_{CC} - e \end{vmatrix} = 0$$

or by setting

$$m = \frac{(\alpha_C - e)}{\beta_{CC}}$$

Table of Electronegativities

The valences used to calculate electronegativities are shown in roman numerals

1 H **Hydrogen** 1·0081																	2 He **Helium** 4·003
I 2																	
3 Li **Lithium** 6·940	4 (Be) **Beryllium** 9·0											5 B **Boron** 10·62	6 C **Carbon** 12·010	7 N **Nitrogen** 14·008	8 O **Oxygen** 16·0000	9 F **Fluorine** 19·00	10 Ne **Neon** 29·183
I 0·55	II 1·10											III 1·85	IV 2·50	III 3·15	II 3·60	I 4·15	
11 Na **Sodium** 22·997	12 Mg **Magnesium** 24·32											13 Al **Aluminium** 26·97	14 Si **Silicon** 28·06	15 P **Phosphorus** 30·98	16 S **Sulphur** 32·06	17 Cl **Chlorine** 35·457	18 A **Argon** 39·944
I 0·50	II 0·90											III 1·25	IV 1·65	III 1·85	II 2·45	I 3·10	
19 K **Potassium** 39·096	20 Ca **Calcium** 40·08	21 Sc **Scandium** 45·10	22 Ti **Titanium** 47·90	23 V **Vanadium** 50·95	24 Cr **Chromium** 52·01	25 Ma **Manganese** 54·93	26 Fe **Iron** 55·84	27 Co **Cobalt** 58·54	28 Ni **Nickel** 58·69	29 Cu **Copper** 63·57	30 Zn **Zinc** 65·38	31 Ga **Gallium** 69·72	32 Ge **Germanium** 72·60	33 As **Arsenic** 74·91	84 Se **Selenium** 78·76	35 Br **Bromine** 79·915	36 Kr **Krypton** 83·7
I 0·40	II 0·65	III 1·35	IV 1·55	II 1·20	II and 1·15 III	II 1·25	II and 1·55 III	II 1·65	II 1·65	II 1·85	II 1·30	III 1·45	IV 1·40	III 1·85	II 2·40	I 2·85	
37 Rb **Rubidium** 85·48	38 Sr **Strontium** 87·63	39 Y **Yttrium** 88·92	40 Zr **Zirconium** 91·32	41 Nb **Niobium** 92·91	42 Mo **Molybdenum** 95·95	43 (Te) **Technetium**	44 Ru **Ruthenium** 101·7	45 Rh **Rhodium** 102·91	46 Pd **Palladium** 106·7	47 Ag **Silver** 107·880	48 Cd **Cadmium** 112·41	49 In **Indium** 114·75	50 Sn **Tin** 118·70	51 Sb **Antimony** 121·76	52 Te **Tellurium** 127·61	53 I **Iodine** 126·92	54 Xe **Xenon** 131·3
I 0·35	II 0·60	III and 0·80 V ?	IV 1	V 1·80	IV and 1·80 V		III and 1·60 IV	II 1·6	II 2·2 ?	I 1·55	II 1·30	III 1·45	II 1·45 IV 1·65	III 1·75 V 2·10 ?	IV 2·20	I 2·45	
55 Cs **Caesium** 132·91	56 Ba **Barium** 136·36	57 La **Lanthanium** 138·92	58 Ce **Cerium** 140·13	59 Pr **Praseodymium** 140·92	60 Nd **Neodymium** 144·27	61 Pm **Promethium**	62 Sm **Samarium** 150·43	63 Eu **Europium** 152·0	64 Gd **Gadolinium** 156·9	65 Tb **Terbium** 159·2	66 Dy **Dysprosium** 162·46	67 Ho **Holmium** 163·5	68 Er **Erbium** 167·2	69 Tm **Thulium** 169·4	70 Yb **Ytterbium** 173·04	71 Lu **Lutecium** 175·0	
I 0·35	II 0·55																
			72 Hf **Hafnium** 178·6	73 Ta **Tantalum** 180·88	74 W **Tungsten** 183·92	75 Re **Rhenium** 186·31	76 Os **Osmium** 190·2	77 Ir **Iridium** 193·1	78 Pt **Platinum** 195·23	79 Au **Gold** 197·2	80 Hg **Mercury** 200·61	81 Tl **Thallium** 204·39	82 Pb **Lead** 207·21	83 Bi **Bismuth** 209·00	84 Po **Polonium** 210	85 At **Astatine**	86 Rn **Radon** 222
									II and 2 IV	I 2·25	I 1·60 II 1·60 ?	I 1·20 III 1·85	II 1·40	III 1·80			
87 Fr **Francium** (223)	88 Ra **Radium** 226·05	89 Ac **Actinium** 227	90 Th **Thorium** 232·12	91 Pa **Protactinium** 231	92 U **Uranium** 238·07	93 Np **Neptunium**	95 Pl **Plutonium**	95 Am **Americium**	96 Cm **Curium**	97 Bk **Berkelium**	98 Cf **Californium**	99 Es **Einsteinium**	100 Fm **Fermium**	101 Md **Mendelevium**	102 No **Nobelium**	103	104

$$\begin{vmatrix} m + \xi_N & \eta_{CN} & 0 & 0 & 0 & \eta_{CN} \\ \eta_{CN} & m & 1 & 0 & 0 & 0 \\ 0 & 1 & m & 1 & 0 & 0 \\ 0 & 0 & 1 & m & 1 & 0 \\ 0 & 0 & 0 & 1 & m & 1 \\ \eta_{CN} & 0 & 0 & 0 & 1 & m \end{vmatrix} = 0$$

The problem then reduces to exactly the same form as in the case of conjugated hydrocarbons provided ξ and η are known. These parameters can be chosen so that the experimental values of certain quantities agree with the calculated values. They can also be chosen *a priori* by means of electronegativities and bonding energies.

Mulliken [339] defines the electronegativity x_A of an atom A as the sum (or half the sum) of its first ionisation energy E_A and its electronegativity I_A. Hence

$$x_A = I_A + E_A.$$

Various other definitions of electronegativity have been proposed [340]. Pauling's definition is particularly interesting as it allows the calculation of electronegativities for a large number of atoms, while the lack of experimental data in various cases prevents the use of Mulliken's method. The quantities introduced by Mulliken and Pauling are in other respects proportional. We shall content ourselves by giving a table constructed [341] using a slightly improved version of Pauling's method. Obviously, the electronegativity so defined is a measure of the affinity of an atom for electrons. The function α will then probably be an increasing function of this electronegativity. Arguments have been given in favour of a linear function of the form [342]

$$(\alpha_X - \alpha_C) = M(x_X - x_C)\beta_{CC},$$

where M is close to unity [343].

In the case of nitrogen,

$$\alpha_N - \alpha_C = 0 \cdot 65\beta_{CC} \quad \xi_N = 0 \cdot 65.$$

Lennard-Jones[344] has proposed the formula

$$\eta_{CX} = \frac{E_{dCX} - E_{sCX}}{E_{dCC} - E_{sCC}}$$

to estimate the η factors. In this formula, E_{dXY} and E_{sXY} denote the energies of the double and single bonds respectively between atoms X and Y.

In Pauling and Wheland's approximation, we can also introduce the overlap integrals which are usually neglected[345].

In the self-consistent field method, applied rigorously, it is clear that the introduction of substituents do not pose a new problem. In Pariser and Parr's method, on the other hand, various parameters have to be estimated, for example the W_{2p} and the β^C.

C. Perturbation Methods

These are various types of perturbation methods. One method consists of considering the hydrocarbon which has the same conjugate system and representing as perturbation the variations which have to be applied to the integrals to obtain the original molecule. A second method, particularly suited to the case of substituents, consists of imagining the substituents separated from the rest of the molecule and considering as perturbation the interactions arising when the two fragments are put together. Many variations can be made between these two points of view.

The first method leads to the important idea of polarisability[346]. The atom–atom polarisability is defined as

$$\pi_{rs} = \frac{\partial q_r}{\partial \alpha_s}.$$

It measures the variation of the charge on atom r with respect to the coulomb integral of atom s. This quantity is called the auto-polarisability of atom r when

$$s = r.$$

The atom–bond and bond–atom polarisability are defined as

$$\pi_{r,st} = \frac{\partial q_r}{\partial \beta_{st}} \qquad \pi_{st,r} = \frac{\partial p_{st}}{\partial \alpha_r}$$

and the bond–bond polarisability as

$$\pi_{rs,tu} = \frac{\partial p_{rs}}{\partial \beta_{tu}}.$$

The use of polarisability can be illustrated in the case of pyridine. If the nitrogen atom is number 1 and if η is assumed to be unity (this is fairly near the result given by Lennard-Jones's formula) we have

$$q_s = 1 + \frac{\partial q_s}{\partial \alpha_1}(\alpha_N - \alpha_C) + \tfrac{1}{2}\frac{\partial^2 q_s}{\partial \alpha_1^2}(\alpha_N - \alpha_C)^2 + \cdots,$$

since in the parent hydrocarbon where $\alpha_N = \alpha_C$ (benzene)

$$q_s = 1$$

for all the carbon atoms.

Taking only first order terms, this reduces to

$$q_s = 1 + \pi_{1s}(\alpha_N - \alpha_C) = 1 + \pi_{1s}\xi_N\beta_{CC}.$$

The results obtained when ξ_N does not exceed unity are very near the results given by the corresponding global method for derivatives of alternant hydrocarbons, but are rather less satisfactory for derivatives of non-alternant hydrocarbons. The polarisabilities can be calculated by means of the formulae

$$\pi_{r,s} = 4\sum_{j=1}^{m}\sum_{k=m+1}^{n}\frac{c_{rj}c_{sj}c_{rk}c_{sk}}{e_j - e_k}$$

$$\pi_{st,r} = 2\sum_{j=1}^{m}\sum_{k=m+1}^{n}\frac{c_{rj}c_{rj}(c_{sj}c_{tk} + c_{tj}c_{sk})}{e_j - e_k}$$

$$\pi_{tu,rs} = 2\sum_{j=1}^{m}\sum_{k=m+1}^{n}\frac{(c_{rj}c_{sk} + c_{sj}c_{rk})(c_{tj}c_{uk} + c_{uj}c_{tk})}{e_j - e_k}.$$

A number of polarisabilities are given in the D.G.T.

The reader is referred to the original papers[347] for the study of the other types of perturbation.

D. *Some General Results*

The presence of hetero-atoms or substituents in a conjugated structure derived from an alternant hydrocarbon usually destroys the symmetrical distribution of the different energies associated with orbitals with respect to the root

$$e = \alpha.$$

It follows that the charges will usually not be unity, as was also shown by the preceding formula containing polarisability.

In the case of alternant hydrocarbons, the atom–atom polarisabilities are positive between atoms of opposite parity and negative between atoms of the same parity. Consequently, in the case of an alternant aza-derivative the charges on atoms are greater than one for those having the same parity as nitrogen, and less than one for atoms with opposite parity. The π system of a conjugated molecule, therefore, usually has a certain polar moment. The total polar moment remains rather difficult to calculate as together with the polar moment of the π system we have to take account of the moment of the σ system which includes a moment due to free pairs which is often important and difficult to estimate.

40. The Aza-derivatives of Conjugated Alternant Hydrocarbons

A. *Pyridine*

The pyridine molecule is a good example of an aza-derivative of an alternant hydrocarbon. It has been the object of a great number of papers from which we shall quote the more essential points. The method of Pauling and Wheland has been used for some time for the study of this molecule. The choice of the parameter ξ_N is a delicate problem. Generally, it is chosen to fit the experimental value of the polar moment but, as we have already mentioned, there is considerable uncertainty associated with the difficulty of estimating the moment of the free pair of the nitrogen and while ξ_N was taken equal to two in earlier papers, it has been given a value of about 0·6 in more recent work [349], which agrees with that we have found using the formula relating the ξ with the electronegativities.

If we fit ξ to values of the charges which McWeeny and Peacock [350] found using a procedure based on the self-consistent field method, however, we find

$$\xi_N = 0\cdot 2.$$

Figure 58 compares the charges obtained using the naïve method with those obtained by McWeeny and Peacock.

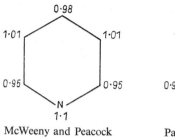

| McWeeny and Peacock | Pauling and Wheland |

Fig. 58

Various authors have studied the effect of introducing overlap integrals and resonance integrals between non-adjacent atoms. Although some of them [351] found that this does not modify the results appreciably, Pritchard and Sumner [352] obtained very different charges (greater than unity for *ortho* and *para*, less than one for *meta*).

As we have already mentioned, McWeeny and Peacock have studied pyridine using the self-consistent field method with Pariser and Parr's approximation. The charges found are given in Fig. 58. Their paper also discusses the electronic spectrum of pyridine together with the spectra of pyridazine, pyrimidine and pyrazine. The energies of excited states are calculated using the configuration interaction method.

In all these cases, the theory gives a good interpretation of the fact that three band systems (α, p and β) are found, the β and β' levels being nearly indistinguishable.

Brown and Heffernan [353] have also studied pyridine using the self-consistent field method. They also treated its ground state using configuration interactions [354]. They found that the effect of the configuration interactions was to lower the polar moment due to the π electrons. The polar moment of pyridine, according to them, is mainly due to the free pair of the nitrogen.

The same authors[355] have tried to improve the self-consistent field method by making the effective number of each atom depend on the charge it carries in Slater's orbitals which are used to calculate the molecular orbitals. They call this the method of variable electronegativity[356]. Unfortunately, there are many possible variants in the use of this procedure and the charge distribution obtained depends very strongly on these variants. The results preferred by the authors are close to McWeeny and Peacock's.

The following table compares experimental results with the results obtained when the corresponding procedure is applied with configuration interaction to the electronic spectrum of pyridine.

	Transition energies in eV	
	Calculated	Observed
α	4·96	4·90
p	5·23	6·38
β	6·97	7·07
β'	7·20	

B. *The n, π Transitions*

The methods used up to now do not take account of the free electrons of the nitrogen in the spectrum of pyridine.

Kasha[357], however, came to the conclusion that the absorption line at 2700 Å in the spectrum of pyridine corresponds to the transition of "one of the electrons" of the free pair of the nitrogen to one of the unoccupied orbitals of the π system. This is usually called an n, π transition. More recently, Rush and Sponer[258] have studied the spectra of picoline vapours in the near ultraviolet and found two band systems: one at 35,500 cm^{-1} and the other at 38,500 cm^{-1}. They concluded that the first corresponds to an n, π transition while the second is a π, π transition.

Now, n, π transitions are found in a great number of spectra arising from aza-derivatives of conjugated hydrocarbons. Various authors[359] have analysed the qualitative properties of these transitions, particularly the weakness of their intensities.

More quantitative investigations have been carried out. We shall first of all look at Goodman and Harrell's[360].

In the self-consistent field method, it is easy to show that the energy of a transition represented by "the passage" of an electron from an orbital φ_a to an orbital φ_b is

$$^{1,3}\Delta E = \varepsilon_b^C - \varepsilon_a^C - [(aa, bb) - (ab, ab)] \pm (ab, ab),$$

the sign being positive or negative depending on whether the excited state is singlet or triplet.

Goodman and Shull[361] have pointed out that it is reasonable to replace

$$\varepsilon_b^C - \varepsilon_a^C$$

by the value that it has in Pauling and Wheland's approximation, i.e.

$$\varepsilon_b^C - \varepsilon_a^C = e_b - e_a = (m_a - m_b)\beta$$

and hence

$$^{1,3}\Delta E = (m_a - m_b)\beta - [(aa, bb) - (ab, ba)] \pm (ab, ba).$$

The integrals can be calculated by means of Pauling and Wheland's method and ΔE then only depends on β which can be determined empirically.

By using a simplified form of this formula, Goodman and Harrel have calculated the energies of some n, π transitions. The following table contains some of their results and the corresponding experimenta data.

	Energy of the n, π singlet transition (in eV)	
	Observed	Calculated
Pyridine	4·27	4·26
Pyridazine	3·30	3·24
Pyrimidine	3·85	4·05
Pyrazine	3·83	3·83
s-Triazine	3·84	3·95
s-Tetrazine	2·23	2·60
2,2,4 Triazine	2·75	2·77
Quinoline	3·6	3·58
Isoquinoline	3·6	2·64

Anno[362] has studied n, π transitions rather more rigorously. He uses the method of Pariser and Parr by introducing explicitly the interaction between the orbital representing the free pair and the

π system. He uses a basis of configuration interaction containing the ground state and the mono-excited configurations. It is obviously necessary to specify the form of the orbital associated with the free pair. It is natural to use a hybrid of the form

$$n = \lambda\, 2s + 2p.$$

Anno carried out his calculations using the regular triagonal hybridisation ($\lambda = 1/\sqrt{2}$) as is frequently done. Hameka and Liquori [363], for example, made this choice in their interpretation of the fact that the angle $C\hat{N}C$ in azo-derivatives of conjugated hydrocarbons is usually less than 120°.

Anno obtained 6·9 eV for the energy of an n, π transition in pyrazine while experiment gives 3·8 eV.

Anno and Sadô [364] have tried to reduce this disparity between theory and experiment by introducing doubly excited configurations. They found that this makes little difference and that the disparity persists unless the value of λ is reduced so that the characteristic of the hybrid associated with the free pair is approximately 0·1.

Anno [365] has again taken up the problem of pyridine in detail and has calculated the set of energies of the first n, π transitions. He found, in particular, that the first π, π transition lies between two n, π transitions. Unfortunately, there is a criticism to be made about these works [366]. When an electron of the free pair passes to the π system, there is a reorganisation of the σ system which is difficult to take account of, *a priori*.

C. *References to Other Studies of Aza-derivatives*

We shall end this section by giving some references to works pertaining to aza-derivations of alternant hydrocarbons. First we mention some studies of the pyridinium ion which is formed when the nitrogen of pyridine fixes a proton. Mataga *et al.* [367] have analysed the effect of protonation on the spectrum of pyridine using the self-consistent field method, as well as the spectrum of methyl-pyridines [367].

A number of works on the azines have been carried out. Murrell [369] has used a perturbation method. Simonetta *et al.* [370] have used the self-consistent field method and the configuration interaction method. Paoloni [371] has used a similar approach.

The effect of protonation of azines have been discussed by Mataga and Mataga[372].

Mataga[373] has, using the same methods, analysed the spectra of acridine and phenazine, while Simonetta et al.[374] have discussed the case of naphthotriazine, and Fernandez and Carbonell[375] have studied azobenzene and the azanaphthalenes. Finally, we mention the analysis of the properties of curious compounds such as the quinolizinium ion[376], cyclazines[377] and diazapyrene[377].

41. OTHER NITROGEN DERIVATIVES

A. *Pyrrole and its Derivatives*

The self-consistent field method (Pariser and Parr's approximation) has been applied to pyrrole[378], as well as the method of variable electronegativities[379]. Other work has also been done on the benzoindoles[380], naphoidines[381] and aza-indoles[382].

B. *Aniline and its Derivatives*

We shall examine in greater detail aniline and amine derivatives in general which have been treated by Bloor† using a perturbation method[383] which has not yet been studied in this book. In the case of aniline it consists of starting from benzene and the NH_2 group and finding how their level are perturbed when the two are brought together to form aniline.

For generality, let us call these two parts R and S. In the present case, S is NH_2 and carries two π electrons. It may be expected, therefore, that, for aniline, a proportion of these electrons will end up in the benzene cycle which normally contains only one π electron per atom, the repulsion between electrons tending to make some sort of equipartition; this is why substituents like NH_2, OH, F, Br, Cl, I are often called *electron donors*. This, therefore, leads to the representation of the last occupied orbital of aniline, φ say, as a linear combination of the π orbital of NH_2, φ_s say, and the first unoccupied orbital of benzene, φ_R say. Hence

$$\varphi = a\varphi_R + b\varphi_s.$$

† Personal communication.

Let H_R and H_S be the Hamiltonians which determine φ_R and φ_S in the isolated systems. We shall set

$$H_R = T + V_R \quad \text{and} \quad H_S = T + V_S$$

and we shall assume that the Hamiltonian associated with φ is

$$H = T + V_R + V_S.$$

By McDonald's theorem, the energy ε_{RS} associated with φ is the solution of the secular equation

$$\begin{vmatrix} H_{11} - \varepsilon_{RS} & H_{12} \\ H_{21} & H_{22} - \varepsilon_{RS} \end{vmatrix} = 0$$

provided the overlap integrals are neglected and

$$H_{11} = \int \varphi_R H \varphi_R \, dv \quad H_{22} = \int \varphi_S H \varphi_S \, dv,$$

$$H_{12} = \int \varphi_R H \varphi_S \, dv = H_{21} = \int \varphi_S H \varphi_R \, dv.$$

Let us calculate H_{11}. We have

$$H_{11} = \int \varphi_R (H_R + V_S) \varphi_R \, dv = \varepsilon_R + \int \varphi_R V_S \varphi_R \, dv,$$

where ε_R is the energy associated with φ_R in R.

As the operator V_S is formed by elements of S and the function φ_R is localised in R, we can neglect the integral

$$\int \varphi_R V_S \varphi_R \, dv.$$

We then have

$$H_{11} = \varepsilon_R.$$

Similarly,

$$H_{22} = \varepsilon_S.$$

In the L.C.A.O. approximation

$$\varphi_R = \sum_i c_{iR} \psi_i$$

$$\varphi_S = \sum_{i'} c_{i'S} \psi_{i'}.$$

The element H_{12} is then

$$H_{12} = \int \varphi_R H \varphi_S \, dv = \sum_i \sum_{i'} c_{iR} c_{i'S} \int \psi_i H \psi_{i'} \, dv.$$

Obviously, if the integrals between non-adjacent atoms are neglected, only one term remains: the one corresponding to the two atoms inducing the union of the two parts. Let β be the corresponding resonance integral. Then

$$H_{12} = c_R c_S \beta,$$

where c_R and c_S denote the coefficients of these atoms. The secular equation then becomes

$$(\varepsilon_R - \varepsilon_{RS})(\varepsilon_S - \varepsilon_{RS}) = c_R^2 c_S^2 \beta^2$$

and hence

$$\varepsilon_{RS} = \varepsilon_R + \varepsilon_S \pm \sqrt{\{(\varepsilon_R - \varepsilon_S)^2 + 4c_R^2 c_S^2 \beta^2\}}.$$

By determining empirically the parameters for aniline, Bloor has calculated the transition energy of the K-band [384] of amine belonging to the family of aza-derivatives of alternant hydrocarbons. The following table gives these results together with experimental results.

Derived amine of:	Transition energies	
	Calculated	Observed
Styrolene	4·53	4·54
Stilbene	3·96	3·92
Diphenyl	4·45	4·52
Terphenyl	3·98	4·19
Naphthalene (α)	3·87	3·98
Anthracene (meso)	3·19	3·18

Magata and Magata [385] have done similar work on the aminopyridines.

42. OTHER CONJUGATED MOLECULES

A. *Carbonyl and Carboxylic Compounds*

Formaldehyde itself has been closely studied using the self-consistent field method and the configuration interaction method [386]. The problem is similar to that of pyridine in as much as it is necessary to take account of π, π and n, π transitions simultaneously. Many papers have been devoted to the study of quinones. Paolini[387] has studied parabenzoquinone and some of its derivatives using Pauling and Wheland's method. Kuboyama[388] has supplied this method to α-naphthoquinone and anthraquinone. Payette and Sandorfy have used a similar method (but including overlap integrals on a series of conjugate quinones[389]). Blinc and Pirkmajer have discussed the case of naphthazarine[390].

Anno *et al.*[391] have devoted a series of works to parabenzoquinone using Pariser and Parr's approximation, making allowance for the free electrons of oxygen explicitly. These works include an analysis of the infrared spectrum. Besnainou and Bratoz[392] have studied the effect of environment on the frequency of valence of the carbonyl group. In particular, they give an expression for the force constant of a conjugated bond in terms of a wave function deduced using Pariser and Parr's approximation. They also give an elegant means of determining penetration integrals by means of ionisation energies of free radicals having certain associations with the molecules under study. The region of applicability of this method is increased if there is a means of predicting ionisation energies of free radicals[393].

As an example of the study of carboxylic compounds, we indicate Goodwin's paper on benzoic acid[394].

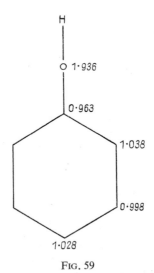

FIG. 59

B. *Phenolic Compounds*

Phenol itself has been studied by Nishimoto and Fujishiro[395] using Pariser and Parr's approximation. Figure 59 shows the charge distribution obtained. As expected, there is a transfer of charge towards the benzene ring which is expressed as an increase of charges in *ortho* and in *para*.

More complex phenolic derivations have only been studied by naïve methods. This has been done for gallol[396], phloroglucine[397] and the naphthalenediols.

C. *Nitro Compounds*

Fernandez[398] has studied mononitrobenzene using Pauling and Wheland's method and found a big difference between the charge distribution for the ground state and for an excited state. Fevini and Carra[399] have discussed α and β nitronaphthalene.

D. *Oxygen, Sulphur, Selenium Compounds*

Among the works on oxygen derivatives, we shall mention one by Kulo, Kurita and Kimura on tropolone[400] and one by Brown and Coller[401] on furan, benzofuran and dibenzofuran (they also treat pyrrole, indole and carbazole).

The appearance of atoms of the third period in a conjugate system poses a new problem. Some authors[402] make allowance for $3D$ orbitals while others[403] do not. Koutecky *et al.*[404] have recently discussed this problem in the case of dibenzothiophene.

Other papers have been written on 1-4 dithiadene[405], the cyclic disulphides[407], thiothiophtene[402] and selenium derivatives[408].

E. *Methyl Compounds*

The problem of hyperconjugation has been made the object of many discussions. We shall content ourselves for the moment by referring the reader to what has been written by the author with R. Lefévre and C. Moser in *Quantum Chemistry*, Section VIII-4 (pp. 194–200) (Interscience New York, 1959). We hope to be able to return to this question in the next book of this series, *Theory of Chemical Reactivity*.

CHAPTER XI

Some Molecules of Biochemical Interest

43. STRUCTURE OF POLYPEPTIDES AND PROTEINS

We shall end this book by looking at some molecules of great interest in biochemistry and biology. Applications of wave mechanics in this field are becoming more and more numerous and will certainly play a very important role in the near future.

Among these molecules, the proteins are particularly important by reason of their abundance and their importance in living creatures. Proteins form most of the molecules making up viruses, numerous hormones, enzymes, animal tissues and, in particular, epidermic tissues and membranes. Proteins can be said to be derived from amino-acids by polymerisation following elimination of water:

The polypeptidic chain:

is discriminated from the remainders R_1, R_2 and R_3 which characterise the different amino-acids.

The amino-acids found in protein are:

1 Glycine

$$H_2N—CH_2—CO_2H$$

alanine

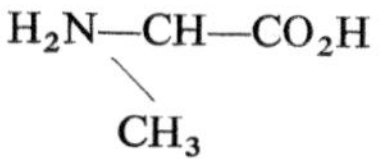

$$H_2N—CH—CO_2H$$
$$CH_3$$

valine

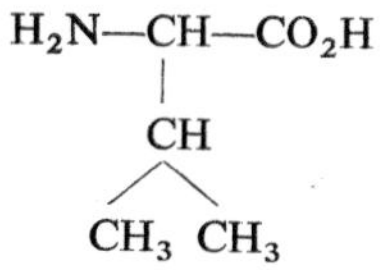

$$H_2N—CH—CO_2H$$
$$CH$$
$$CH_3 \quad CH_3$$

leucine

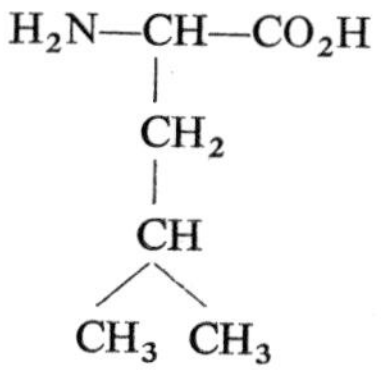

$$H_2N—CH—CO_2H$$
$$CH_2$$
$$CH$$
$$CH_3 \quad CH_3$$

isoleucine

$$H_2N—CH—CO_2H$$
$$CH$$
$$CH_3$$
$$CH_2$$
$$CH_3$$

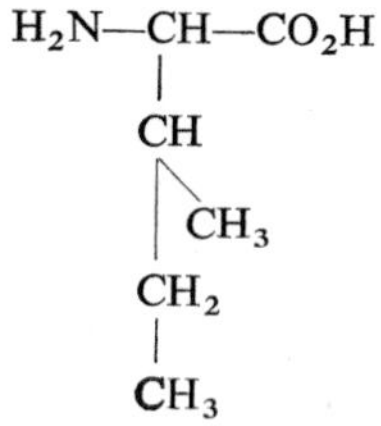

phenylalanine

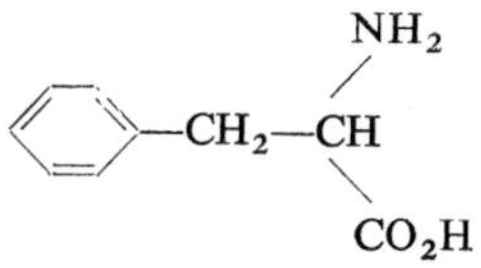

tryptophan

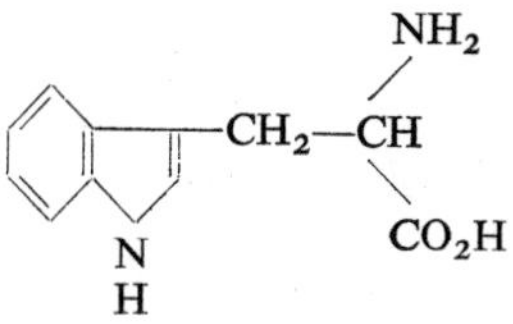

histidine

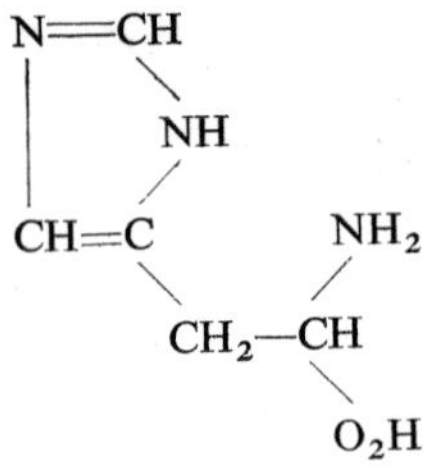

$$N=CH$$
$$\diagdown NH$$
$$CH=C \qquad NH_2$$
$$\diagdown CH_2-CH$$
$$\diagdown O_2H$$

and proline

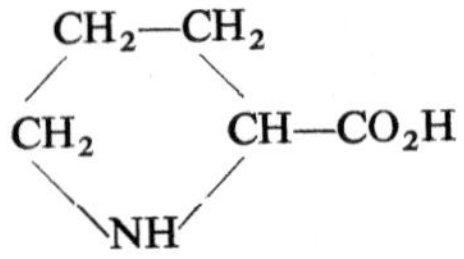

$$CH_2-CH_2$$
$$CH_2 \qquad CH-CO_2H$$
$$\diagdown NH \diagup$$

2 Hydrated amino acids:

serine

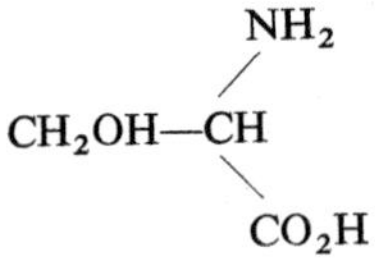

$$NH_2$$
$$CH_2OH-CH$$
$$\diagdown CO_2H$$

threonine

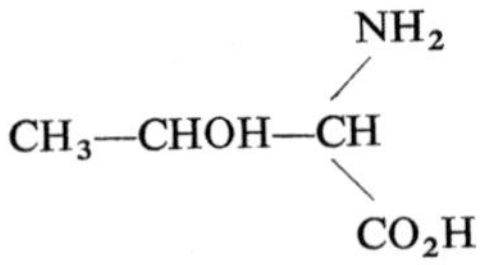

$$NH_2$$
$$CH_3-CHOH-CH$$
$$\diagdown CO_2H$$

tyrosine

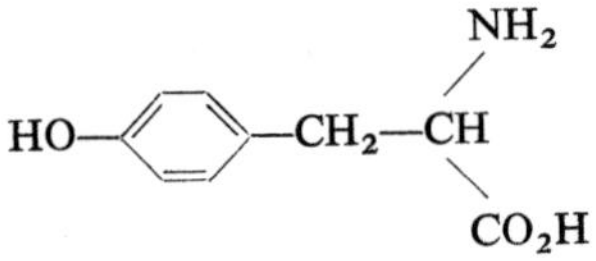

$$NH_2$$
$$HO-\langle\bigcirc\rangle-CH_2-CH$$
$$\diagdown CO_2H$$

and hydroxyproline.

3 Basis amino acids:

lysine

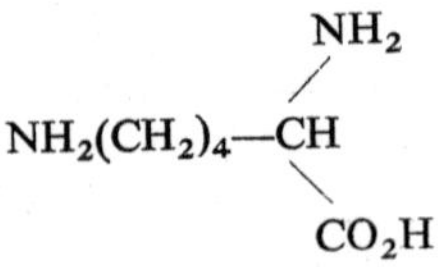

$$NH_2$$
$$NH_2(CH_2)_4-CH$$
$$\diagdown CO_2H$$

and arginine

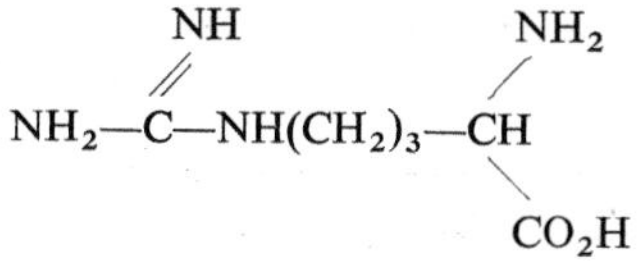

$$NH_2-\overset{\overset{\displaystyle NH}{\|}}{C}-NH(CH_2)_3-\overset{\overset{\displaystyle NH_2}{/}}{\underset{\underset{\displaystyle CO_2H}{\backslash}}{CH}}$$

4 Acid amino acids:

aspartic acid

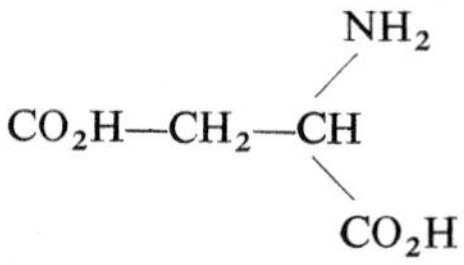

$$CO_2H-CH_2-\overset{\overset{\displaystyle NH_2}{/}}{\underset{\underset{\displaystyle CO_2H}{\backslash}}{CH}}$$

and glutamic acid

$$CO_2H-(CH_2)_2-\overset{\overset{\displaystyle NH_2}{/}}{\underset{\underset{\displaystyle CO_2H}{\backslash}}{CH}}$$

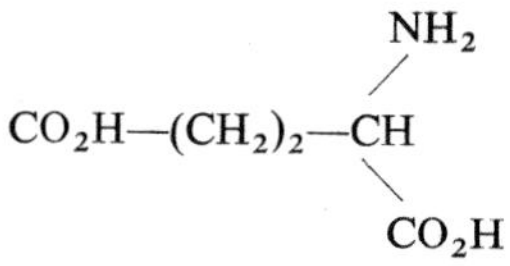

5 Sulphuretted amino acids:

cysteine

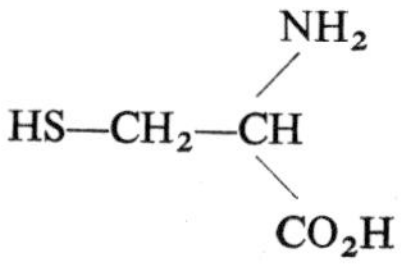

$$HS-CH_2-\overset{\overset{\displaystyle NH_2}{/}}{\underset{\underset{\displaystyle CO_2H}{\backslash}}{CH}}$$

and methionine

$$CH_3-S-(CH_2)_2-\overset{\overset{\displaystyle NH_2}{/}}{\underset{\underset{\displaystyle CO_2H}{\backslash}}{CH}}$$

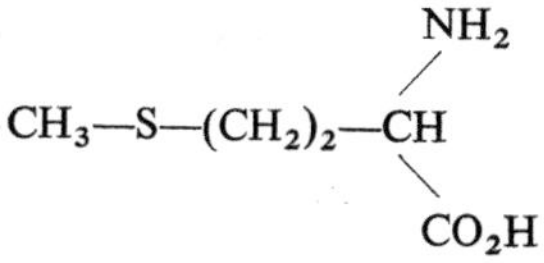

The proteins are generally subdivided into two large classes: globular soluble proteins and fibrous insoluble proteins.

The fibrous proteins are themselves usually divided into two groups: the keratin group and the collagen group. Figure 60 gives an idea of the structure of the keratin β [409].

We see that the protein is made up of parallel planes formed of parallel polypeptidic chains connected by a large number of hydrogen bonds. The distance between the planes is approximately 10 Å and the displacement of chains in the same plane is 4·65 Å.

Note that the symbols R denote various remainders of amino-acids.

In keratin α the chains are partially coiled.

In non-denatured globular proteins it is assumed (Pauling, Corey and Branson[410]) that the polypeptidic chains are coiled helically. In this case the "hydrogen" bonds are connected to the interior of the same chain of peptidic groups $O=C-NH$.

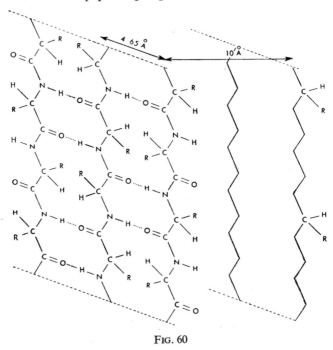

FIG. 60

To end this general description of proteins, we give in Fig. 61 a schematic diagram of the structure of one of the smallest proteins: insulin.

Polypeptides are sometimes called proteinic molecules of small molecular weight.

Szent Gyorgi[411] has inferred that the presence of a system formed of peptidic bonds connected by "hydrogen" bonds will allow electrons to circulate in the proteins rather like the flow of electricity in a conductor.

The theoretical study of questions of this type has been ap-

proached by Bayliss[412] using the method of the free electron and by
Evans and Gergely[413] using Pauling and Wheland's method.

We shall only analyse this last paper. According to Pauling and
Wheland's method, a peptidic bond $O=C-NH$ can be treated as a

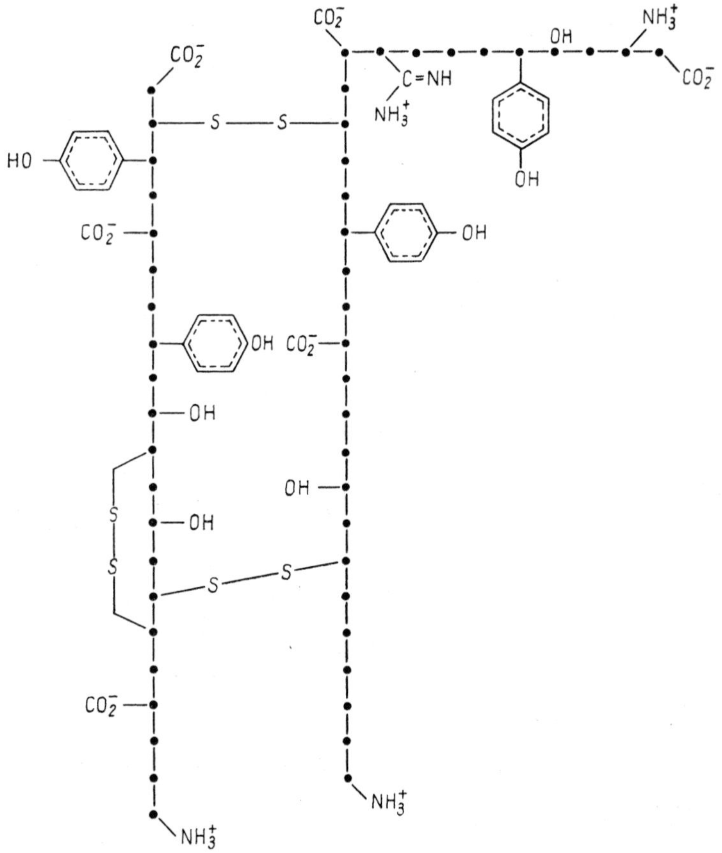

FIG. 61. Each point represents an amino acid group for which only the
characteristic part is given explicitly (from K. HARRISON, *A Guide Book
to Biochemistry* (1959), University Press, Cambridge).

bond delocalised to three centres and containing four electrons, as
C and O each contribute one π electron while NH introduces two.
The solution of the secular system therefore gives three orbitals:
the first two doubly occupied and the third unoccupied. The exis-

tence of hydrogen bonds introduce integrals β_{ON} between the different peptidic bonds and the secular system is

$$
0 = \begin{vmatrix}
\alpha_N - e & \beta_{NC} & 0 & & & & \\
\beta_{NC} & \alpha_C - e & \beta_{CO} & & & & \\
0 & \beta_{CO} & \alpha_O - e & \beta_{ON} & & & \\
& & \beta_{ON} & \alpha_N - e & \beta_{CN} & 0 & \\
& & & \beta_{NC} & \alpha_C - e & \beta_{CO} & \\
& & & 0 & \beta_{CO} & \alpha_O - e & \beta_{ON} \\
& & & & & \beta_{ON} & \alpha_N - e
\end{vmatrix}
$$

First of all, the parameters must be chosen. The authors set

$$\alpha_i = \alpha_M + \delta_i,$$

where α_M is the mean value of the α, chosen to be $-13 \cdot 24$ eV from an examination of the electronegativities of NH, O= and C=O.

Moreover they take

$$\delta_N = -0 \cdot 58 \quad \text{or} \quad 1 \qquad \delta_O = -1 \cdot 49 \quad \text{and} \quad \delta_C = 2 \cdot 07.$$

The β was taken as half the energy of the π bond in C=O, N=O and N=C calculated for the distances found experimentally in the proteins [414], i.e.

$$d_{NO} = 2 \cdot 65 \text{ Å}, \qquad d_{CO} = 1 \cdot 25 \text{ Å}, \qquad d_{CN} = 1 \cdot 33 \text{ Å}.$$

In this way they obtained

$$\beta_{NO} = -0 \cdot 2, \qquad \beta_{CO} = -2 \cdot 3, \qquad \beta_{ON} = -1 \cdot 5 \dagger.$$

They have also tried $\beta_{CN} = -2 \cdot 3$.

The secular system was solved using Ursell's method. One band of levels now corresponds to each orbital of a peptidic bond. The following table gives the positions and widths of these bands.

† This calculation applies mainly to fibrous proteins where all the π orbitals are parallel.

	$\delta_N = -0.58$ $\beta_{CN} = -1.5$	$\delta_N = 1$ $\beta_{CN} = -1.5$	$\delta_N = -0.53$ $\beta_{CN} = -2.3$
Band 1 doubly occupied	0–0·20	0–0·13	0–0·26
Band 2 doubly occupied	2·04–2·34	3·17–3·43	2·50–2·89
Band 3 unoccupied	6·57–6·67	6·48–6·60	7·65–7·79

The authors have observed that the jump between the second occupied band and the conduction band is very large (> 3 eV). They concluded from this that the proteins can exhibit a photo-conduction but practically no semi-conduction.

Semi-conducting properties of molecules which carry π electrons have been made the object of many experimental studies. Vartanyan[415] has found semi-conductivity in the phthalocyanins. Inokuchi[416] and collaborators have observed this property in numerous conjugated hydrocarbons. Eley[417] and collaborators have made a special study of proteins.

Their method consists of introducing the proteins as a dry powder between the plates of a condenser which can move together to compress the powder with pressures from 0 to 80 kg/cm². The apparatus is installed in an oven through which a current of hydrogen or nitrogen can be passed to remove the air. Hence, the conductivity can be measured as a function of temperature which is found to be of the form

$$\varrho = \varrho_0 \, e^{\Delta e/2RT},$$

where Δe can be interpreted as the separation of the bands previously mentioned.

The more recent results are summarised in the following table:

Nucleoprotein of the thymus	2·57 eV
Thrombine	2·59
Cytochrome C	2·60
Lysozyme	2·62
Fibrinogene	2·69
Insulin (of pig)	2·91
Globine	2·97
Collagene	2·73
Polyglycine	2·99

One can conclude that Δe is practically invariant from one protein to another and that the variations observed can be attributed to a variable amount of denaturation of the protein in the course of its treatment.

The order of magnitude of Δe is compatible with the value calculated by Evans and Gergely.

Eley and Spivey *(loc. cit.)* have measured the mobility of electrons in the proteins and have constructed a model which illustrates this mobility as well as Δe and the non-ohmic behaviour of proteins. Cardew and Eley *(loc. cit.)* have inquired into the biochemical consequences of the existence of the conduction band. They arrived at three conclusions.

Szent Gyorgi has postulated that the respiration of sea-urchin eggs may be carried out through the intermediary of an electric current through protein fibres. It is necessary to envisage a current of approximately 16.8×10^{-11} A, i.e. a resistance of 0.6×10^{10} Ω, assuming an oxy-reduction potential of the order of 1 V. The preceding measurements show that a protein fibre of 50 Å diameter and 1 micron thick corresponds to a resistance of 2×10^{24} Ω. It is, therefore, improbable that the mechanism suggested by Szent Gyorgi fits.

On the other hand, the phenomenon of photo-excitation might be very important. A photo-excitation of energy greater than 3 eV must be able to induce the formation of an exciton capable of propagation through the protein chain and capable of producing perturbations at various points of the protein. The lack of photochemical activation of urease by photons of wavelengths between 1960 and 3660 Å (3·39 eV) may be explained by this. Note that by applying a potential separating the two components of the exciton, one can form an oxy-reduction chain.

Finally, the authors have wondered whether the catalytic effect of enzymes might be due to a diminution of the energy of an intermediary of the reaction by the coupling of its delocalised system with the protein.

It is accepted that in certain dehydrogenisation reactions, the speed of reaction is controlled by the formation of semi-quinones. These semi-quinones can be stabilised by such a coupling. The smallness of β_{ON} indicates that this effect can only be significant for peptidic bonds near the reaction.

All these conclusions, however, are subject to various criticisms.

In particular, the effect of water normally included in the proteins has been neglected. No account has been taken of the field of the hydrogen bond in calculating β_{ON}. Also, certain specialists consider that impurities are responsible for the semi-conductivity measured by Eley and his collaborators.

Douzou and Thuillier[418] have given a preliminary report on work in which they have observed the photo-conductive property of proteins.

44. The Structure of Some Molecules Arising in the Phenomena of the Absorption, Storage and Utilisation of Energy by Living Organisms

A. *Introduction*

It is known that plants use solar energy to transform carbonic acid of the air by *reduction* to oxygen and organic materials (sugars, starch, cellulose, etc.). Animals, on the other hand, consume organic material (arising mainly from plants and other animals) and by *oxidation* regenerate the carbonic acid. This reduction is called photo-synthesis and the oxidation corresponds to the respiratory chain. Symbolically we have:

$$CO_2 + H_2O \underset{\text{respiratory chain}}{\overset{\text{photo-synthesis}}{\rightleftharpoons}} \text{organic matter}$$

In the course of this extremely complex process, many problems arise. Some of them require precise knowledge of the structure of conjugated molecules and have been approached by wave mechanical methods.

B. *The Mechanism of the Respiratory Chain*

Let us take the example of the oxidation of lactic acid:

$$CH_3\text{—}CHOH\text{—}CO_2H.$$

It is assumed, at the moment, that this oxidation is carried out with the help of an enzyme and a co-enzyme. The co-enzyme is called diphosphopyridine nucleotide (DPN) (or co-enzyme I); its formula is the following:

The reaction can be symbolised by

$$CH_3—CHOH—CO_2H + DPN \rightleftarrows CH_3—CO—CO_2H + DPNH_2 + enzyme$$
$$\diagdown enzyme \diagup$$

(lactic dehydrogenase)

The hydrogen acquired by the DPN is then transferred to a new enzyme of the dehydrogenase type: a flavo-protein (yellow enzyme). For example, here is the formula of a flavo-adenine dinucleotide which forms a flavo-protein when connected to a protein.

Then, if FP denotes a flavo-protein, we have:

$$DPNH_2 + FP \rightleftarrows FPH_2 + DPN.$$

The FPH_2 molecules are then oxidised by cytochrome C which is a carrier of electrons. This cytochrome is made up of the following prosthetic group associated with a protein:

Hence we have

$$FPH_2 + 2 \text{ cytochrome C (Fe}^{+++}) \rightleftharpoons FP + 2 H^+ + 2 \text{ cytochrome C (Fe}^{++}).$$

The reduced cytochrome C is then oxidised by cytochrome a_3, a protein analogous to cytochrome C but which is strongly associated with the insoluble part of cells and which acts as an oxidiser and is often called oxidising cyctochromes:

$$\text{cytochrome C (Fe}^{++}) + \text{cytochrome } a_3 + H^+ \rightleftharpoons \text{cytochrome C (Fe}^{+++})$$
$$+ (\text{cytochrome } a_3H).$$

It is this reduced form of cytochrome a_3 which is suitable to react directly with the oxygen thus completing the chain by the reaction

$$4(\text{cytochrome } a_3H) + O_2 \rightarrow 2 H_2O + 4 \text{ cytochrome } a_3.$$

To summarise, the respiratory chain is made up of the following links:

$$CH_3\text{—}CHOH\text{—}CO_2H + DPN \rightleftharpoons CH_3\text{—}CO\text{—}CO_2H + DPNH_2 \quad \text{(I)}$$
$$\diagdown \text{ enzyme } \diagup \qquad\qquad + \text{ enzyme}$$

$DPNH_2 + FP \rightleftharpoons DPN + FPH_2$ (II)

$FPH_2 + 2$ cyto. $C (Fe^{+++}) \rightleftharpoons FP + 2$ cyto. $C Fe^{++} + 2 H^+$ (III)

cyto. $C (Fe^{++}) + H^+ +$ cyto. $a_3 \rightleftharpoons$ cyto. $C (Fe^{+++}) + ($cyto. $a_3 H)$ (IV)

$4 ($cyto. $a_3 H) + O_2 \rightarrow 2 H_2O + 4$ cyto. a_3 (V)

Three of these reactions liberate energy (II, III and V) and it is assumed that this energy is stored by means of the formation of "rich bonds". This mainly comes about by the transformation of a molecule of adenosine diphosphate (ADP) to adenosine triphosphate (ATP). The energy thus stored can then be used by the organism in different syntheses, e.g. protein syntheses.

C. *Nature of Rich Bonds*

The complex problem of the respiratory chain has been discussed from the theoretical point of view by Grabe[419]. As this book is limited to the study of structures (the next book will be devoted to reactions), we shall concentrate on studies which specify the structure of some of the molecules which arose in Section 44B.

As a first example we shall examine the nature of rich bonds. Let us state precisely the definition of such bonds. The hydrolysis of a phosphoric ester derived from an alkyl R corresponds generally to a variation of standard free energy $-\Delta F^0$ of approximately 3 kcal/mole:

$$\begin{array}{c} O \\ \| \\ R-O-P-OH + H_2O \rightarrow R-OH + PO_4H_3 \\ | \\ OH \end{array}$$

$$(-\Delta F^0 = 3 \text{ kcal/mole}).$$

The hydrolysis of the OP bond in certain more complex phosphoric compounds corresponds to a variation of free standard energy of the order of 10 kcal/mole, e.g.

$$\begin{array}{cc} O & O \\ \| & \| \\ R-C-O-P-OH + H_2O \rightarrow RCO_2H + PO_4H_3 \\ & | \\ & OH \end{array}$$

$$(-\Delta F^0 = 12 \text{ kcal/mole}).$$

The OP bond of such a compound is called "rich" and the compound is symbolised by the simplified formula

$$
\begin{array}{c}
O \\
\parallel \\
R-C-O \sim \text{\textcircled{P}}
\end{array}
$$

The adenosine diphosphate which we have just mentioned and whose formula is

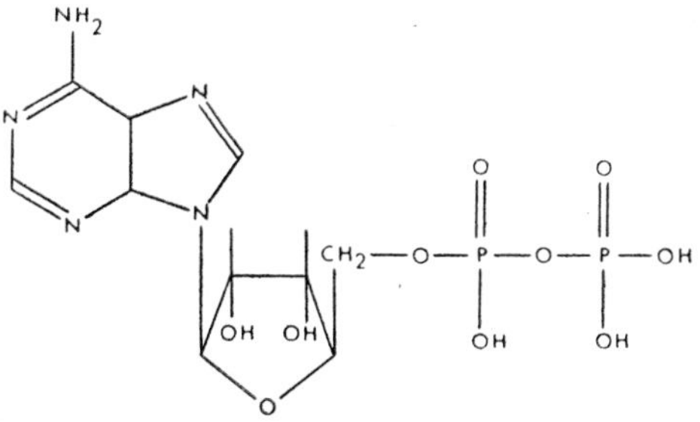

can be symbolised as

$$A-O-\text{\textcircled{P}} \sim \text{\textcircled{P}}$$

if we only want to emphasise the position of the rich bond.

Similarly, ATP can be denoted by

$$A-O-\text{\textcircled{P}} \sim \text{\textcircled{P}} \sim \text{\textcircled{P}}.$$

This illustrates what we mean when we speak of the appearance of an extra rich bond when one passes from ADP to ATP.

Grabe[420] has studied the distribution of electric charge in carboxyl phosphate, adenosine diphosphate and adenosine triphosphate. The principle of his calculation will be analysed for the case of carboxyl phosphate. Figure 62 shows the notations used. The problem has been reduced to the examination of a system of six π electrons, one from the carbon atom, one from oxygen O_α, two from oxygen O_β, one from the phosphorus and one from the $O_{\gamma_1}, O_{\gamma_2}, O_{\gamma_3}$ group, hence applying ideas used in the study of hyperconjugation. For the first four atoms a $2p_z$ orbital is used. For the group we use an orbital of the type

$$\varphi = 2p_{\gamma_1} - \tfrac{1}{2}(2p_{\gamma_2} - 2p_{\gamma_3}),$$

where the $2p$ orbitals are directed along the corresponding PO bonds. This is once again based on methods used to study hyperconjugation.

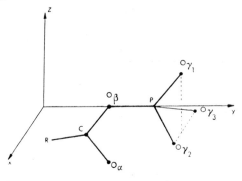

FIG. 62

The calculation is then continued using Pauling and Wheland's approximation, but without neglecting overlap integrals. The α are chosen as functions of the ionisation energies of p-orbitals estimated by Skinner and Pritchard [421]. The β are calculated by means of a formula which is valid for an isolated bond

$$\beta = -\frac{D'S_{\mu v}}{2} \pm \sqrt{\left\{\frac{D'^2}{4} - \frac{(\alpha_\mu - \alpha_v)^2}{4}\right\}},$$

where D is the difference between the energies of a double bond and the corresponding simple bond.

$$\left[\begin{array}{c} \begin{array}{c} -0.68 \\ O \\ +0.36 \\ O \underset{-0.68}{} P \underset{O}{\overset{-0.68}{\diagdown}} \\ O \\ -0.68 \end{array} \end{array} \right]^{-3} \qquad \begin{array}{c} -0.34 \qquad\qquad -0.5 \\ O \qquad\qquad\qquad O \\ \| \\ R -\!\!-\!\!- C -\!\!-\!\!- O -\!\!-\!\!- P \overset{-0.5}{\underset{O}{\diagup}} O \\ +0.18 \; +0.32 \; +0.35 \qquad O \\ -0.5 \end{array}$$

FIG. 63(a)

Figure 63 illustrates the charge distribution calculated from this.

Grabe reached various conclusions from this concerning the stability of OP bonds and chemical reactions in which ADP can participate.

The same study has been carried out by A. and B. Pullman [422] by an analogous method. They also calculated the energy of electrostatic repulsion between these charges appearing on the atoms and,

$$
\begin{array}{ccc}
O^{-0,5} & & O^{-0,5} \\
| & & | \\
A-O-P-O-P-O^{-0,5} \\
{}^{+0,35}| \quad {}^{+0,31} \quad |^{+0,35} \\
O^{-0,5} & & O^{-0,5}
\end{array}
$$

Fig. 63(b)

in particular, the excess of this repulsion when compared with an ester with no rich bonds. They find that this excess is 1·4 kcal/mole in ADP and 2 kcal/mole for ATP. They think that this explains, in part, the existence of rich bonds in these molecules. Another part of this richness arises from the fact that the delocalised bonds in ADP and ATP have a smaller bonding energy than in the fragments which constitute them.

To be more precise on this point, let us take an example: the resonance energy is $0·137\beta$ in the part CH_2-O and $1·185\beta$ in the ion PO^{-3}. With the combination of these elements corresponding to ATP, the resonance energy would be

$$0·137 + 2 \times 1·185 = 2·507,$$

provided this phenomenon is additive. In fact the calculation gives a resonance energy of $2·412 \beta$ for ADP, i.e. a decrease of $0·095\beta$.

If, with Pullman, we take $\beta = 40$ kcal/mole, this fall corresponds to 4 kcal/mole, i.e. an enrichment of approximately 2 kcal/mole by the phosphoric part.

This explains why the free energy of hydrolysis of rich bonds of ADP and ATP exceed the corresponding energy for a simple alkyl phosphoric ester.

D. *Structure and Action of Co-enzyme I (DPN) and Enzymes of the Flavo-protein Type*

B. and A. Pullman [423] studied the structure of co-enzyme (DPN) and flavo-proteins using Pauling and Wheland's method. Grabe [424] has discussed the same problem using both the same approximation and Pariser and Parr's approximation.

ESM 14

It is interesting to compare the results.

In Grabe's work, the structures studied are the following:

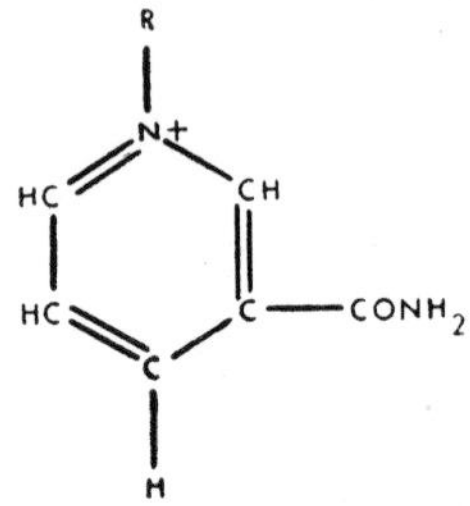

DPN+

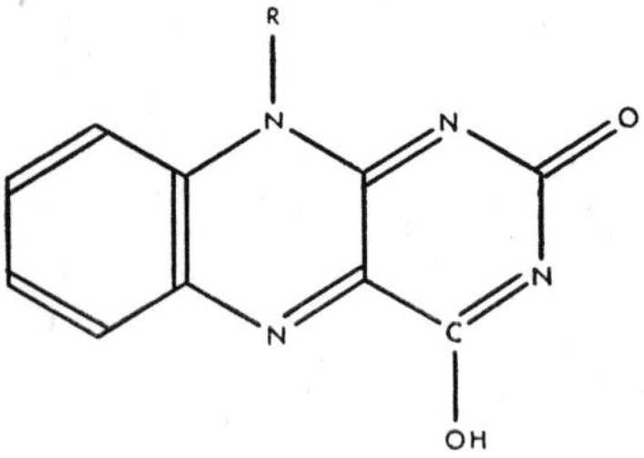

FAD

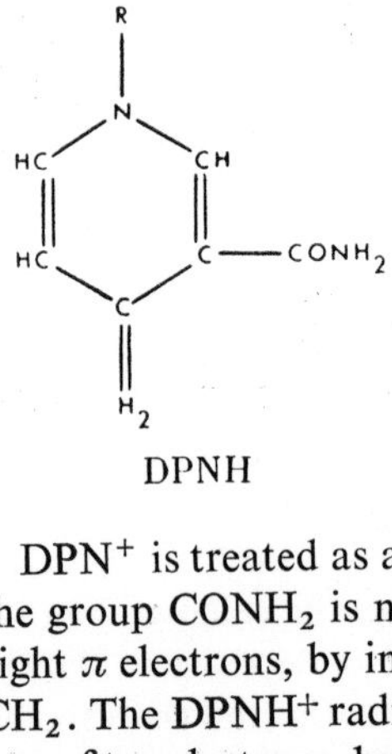

DPNH

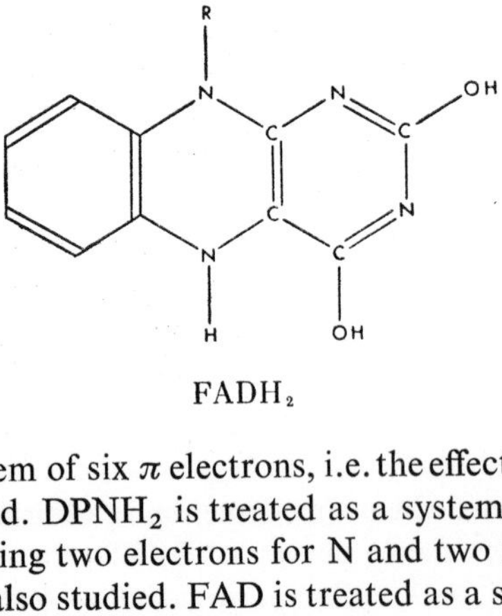

FADH$_2$

DPN$^+$ is treated as a problem of six π electrons, i.e. the effect of the group $CONH_2$ is neglected. DPNH$_2$ is treated as a system of eight π electrons, by introducing two electrons for N and two for CH_2. The DPNH$^+$ radical is also studied. FAD is treated as a system of ten electrons, by neglecting one of the benzene parts, and the group OH.RADH$_2$ is considered as a system of twelve electrons. The case of the FAD$^-$ radical is treated similarly.

These are gross simplifications and these calculations can be considered as only a starting point for more exact researches.

In Pullman's work, a greater number of π electrons are taken into consideration, but only Pauling and Wheland's approximation is used.

All the authors have seriously discussed the choice of parameters but end with different choices. The distribution of charge and bond orders is given, but the most interesting subject here seems to be the examination of orbital energies.

The following tables allow comparison of Grabe's results.

We see that, for neutral molecules, the two methods agree fairly well for occupied orbitals but much less well for unoccupied orbitals.

For the radical DPNH$^+$, the differences are already significant for occupied orbitals, as might be expected.

Be this as it may, both methods show DPN$^+$ is a much greater acceptor of electrons than DPNH, in agreement with the fact that DPN$^+$ acts as an oxidising agent and DPNH as a reducing agent.

	DPN$^+$		DPNH		DPNH$^+$	
	P and P	P and W	P and P	P and W	P and P	P and W
Occupied orbitals	-0.913	-1.030	-0.603	-0.635	-0.846	-0.635
	-0.700	-0.790	-0.515	-0.602	-0.745	-0.602
	-0.694	-0.780	-0.487	-0.540	-0.708	-0.540
			-0.414	-0.489	-0.667	-0.489
Un-occupied orbitals	-0.265	-0.655	-0.006	-0.370		
	-0.246	-0.585	$+0.021$	-0.308		

Energies in atomic units   { P and P = Pariser and Parr
P and W = Pauling and Wheland

Pullman's results agree with Grabe's for DPNH, FAD and FADH$_2$, but differ significantly for DPN$^+$.

E. *Structure of the Porphyrines:*
The Particular Case of Cytochrome

The following types of porphyrines

Porphine   Chlorine

have been studied using Pauling and Wheland's approximation [425] and the free electron method [426].

We shall only discuss here Seely's work which studied six porphyric structures.

In this article, there are calculations both including and neglecting overlap integrals. Contrary to expectation, the results obtained when overlap integrals are included are less appropriate in the study of spectroscopic properties of porphyrines and hence we shall only discuss the case where they are neglected.

The table opposite shows how the calculated frequencies correspond to observed frequency (the value of β was chosen empirically — the calculations having been made by assuming that the nitrogen atoms supply six π electrons; the spectra used correspond to zinc complexes).

It can be seen that the overall agreement is good and the table interprets well the bathochrome or hypsochrome displacements produced as one goes from one porphyrine to another. Moreover, the authors have been able to attribute assignations to different band systems, i.e. to identify the nature of the electron transitions which produce them.

	Wavelengths in mμ	
	Calculated	Observed
Porphine	603	620
	433	422
Chlorine	616	625
	569	540
	467	420
	440	400
OPPTHP	742	750
	635	600
	354	396
	328	320
ADJTHP	560	602
	500	495
	449	415
	409	?
HHP	619	642
	457	420
	442	405
	352	365

In a similar manner, Pullman, Spanjaard and Berthier[427] have studied porphine and iron complexes. These complexes are frequently classed in two families: those called ionic, as in haemoglobin and myloglobin which have a large number of "unmarried electrons", and covalent complexes such as oxyhaemoglobin and the ferrocytochromes C which have at most one unmarried electron. In the first case, it is assumed that the $3d$ orbitals of iron do not take part in the bonds while they do in the second case. The electron configuration of the M-shell of atomic iron is usually taken as

$$(3s)^2 \quad (3p)^6 \quad (3d)^6 \quad (4s)^2 .$$

In Fe^{++}, the $4s$ orbital is assumed to be empty, six electrons occupying the $3d$ state. In Fe^{+++} the number of electrons occupying the $3d$ state is reduced to five. Measurement of magnetic susceptability and electron resonance of porphyric complexes lead to the adoption of the following order of the d orbitals[428]

$$3d_{xy}, 3d_{yz}, 3d_{zx}, 3d_{x^2}, 3d_{x^2-y^2},$$

where the z-axis is perpendicular to the plane of the molecule.

Now, it can be easily seen from the symmetry of the π orbitals of porphine that only the orbitals $3d_{xy}$, $3d_{yz}$ and $4p_z$ can enter into combination with one another.

The porphine group contains 26π electrons and a basis of 24 orbitals. The ferrous or ferric ionic complexes correspond then to systems of 26π electrons and a base of 25 orbitals (including the $4p_z$ orbital) which reduces to saying that the ferrous–ferric transition occurs on the iron atom; the covalent ferrous complexes correspond to 27 orbitals and 30 electrons (4 from orbitals $3d_{xy}$ and $3d_{yz}$); here it is assumed that the ferrous–ferric transition does affect the π system.

By choosing convenient parameters, the authors found that in ferrocytochrome the last occupied level is -0.085γ (overlap integrals were included). This is a very high value for an occupied level. Ferrocytochrome C, therefore, will be a generous electron donor and therefore an active reducing agent.

In ferricytochrome, this level becomes half empty. Although an empty level, this is a low level. Ferricytochrome C will, therefore, be a good oxidiser. Hence, the results of quantal calculations give a good interpretation of experimental data by specifying the nature of this important group of enzymes.

F. Eventual Role of Carotenide in the Mechanism of Photo-synthesis

Platt[429] has attempted to see whether the methods of quantum molecular physics can be applied to illustrate the role of carotene in photo-synthesis.

This question was posed by B. L. Strehler (Rhythmic and Synthetic Processes in Growth, D. Rudnick, Princeton (1957), p. 171) as the carotenides almost always accompany chlorophyll, their speed of formation follows that of chlorophyll and the presence of these carotenides modify the structure of characteristic bands of chlorophyll, as if there were an interaction between these molecules.

More exactly, Strehler inquires whether the carotenides, by trapping energy received by the chlorophyll, may not act as mediators in a transfer of electrons between a donor and a receiver.

At first sight, this process seems impossible, as the first excited level of a carotenide is higher than the corresponding level in chlorophyll. However, a carotenide contains a very long polarisable chain:

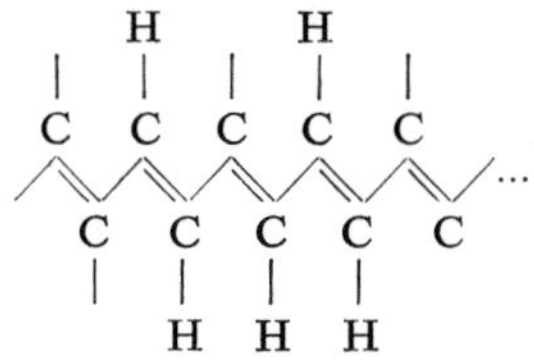

Instances are known where the effects of polarisation make a considerable change in the position of the first excited state with respect to the ground state. This is how the effect of solvents can modify, by some thousands of angströms, the position of the first absorption band system of merocyanines of Brooker[430]. A mesomeric argument allows the origin of this phenomenon to be understood.

For one such cyanine, there is a unique Kékulé formula

$$O=C—CH=CH—CH=CH—\cdots—CH=CH—NH_2$$

and a favoured ionic formula

$$-O—C=CH—CH=CH\cdots CH—CH=NH_2^+$$

as the nitrogen of NH_2 yields two π electrons to the conjugate system and oxygen only one. If Ψ_I and Ψ_{II} are the functions associated with these two functions respectively, we might try to represent the molecule by the very simple function

$$\Psi = a\Psi_I + b\Psi_{II}.$$

Using obvious notation, the secular equation is

$$(H_{II} - E)(H_{II\,II} - E) = H_{I\,II}$$

if the overlap integrals are neglected.

If the energies H_{II} and $H_{II\,II}$ are very different, $H_{I\,II}$ is small and obviously a is large and b is small for the ground state and the opposite is true for the excited state. The energy of the ground state is then near H_{II} and the energy of the excited state near $H_{II\,II}$. If the substance is placed in a polar solvent S, we have to consider the energy associated with the formula

$$\overset{\leftarrow+}{\underset{S}{}}\ ^-O—C=CH\cdots CH=CH—NH_2^+\ \overset{\leftarrow+}{\underset{S}{}}$$

The stabilising effect of the solvent which varies with its polarity will bring the values of H_{II} and H_{IIII} together and hence will bring the excited level and the ground state together.

In the case of carotenides, Platt supposes that the effect of the solvent may be set going by the presence of a molecule, D, a donor of electrons and molecule, A, an acceptor of electrons, the set forming a complex by a transfer of charge of the type

$$D \diagup\!\diagdown\!\diagup\!\diagdown\!\diagup\!\diagdown\!\diagup\!\diagdown\!\diagup A$$

Besides this formula, we are also lead to consider the formula

$$D^+ - \diagdown\!\diagup\!\diagdown\!\diagup\!\diagdown\!\diagup\!\diagdown\!\diagup + A^-$$

and the same reasoning applies[431].

This indicates that the first excited level of this complex may be lower than that of chlorophyll and that in the first excited state it will have a structure rather like the ionic structure.

Following Platt, therefore, we may assume that the photons absorbed by the chlorophyll can be trapped by molecules of a carotenide complex which is in its first excited level. Moreover, it may act as first singlet level or first triplet level. The excited state of this complex can be dissociative, forming free D^+ and A^- and regenerating the carotenide. *The latter will then act as a reservoir of energy and a mediator in the transfer of an electron from D to A.*

If the state is triplet, without being dissociative, it has time to receive a new photon and the energy of the two photons thus accumulated causes the dissociation which explains why photosynthesis seems to carry out reactions whose energy is greater than the energy of a single photon.

45. STRUCTURE OF NUCLEIC ACIDS. VARIOUS STUDIES

We shall finish by giving some references to works discussing the structure of nucleic acids[432], puric bases[433], pyrimidic bases[434], vitamins and retinene[435].

References

1. E. A. HYLLERAAS, *Z. f. Phys.*, **71** (1931), 739. G. JAFFE, *Z. f. Phys.*, **87** (1934), 535. E. TELLER, *Z. f. Phys.*, **61** (1930), 458. S. K. CHAKRAVARTY, *Phil. Mag.*, **28** (1939), 423. D. R. BATES, K. LEDSHAM and A. L. STEWART, *Phi. Trans. Roy. Soc.*, A **246** (1953), 215.
2. H. M. JAMES, *J. Chem. Phys.*, **3** (1935), 9.
3. V. GUILLEMIN and C. ZENER, *Proc. Nat. Acad. Sci.*, **15** (1929), 314.
4. L. PAULING, *Chem. Rev.*, **5** (1928), 173.
5. B. N. FINKELSTEIN and G. E. HOROWITZ, *Z. f. Phys.*, **48** (1928), 118.
6. B. N. DICKENSON, *J. Chem. Phys.*, **1** (1933), 317.
7. A. C. HURLEY, *Proc. Roy. Soc.*, A **226** (1954), 179.
9. S. A. BOYS, *Proc. Roy. Soc.*, A **200** (1950), 542. A. MECKLER, *J. Chem. Phys.*, **21** (1953), 1750. C. MUELLER and J. CAHILL, *Texas J. Science*, **8** (1956), 147.
10. F. A. MATSEN, *J. Chem. Phys.*, **21** (1953), 928.
11. See for example: *Théorie de la quantification dans la nouvelle mécanique*, L. DE BROGLIE, Paris (1932), 187.
12. WILSON, *Phys. Rev.*, **48** (1935), 536.
13. ROOTHAAN, Colloque international sur le calcul des fonctions d'onde moléculaires (Editions du C.N.R.S., Paris, 1957).
14. H. SHULL and P. O. LÖWDIN, *J. Chem. Phys.*, **23** (1955), 1565.
15. D. R. HARTREE and A. L. INGMAN, *Memoirs and Proc. of Manchester Literary and Phil. Soc.*, **77** (1933), 69.
16. C. A. COULSON, *Trans. Far. Soc.*, **33** (1937), 1479.
17. H. A. AGHAJANIAN, *Quarterly Progress Report* (M.I.T. Slater Group), 15 April and 15 July, 1957.
18. N. ROSEN, *Phys. Rev.*, **38** (1931), 2099.
19. E. F. GURNEE and J. L. MAGEE, *J. Chem. Phys.*, **18** (1950), 142.
20. T. INUI, *Proc. Math. Soc. Japan*, **20** (1938), 770; **23** (1941), 992.
21. C. A. COULSON and I. FISCHER, *Phil. Mag.*, **40** (1949), 386.
22. C. R. MUELLER and H. EYRING, *J. Chem. Phys.*, **19** (1951), 1495.
23. J. LENNARD-JONES and J. A. POPLE, *Proc. Roy. Soc.*, A **210** (1951), 190.
24. J. O. HIRSCHFELDER and J. W. LINNETT, *J. Chem. Phys.*, **18** (1950), 130.
25. A. A. FROST and J. BRAUNSTEIN, *J. Chem. Phys.*, **19** (1951), 1133.
26. H. SHULL and F. O. ELLISON, *J. Chem. Phys.*, **19** (1951), 1215.
27. D. P. CRAIG, *Colloque international sur le calcul des fonctions d'onde moléculaires* (Editions du C.N.R.S., Paris, 1958).
28. I. FISHER-HJALMARS, *Colloque international sur le calcul des fonctions d'onde moléculaires* (Editions du C.N.R.S., Paris, 1958).
29. W. MOFFITT, *Proc. Roy. Soc.*, A **210** (1951), 245.
30. W. BINGEL, *Z. Naturforsch.*, A **12** (1957), 59.
31. H. PREUSS, *Z. Naturforsch.*, A **13** (1958), 363.

32. G.HERZBERG, *Spectra of diatomic molecules*, Van Nostrand, New York (1950), p. 343.

33. J.W.LINNETT, *J. Chem. Soc.* (1956), p. 275.

34. H.EYRING, J.WALTER and G.E.KIMBALL, *Quantum Chemistry*, John Wiley, New York (1957), p. 210.

35. C.C.J.ROOTHAAN, *Rev. Modern Phys.*, **23** (1951), 69.

36. G.BERTHIER, *J. Chimie Phys.* (1954), 363. J.A.POPLE and R.K.NESBET, *J. Chem. Phys.*, **22** (1954), 571.

37. R.LEFEBVRE and C.MOSER, *J. Chimie Phys.* (1956), 393. R.LEFEBVRE, *J. Chimie Phys.* (1957), 168. H.BRION, R.LEFEBVRE and C.MOSER, *J. Chimie Phys.* (1957), 363. R.LEFEBVRE, *Colloque international sur le calcul des fonctions d'ondes moléculaires*, Editions du C.N.R.S. (1958).

38. R.MACWEENY, *Proc. Roy. Soc.*, A **235** (1956), 496; A **237** (1956), 355.

39. S.BRATOZ, *Calcul des fonctions d'onde moléculaire* (1958), p. 287 (Editions du C.N.R.S., Paris).

40. R.S.MULLIKEN, *J. Chem. Phys.*, **23** (1955), 1833, 2338.

41. R.DAUDEL, A.LAFORGUE and C.VROELANT, *J. Chimie Phys.*, **49** (1952), 544.

42. J.FAULKNER, *J. Chem. Phys.*, **27** (1957), 369.

43. J.FAULKNER, *J. Chem. Phys.*, **27** (1957), 369.

44. C.W.SCHERR, *J. Chem. Phys.*, **23** (1955), 569.

45. M.KOTANI, Y.MIZUNO, K.KAYAMA and E.ISHIGURO, *J. Phys. Soc. Japan*, **12** (1957), 707.

46. J.EVE, *Proc. Roy. Soc.*, A **246** (1958), 582.

47. R.C.SAHNI, *J. Chem. Phys.*, **25** (1956), 332.

48. M.KRAUSS, *J. Chem. Phys.*, **28** (1958), 1021.

49. H.BRION, *Cahiers de Physique*, **12** (1958), 100.

50. A.J.FREEMAN, *J. Chem. Phys.*, **28** (1958), 230.

51. S.ABURTO, R.DAUDEL, R.GALLARDO, R.LEFEBVRE and R.MUNOZ, *C.R.*, **247** (1958), 1859.

52. J.HIGUCHI, *J. Chem. Phys.*, **22** (1954), 1399.

53. K.TOMITA and K.FUKUI, *Prog. Th. Phys.*, **10** (1953), 362.

54. R.C.SANHI, *Trans. Far. Soc.*, **49** (1953), 1245.

55. E.ISHIGURO, K.KAYAMA, M.KOTANI and Y.MIZUNO, *J. Phys. Soc. Japan*, **12** (1957), 1355.

56. M.ROUX, S.BESNAINOU and R.DAUDEL, *J. Chimie Phys.*, (1956), 218; (1956), 939; and M.ROUX, *J. Chimie Phys.*, (1958), 754.

57. I.FISCHER, *Arkiv. für Fysik*, **5** (1952), 349.

58. W.MOFFITT, *Proc. Roy. Soc.*, A **210** (1951), 224, 245.

59. A.C.HURLEY, *Proc. Phys. Soc.*, A **68** (1955), 149; A **69** (1956), 49.

60. A.C.HURLEY, *Proc. Phys. Soc.*, A **69** (1956), 301.

61. W.BINGEL, *Z. Naturforsch*, A **12** (1957), 59.

62. H.PREUSS, *Z. Naturforsch*, A **13** (1958), 363.

63. S.F.BOYS, G.B.COOK, C.M.REEVES and I.SHAVITT, *Nature*, **178** (1956), 1207.

64. L.GERÖ, G.HERZBERG and R.SCHMID, *Phys. Rev.*, **52** (1937), 467.

65. W.H.BRAGG and W.L.BRAGG, *Proc. Roy. Soc.*, A **89** (1913), 277. W.ENRENBERG, *Z. Krist.*, **63** (1926), 320.

66. L.PAULING and L.O.BROCKWAY, *J. Amer. Chem. Soc.*, **59** (1937), 1227.

67. E.H.EYSTER, *J. Chem. Phys.*, **6** (1938), 580.

68. L.O.BROCKWAY, *Rev. of Mod. Phys.*, **8** (1936), 231.
69. H.VERIEGER, *Physikal. Z.*, **38** (1937), 83.
70. S.H.BAUER and J.Y.BEACH, *J. Am. Chem. Soc.*, **64** (1942), 1142.
71. J.M.ROBERTSON, *J. Chimie Phys.*, **47** (1950), 47.
72. T.K.SYRKIN and M.E.DYATKINA, *Structure of Molecules*, Interscience, New York, 1950, p. 73.
73. C.A.BURRUS and W.GORDY, *Phys. Rev.*, **52** (1953), 274.
74. M.LISTER and L.E.SUTTON, *Trans. Far. Soc.*, **37** (1941), 393.
75. M.T.ROGERS and R.A.SPURR, *J. Am. Chem. Soc.*, **69** (1947), 2102.
76. L.PAULING, *The nature of the chemical bond*, Cornell University Press, Ithaca, New York (1944), p. 79.
77. L.PAULING, *The nature of the Chemical bond*, p.79.
78. J.M.ROBERTSON, *Annual Rep. Prog. Chem.*, **39** (1942), 95.
79. R.MECKE and W.BAUMANN, *Physikal, Z.*, **33** (1932), 833.
80. L.PAULING and L.O.BROCKWAY, *J. Am. Chem. Soc.*, **59** (1937), 13.
81. Y.K.SYRKIN and M.E.DIATKINA, *Structure of molecules*, p. 73.
82. D.P.STEVENSON and J.Y.BEACH, *J. Am. Chem. Soc.*, **60** (1938), 2872.
83. J.M.O'GORMAN, after ALLEN and SUTTON (*loc. cit.* ref. 131).
84. S.H.BAUER, *J. Am. Chem. Soc.*, **69** (1947), 3104.
85. L.PAULING and L.O.BROCKWAY, *J. Am. Chem. Soc.*, **159** (1937), 13.
86. L.PAULING, *The nature of the chemical bond*, p. 247.
87. S.CLUESSON, J.DONOHUE and V.S.SCHOMAKER, *J. Chem. Phys.*, **16** (1948).
88. J.A.A.KETELAAR and K.J.PALMER, *J. Am. Chem. Soc.*, **59** (1937), 2629.
89. L.O.BROCKWAY, *Rev. Mod. Phys.*, **8** (1936), 231.
90. L.O.BROCKWAY, *Rev. Mod. Phys.*, **8** (1936), 231; V.SCHOMAKER and R.A.SPURR, *J.Am.Chem.Soc.*, **6A** (1942), 1184; D.H.COLES, E.S.ELYASH and J.O'GORMAN, *Phys. Rev.*, **72** (1947), 973.
91. L.O.BROCKWAY (*loc. cit.*) and C.FINBACK and O.HASSEL, *Arch. Math. Nat.*, **44**, no 3.
92. D.P.STEVENSON and J.Y.BEACH, *J. Chem. Phys.*, **6**, (1938), 75.
93. J.A.HUGILL,I.E.COOP and L.E.SUTTON, *Trans. Far. Soc.*, **34** (1938), 1518.
94. O.HASSEL and T.TAARLAND, *Tidsskr. Kemi. Bergv.*, **26** (1946), 152.
95. L.O. BROCKWAY, *Rev. Mod. Phys.*, **8**, (1936).
96. R.A.SPURR and V.SCHOMAKER, *J. Am. Chem. Soc.*, **64** (1942), 2693.
97. J.M.ROBERTSON, *J. Chim. Phys.*, **47** (1950), 47.
98. D.P.STEVENSON, J.LU VALLE and V.SCHOMAKER, *J. Am. Chem. Soc.*, **61** (1939), 2508.
99. D.P.STEVENSON, H.D.BURNHAM and V.SCHOMAKER, *J. Am. Chem. Soc.*, **61** (1959), 2928.
100. V.SCHOMAKER and J.H.O'GORMAN, *J. Am. Chem. Soc.*, **69** (1947), 2638.
101. J.H.O'GORMAN, after ALLEN and SUTTON (*loc. cit.*; ref. 131).
102. J.E.LU VALLE, after ALLEN and SUTTON.
103. V.SCHOMAKER and L.PAULING, *J. Am. Chem. Soc.*, **61** (1939), 1769.
104. S.H.BAUER and J.M.HASTINGS, *J. Am. Chem. Soc.*, **64** (1942), 2686.
105. H.A.LEVY and L.O.BROCKWAY, *J. Am. Chem. Soc.*, **59** (1937), 2085.
106. S.H.BAUER and J.Y.BEACH, *J. Am. Chem. Soc.*, **63** (1941), 1394.
107. J.S.BROADLEY and J.M.ROBERTSON, *Nature*, **164** (1949), 915.
108. J.S.BROADLEY and J.M.ROBERTSON, *Nature*, **164** (1949), 915.
109. A.J.STOSICK, *J. Am. Chem. Soc.* (1938), **61** (1939), 1127.

220   REFERENCES

110. K.J.PALMER, *J. Am. Chem. Soc.*, **60** (1938), 2360.
111. J.WASER and V.SCHOMAKER, *J. Am. Chem. Soc.*, **65** (1943), 1451.
112. S.H.BAUER and J.Y.BEACH, *J. Am. Chem. Soc.*, **64** (1942), 1142.
113. V.SCHOMAKER, after ALLEN and SUTTON (ref. 131).
114. D.P.STEVENSON and V.SCHOMAKER, *J. Am. Chem. Soc.*, **62**, (1940) 1913.
115. C.S.LU and V.SCHOMAKER, same source as 116.
116. A.H.GREGG, G.C.HAMPSON, G.I.JENKINS, P.L.F.JONES and L.E.SUTTON, *Trans. Far. Soc.*, **33** (1957), 852.
117. H.A.SKINNER and L.E.SUTTON, *Trans. Far. Soc.*, **40** (1944), 164.
118. O.BASTIANSEN and H.VIERVOLD, *Acta Chemi. Scand.*, **2** (1948), 702.
119. D.P.STEVENSON and R.A.COOLEY, *J. Am. Chem. Soc.*, **62** (1940), 2477, and J.K.PALMER, *J. Am. Chem. Soc.*, **60**, 2360.
120. L.O.BROCKWAY, *Rev. Mod. Phys.*, **8** (1936), 231.
121. H.A.SKINNER, Thesis (Oxford) (1941).
122. L.O.BROCKWAY, *Rev. Mod. Phys.*, **8** (1936), 231; H.A.LEVY and L.O. BROCKWAY, *J. Am. Chem. Soc.*, **59** (1937), 1662; S.H.BAUER and J.Y. BEACH, *J. Am. Chem. Soc.*, **63** (1941), 1344; O.BASTIANSEN, *Tidsskr. Kemi Bergv. Met*, **6** (1946), 1.
123. H.A.SKINNER and L.E.SUTTON, *Trans. Far. Soc.*, **40** (1944), 164.
124. J.Y.BEACH and D.P.STEVENSON, *J. Am. Chem. Soc.*, **61** (1939), 2643.
125. R.E.RUNDLE, after ALLEN and SUTTON, ref. 131.
126. J.K.PALMER, *J. Am. Chem. Soc.*, **60** (1938), 2360.
127. G.C.HAMPSON and A.J.STOSICK, *J. Am. Chem. Soc.*, **60** (1938), 1814.
128. L.O.BROCKWAY and J.Y.BEACH, *J. Am. Chem. Soc.*, **60** (1938), 1836.
129. O.BASTIANSEN and L.HASSEL, *Tidsskr. Kemi Bergv. Met*, **6** (1946), 71.
130. J.DONOHUE, G.L.HUMPHREY and V.SCHOMAKER, *J. Am. Chem. Soc.*, **67** (1945), 322.
131. P.W.ALLEN and L.E.SUTTON, *Acta Crystallographica*, **3** (1950), 46.
132. TA YOU WU, *J. Chem. Phys.*, **22** (1954), 1125.
133. L.PAULING, see for example: *The nature of the chemical bond.*
134. L.PAULING and J.SHERMAN, *J. Am. Chem. S.*, **59** (1937), 1450.
135. C.A.COULSON, *Valence*, Clarendon Press, Oxford (1952), p. 160.
136. D.P.CRAIG, *Calcul des fonctions d'onde moléculaires* (Editions du C.N.R.S., Paris (1958), p. 63).
137. MACCOLL, *Trans. Faraday Soc.*, **46** (1950), 369.
138. C.A.COULSON, *Proc. Camb. Phil. Soc.*, **33** (1937), 111.
139. R.S.MULLIKEN, *J. Am. Chem. Soc.*, **72** (1950), 4493.
140. R.S.MULLIKEN, *J. Phys. Chem.*, **56** (1952), 295.
141. A.D.WALSH, *J. Chem. Soc.*, (1953), 2260 to 2331.
142. P.J.WHEATLEY, *J. Chem. Soc.*, (1956), 4514.
143. S.ODIOT, thèse sciences, Paris (1956), *Revue d'Optique.*
144. *Handbook of Chem. and Phys. Chem.*, Rubber Co., Cleveland, (1958), 1742.
145. A.ALBERT, *Acridine*, E.Arnold, London (1951), p. 114.
146. C.A.COULSON, *La liaison chimique* (Edition du C.N.R.S., Paris (1950), p. 12).
147. C.A.COULSON, *Trans. Far. Soc.*, **33** (1937), 388.
148. R.E.HONIG, *J. Chem. Phys.*, **16** (1948), 105.
149. S.BESNAINOU and M.ROUX, *J. Chim. Phys.*, (1959), 250.
150. R.S.MULLIKEN, *J. Chim. Phys.*, **46** (1949), 675.

151. I. M. MILLS, *Molecular physics*, **1** (1958), 99.
152. C. R. MUELLER, *J. Am. Chem. Soc.*, **74** (1952), 3466.
153. K. FUNABASHI and J. L. MAGEE, *J. Chem. Phys.*, **26** (1957), 407.
154. R. A. BUCKINGHAM, H. S. W. MASSEY and E. R. TIBBS, *Proc. Roy. Soc.*, A **178** (1941), 119.
155. K. E. BANYARD and N. H. MARCH, *Acta Crystallographica*, **9** (1956), 385.
156. G. THOMER, *Phys. Z.*, **38** (1937), 48.
157. M. J. M. BERNAL, *Proc. Phys. Soc.*, A **66** (1953), 514.
158. I. M. MILLS, *Molecular Physics*, **1** (1958), 99 and 107.
159. C. CARTER, *Proc. Roy. Soc.*, A **235** (1956), 321.
160. S. KOIDE, H. SEKIYAMA and T. NAGASHIMA, *J. Phys. Soc. Japan*, **12** (1957), 1016.
161. E. KAPUY, *Acta Physica Hungaricae*, **9** (1959), 445.
162. N. H. MARCH, *Proc. Camb. Phil. Soc.*, **48** (1952), 665.
163. M. KARPLUS and D. H. ANDERSON, *Chem. Phys.*, **30** (1959), 6.
164. T. FELDMAN, J. ROMANKO and H. L. WELSH, *Canad. J. Phys.*, **33** (1955), 138.
165. G. E. HANSEN and D. M. DENNISON, *J. Chem. Phys.*, **20** (1952), 313.
166. L. PAULING and O. BROCKWAY, *J. Am. Chem. Soc.*, **59** (1937), 1223.
167. See 166. and J. Y. BEACH and D. P. STEVENSON, *J. Am. Chem. Soc.*, **60** (1938), 475; J. Y. BEACH and J. WALTER, *J. Chem. Phys.*, **8** (1940), 303.
168. O. HASSEL and B. OTTAR, *Arch. Math. Naturv.*, B **45** (1942), no. 10; O. HASSEL and H. VIERVOLL, *Acta Chemica Scandinavia*, **1** (1947), 149.
169. See, for example, M. G. EVANS, *Proc. Roy. Soc.*, A **207** (1951), 1.
170. After G. W. WHELAND, *Resonance in organic chemistry*, John Wiley, New York (1955).
171. G. G. HALL, *Proc. Roy. Soc.*, A **205** (1951), 541.
172. R. D. BROWN, *J. Chem. Soc.*, (1953), 2615.
173. M. J. S. DEWAR and R. PETITT, *J. Chem. Soc.*, (1954), 1625.
174. J. LENNARD-JONES and G. G. HALL, *Trans. Faraday Soc.*, **48** (1952), 581.
175. C. SANDORFY and R. DAUDEL, *C.R. Acad. Sci.*, **238** (1954), 93.
176. C. SANDORFY, *Canadian Jour. Chemistry*, **33** (1955), 1337.
177. H. YOSHIZUMI, *Trans. Faraday Soc.*, **53** (1957), 125.
178. A. JULG, *J. Chimie Physique* (1956), 548.
179. R. S. PITZER and E. CATALANO, *J. Am. Chem. Soc.*, **78** (1956), 4844. See also: K. S. PITZER and W. E. DONATH, *Texas J. Science*, **8** (1956), 150.
180. W. HEITLER, *J. Chimie Physique*, (1957), 265.
181. J. E. KILPATRICK and R. S. PITZER, *J. Chem. Phys.*, **14** (1946), 463.
182. O. BASTIANSEN and O. HASSEL, *Tids. Kjemi, Bergv. Met.*, **6** (1946), 71.
183. M. MASHIMA, *J. Chem. Phys.*, **22** (1954), 1785.
184. M. SIMONETTA, G. FAVINI and P. BELTRAME, *Rendiconti, Ist. Lombardo Scienze e Lettere*, **91** (1957), 311.
185. J. D. DUNITZ and V. SCHOMAKER, *J. Chem. Phys.*, **20** (1952), 1703.
186. B. D. SAKSENA, *Proc. Ind. Acad.*, **10** A (1939), 449.
187. C. A. COULSON and W. MOFFITT, *J. Chem. Soc.*, **15** (1947), 151; *Phil. Mag.*, **40** (1949), 1.
189. See, for example: O. HASSEL, *Quarterly Rev.*, **7** (1953), 221.
190. VAN VLECK and SHERMAN, *Rev. Mod. Physics*, **7** (1935), 167.
191. MOFFITT, *Proc. Roy. Soc.*, A **196** (1949), 524.
192. ROBINSON, *J. Chem. Phys.*, **17** (1949), 1022.

193. LENNARD-JONES and POPLE, *Proc. Roy. Soc.*, A **202** (1950), 166.

194. POPLE, *Proc. Roy. Soc.*, A **202** (1950), 323.

195. A.B.F.DUNCAN and J.A.POPLE, *Trans. Far. Soc.*, **49** (1953), 217.

196. H.KAPLAN, *J. Chem. Phys.*, **26** (1957), 1704.

197. J.HIGUCHI, *J. Chem. Phys.*, **24** (1956), 535.

198. A.B.F.DUNCAN, *J. Chem. Phys.*, **27** (1957), 423.

199. M.P.BARNETT and C.A.COULSON, *Trans. Roy. Soc.*, A **243** (1951), 221.

200. S.O.LUNDQVIST and P.O.LÖWDIN, *Arkiv. Fysik*, **3** (1951), 147.

201. R.K.NESBET, Quart. Prog. Report, Solid State and Molecular Theory Group, *M.I.T.*, October 15 (1955), 4.

202. H.SUN and G.L.WEISSLER, *J. Chem. Phys.*, **23** (1955), 1160.

203. F.O.ELLISON and H.SHULL, *J. Chem. Phys.*, **23** (1955), 2348.

204. W.C.HAMILTON, *J. Chem. Phys.*, **26** (1957), 345.

205. K.FUNABASHI and J.L.MAGEE, *J. Chem. Phys.*, **26** (1957), 407.

206. K.E.BANYARD and N.H.MARCH, *J. Chem. Phys.*, **27** (1957), 977.

207. K.E.BANYARD and N.H.MARCH, *Acta Crist.*, **9** (1956), 385.

208. S.F.BOYS, G.B.COOK, C.M.REEVES and I.SHAVITT, *Nature*, **178** (1956), 1207.

209. W.KOLOS, *Acta Phys. Polonica*, **14** (1955), 471.

210. G.HERZBERG, *Infrared and Raman Spectra f Polyatomic Molecules*, New York (1945).

211. V.M.McCONAGLIRE and H.H.NIELSEN, *J. Chem. Phys.*, **21** (1953), 1836.

212. G.W.WHELAND and P.S.K.CHEN, *J. Chem. Phys.*, **24** (1956), 67.

213. M.SIMONETTA and A.VACIAGO, *Il nuovo Cimento*, **5** (1957), 587.

214. HEATH and LINETT, *Trans. Far. Soc.*, **45** (1949), 33.

215. N.V.COHAN and C.A.COULSON, *Trans. Far. Soc.*, **52** (1956), 1163.

216. DUCHESNE and OTTELET, *J. Phys.*, **11** (1950), 119.

217. J.C.LORQUET and H.LEFEBVRE-BRION, *J. Chimie Phys.*, **57** (1960), 85.

218. P.BELTRAME and M.SIMONETTA, *Ist. Lombardo di Scienze e Lettere*, **91** (1957), 849.

219. W.S.GALLOWAY and E.F.BARKER, *J. Chem. Phys.*, **10** (1942), 88.

220. R.G.PARR and B.L.CRAWFORD, *J. Chem. Phys.*, **16** (1948), 526.

221. M.GOEPPERT-MAYER and A.L.SKLAR, *J. Chem. Phys.*, **6** (1938), 645.

222. R.S.MULLIKEN, *J. Chimie Phys.*, **46** (1949), 497, 675.

223. P.G.WILKINSON and H.L.JOHNSTON, *J. Chem. Phys.*, **18** (1950), 190.

224. W.C.PRICE and W.T.TUTTE, *Proc. Roy. Soc.*, A **174** (1940), 207.

225. H.SPONER and P.O.LÖWDIN, *J. Phys. Radium*, **15** (1954), 607.

226. C.MOSER, *Trans. Far. Soc.*, **49** (1953), 1239.

227. R.PARISER and P.PARR, *J. Chem. Phys.*, **21** (1953), 466, 767.

228. R.PARR, *J. Chem. Phys.*, **20** (1952), 1499.

229. R.MacWEENY, *Proc. Roy. Soc.*, A **227** (1955), 288; G.G.HALL, *Trans. Far. Soc.*, **50** (1954), 773; F.PERADEJORDI, *Comptes Rendus*, **243** (1956), 276; F.G.FUMI and R.PARR, *J. Chem. Phys.*, **21** (1953), 1864.

230. P.O.LÖWDIN, *J. Chem. Phys.*, **18** (1950), 365.

231. S.C.ABRAHAMS and J.M.ROBERTSON, *Acta Cryst.*, **2** (1949), 65.

232. A.O.McINTOSH, J.M.ROBERTSON and C.VANDT, *Nature*, **169** (1952), 322.

234. F.SONDHEIMER, *Tetrahedron Letters*, no. 3 (1959), 3.

235. I.L.KARLE, *J. Chem. Phys.*, **20** (1952), 63; K.HEDBERG, after R.L.LIVINGSTON, *Ann. Rev. Phys. Chem.*, **5** (1954), 395.

236. C.A.COULSON, L.J.SCHAAD and L.BURNELLE, *Proc. of 1957 Conference on Carbon*, Pergamon Press, p. 27.
237. C.A.COULSON and G.S.RUSHBROOKE, *Proc. Camb. Phil. Soc.*, **36** (1940), 193.
238. H.C.LONGUET-HIGGINS, *J. Chem. Phys.*, **18** (1950), 265.
239. M.J.S.DEWAR and H.C.LONGUET-HIGGINS, *Proc. Roy. Soc.*, A **214** (1952), 482.
240. I.SAMUEL, *C.R.*, **247** (1958), 293.
241. G.W.WHELAND, *Resonance in organic chemistry*, John Wiley, New York, 1955.
242. For more on this subject, see: D.P.CRAIG, *Kékulé symposium*. Butterworths, 1958, p. 20.
243. After B.PULLMAN, *Proc. of the third Conference on Carbon*, Pergamon Press (1959), p.3.
244. R.S.MULLIKEN, C.A.RIEKE and W.G.BROWN, *J. Am. Chem. Soc.*, **63** (1941), 41; J.VAN DRANEN, Thesis, Amsterdam (1951); C.A.COULSON, *Valence*, Oxford (1952); C.A.COULSON and S.L.ALTMANN, *Trans. Far. Soc.*, **48** (1952), 293.
245. After R.DAUDEL, R.LEFEBVRE and C.MOSER, *Quantum chemistry, methods and applications*, Interscience (1959), 189.
246. C.A.COULSON and G.S.RUSHBROOKE, *Proc. Camb. Phil. Soc.*, **36** (1940), 193.
247. C.P.SMYTH, *J. Org. Chem.*, **1** (1936), 17; K.B.MCALPINE and C.P.SMYTH, *J. Am. Chem. Soc.*, **55** (1933), 453; N.B.HANNAY and C.P.SMYTH, *J. Am. Chem. Soc.*, **65** (1943), 1931 and **68** (1946), 244; H.LUMBROSO, *C.R.*, **225** (1947), 1003 and **228** (1949), 1425; A.LAFORGUE, *J. Chimie Phys.*, **46** (1949), 568.
248. C.SANDORFY, N.Q.TRINH, A.LAFORGUE and R.DAUDEL, *J. Chim. Phys.* (1949), 44.
249. Estimé par A. et B.PULLMAN, *Les theories éléctroniques de la chimie organique*, Masson (1952), 402.
250. G.W.WHELAND and D.E.MANN, *J. Chem. Phys.*, **17** (1949), 264.
251. A.PULLMAN, B.PULLMAN, E.D.BERGMANN, G.BERTHIER, E.FISCHER, Y.HIRSHBERG and J.PONTIS, *J. Chim. Phys.*
252. N.Q.CHAKO, *J. Chem. Phys.*, **2** (1934), 644.
253. R.S.MULLIKEN and C.A.RIEKE, *Rep. Progress Phys.*, **8** (1941), 231; R.S.MULLIKEN, *J. Chem. Phys.*, **7** (1939), 14.
254. C.A.COULSON, *Proc. Roy. Soc.*, **60** (1948), 257.
255. R.PASSERINI and I.G.ROSS, *J. Chem. Phys.*, **22** (1954), 1012.
256. D.S.MCCLURE, *J. Chem. Phys.*, **22** (1954), 1668.
257. E.AHMED and D.J.W.CRUICKSHANK, *Acta Cryst.*, **5** (1952), 852.
258. C.A.COULSON, *Proc. Roy. Soc.*, A **169** (1939), 413.
259. R.DAUDEL, *Adv. Chem. Phys.*, **1** (1958), 180.
260. J.E.LENNARD-JONES, *Proc. Roy. Soc.*, A **158** (1937), 280.
261. M.J.S.DEWAR, *J. Chem. Soc.*, (1952), 3546.
262. H.LABHART, *J. Chem. Phys.*, **27** (1957), 957.
263. Y.OOSHIKA, *J. Phys. Soc. Japan*, **12** (1957), 1238, 1246.
264. H.C.LONGUET-HIGGINS and L.SALEM, *Proc. Roy. Soc.*, A **251** (1959), 172; A **255** (1960), 435; A **257** (1960), 445.

265. L. SALEM and H. C. LONGUET-HIGGINS, *Proc. Roy. Soc.*, A **255** (1960), 435.
266. A. O. MCINTOSH, J. M. ROBERTSON and V. VAND, *J. Chem. Soc.*, (1954), 1661.
267. C. A. COULSON and S. SENENT, *J. Chem. Soc.*, (1955), 1813.
268. S. SENENT and M. A. HERRAEZ, *An. Real. Soc. Española Fis. Quim.*, **53** (1957), 257.
269. R. S. MULLIKEN, C. RIEKE and W. G. BROWN, *J. Am. Chem. Soc.*, **63** (1941), 41.
270. B. PULLMAN, *Proc. third Conference on Carbon*, Pergamon Press (1959), 3.
271. B. H. CHIRGWIN and C. A. COULSON, *Proc. Roy. Soc.*, A **201** (1950), 196.
272. V. W. MASLEN and C. A. COULSON, *J. Chem. Soc.* (1957), 4041.
273. A. and B. PULLMAN, *Les théories électroniques de la chimie organique*, Masson (1952), 524.
274. B. H. CHIRGWIN and C. A. COULSON, *Proc. Roy. Soc.*, A **201** (1950), 196.
275. J. C. SLATER, *Rev. Modern. Phys.*, **25** (1953), 199.
276. See, for example, G. W. WHELAND, *Resonance in organic chemistry*, Wiley, New York (1955).
277. W. G. PENNEY, *Proc. Roy. Soc.*, A **158** (1937), 306.
278. See, for example, C. A. COULSON, R. DAUDEL and J. M. ROBERTSON, *Proc., Roy. Soc.*, A **207** (1951), 306.
279. A. A. FROST, *J. Chem. Phys.*, **25** (1956), 1150.
280. A. A. FROST and F. E. LELAND, *J. Chem. Phys.*, **25** (1956), 1154.
281. L. PAULING, *J. Chem. Phys.*, **4** (1936), 673; O. SCHMIDT, *Ber.*, **73** A (1940), 97; J. R. PLATT, *J. Chem. Phys.*, **17** (1949), 484; H. KUHN, *Helv. Chim. Acta*, **31** (1948), 1441; **31** (1948), 1780; *J. Chem. Phys.*, **16** (1948), 840; **17** (1940), 1198; *Helv. Chim. Acta*, **32** (1949), 2247; *Z. Electrochem.*, **53** (1949), 165; *Helv. Chim. Acta*, **34** (1951), 1308; **34** (1951), 2371; N. S. BAYLISS, *J. Chem. Phys.*, **16** (1948), 287; **17** (1949), 1853; *Aust. J. Sci. Research*, A **3** (1950), 109; *Quarterly Reviews*, **6** (1952), 319; M. V. VOLKENSTEIN and L. A. BOROVINSKI, *Dokl. Acad. Nauk* (SSSR), **85** (1952), 737.
282. WALSH, *Quarterly Reviews*, **2** (1948), 73.
283. K. RUEDENBERG and C. W. SCHERR, *J. Chem. Phys.*, **21** (1953), 1565; C. W. SCHERR, *J. Chem. Phys.*, **21** (1953), 1582; J. R. PLATT, *J. Chem. Phys.*, **21** (1953), 1597; C. W. SCHERR, *J. Chem. Phys.*, **21** (1953), 1413; K. RUEDENBERG and C. W. SCHERR, *J. Chem. Phys.*, **22** (1954), 151; K. RUEDENBERG, *J. Chem. Phys.*, **22** (1954), 1878; J. R. PLATT, *J. Chem. Phys.*, **22** (1954), 1448.
284. H. KUHN, *J. Chem. Phys.*, **25** (1956), 293.
285. A. A. FROST, *J. Chem. Phys.*, **23** (1955), 985.
286. J. I. FERNANDEZ-ALONSO, J. MIRA and J. L. OLIETE, *J. Chimie Phys.*, (1957), 822; J. I. FERNANDEZ-ALONSO, J. L. OLIETE and R. DOMINGO, *J. Chimie Phys.*, (1959), 548.
287. H. LABHART, *J. Chem. Phys.*, **27** (1957), 957, 963.
288. N. S. HAM and K. RUEDENBERG, *J. Chem. Phys.*, **25** (1956), 1, 13; S. HUZINAGA, *Prog. Th. Phys.*, **15** (1956), 495.
289. R. LEFEBVRE, *C. R.*, **240** (1955), 1094; R. LEFEBVRE and C. MOSER, *J. Chim. Phys.*, **53** (1956), 393; R. LEFEBVRE, *Cah. Phys.*, **13** (1959), no. 110, 1.
290. R. MCWEENY, *Proc. Roy. Soc.*, A **235** (1956), 496.
291. C. C. J. ROOTHAAN, *Rev. Mod. Phys.*, **32** (1960), 179.

292. J. L. MASSE, Science Thesis, Paris (in press).
293. L. BRILLOUIN, *Les champs «self-consistents» de Hartree et de Fock*, Hermann, Paris (1934).
294. J. A. POPLE, *Trans. Far. Soc.*, **49** (1953), 1375.
295. A. BRICKSTOCK and J. A. POPLE, *Trans. Far. Soc.*, **50** (1954), 901.
296. R. LEFEBVRE, *J. Chimie Phys.*, **54** (1957), 168.
297. MCLAHLAN, *Molecular Physics*, **2** (1959), 271.
298. F. A. MATSEN, *J. Chem. Phys.*, **24** (1956), 602; R. M. HEDGES and F. A. MATSEN, *J. Chem. Phys.*, **28** (1958), 950.
299. N. S. HUSH and J. A. POPLE, *Trans. Far. Soc.*, **51** (1955), 600.
300. R. PARISER, *J. Chem. Phys.*, **24** (1956), 250.
301. J. A. POPLE, *J. Phys. Chem.*, **61** (1957), 6.
302. N. S. HUSH and J. A. POPLE, *Trans. Far. Soc.*, **51** (1955), 600.
303. J. A. POPLE, *J. Phys. Chem.*, **61** (1957), 6.
304. J. A. POPLE, *Proc. Phys. Soc.*, A **68** (1955), 81.
305. G. G. HALL, *Proc. Roy. Soc.*, A **213** (1952), 113.
306. R. LEFEBVRE, *Cah. Phys.*, **13** (1959), no. 110, 56.
307. G. BERTHIER, *J. Chim. Phys.*, **50** (1953), 344; *J. Chem. Phys.*, **21** (1953), 953.
308. J. A. POPLE, *J. Chem. Phys.*, **61** (1957), 6.
309. G. G. HALL, *Trans. Far. Soc.*, **53** (1957), 573.
310. H. O. PRITCHARD and F. H. SUMNER, *Trans. Far. Soc.*, **51** (1955), 457.
311. H. O. PRITCHARD and F. H. SUMNER, *Proc. Roy. Soc.*, A **226** (1954), 128.
312. T. E. PEACOCK, *Trans. Far. Soc.*, **53** (1957), 1.
313. D. N. J. CRUICKSHANK and R. A. SPARKS, *Proc. Roy. Soc.*, A **258** (1960), 270.
314. R. G. PARR and R. S. MULLIKEN, *J. Chem. Phys.*, **18** (1950), 1338; R. K. NESBET, *Proc. Roy. Soc.*, A **230** (1955), 312, 322; R. S. BERRY, *J. Chem. Phys.*, **26** (1957), 1660; R. LEFEBVRE (306).
315. R. MCWEENY, *Proc. Roy. Soc.*, A **235** (1956), 496.
316. S. KOLBOE and A. PULLMAN, *Calcul des fonctions d'onde moléculaires*, C.N.R.S., Paris (1958), 213; T. E. PEACOCK, *J. Chem. Soc.* (1959), 324.
317. E. T. STEWART, *J. Chem. Soc.* (1958), 4016.
318. G. BERTHIER, *J. Chimie Phys.*, **52** (1955), 141; R. LEFEBVRE (306).
319. A. A. VERRIJN STUART and E. L. MACKOR, *J. Chem. Phys.*, **27** (1957), 826.
320. G. J. HOIJKINK, *Calcul des fonctions d'onde moléculaires*, C.N.R.S. ed., Paris (1958), 239; W. P. WEIJLAND, Thesis, Amsterdam (1958); P. BALK, S. and BRUIJN and G. J. HOIJTINK, *Mol. Physics*, **1** (1958), 151; P. J. ZANDSTRA, Thesis, Groningen (1959).
321. M. J. S. DEWAR and H. C. LONGUET-HIGGINS, *Proc. Phys. Soc.*, A **67** (1954), 795.
322. J. A. POPLE, *Proc. Phys. Soc.*, A **68** (1955), 81.
323. R. PARISER, *J. Chem. Phys.*, **24** (1956), 250.
324. P. O. LÖWDIN, *Symposium on Molecular Physics*, Nikko, Japan (1953), 13.
325. I. ITOH and H. YOSHIZUMI, *J. Phys. Soc. Japan*, **10** (1955), 201.
326. Conférence au Colloque d'Uppsal (1960).
327. R. LEFEBVRE, DEARMAN and H. MCCONNELL, *J. Chem. Phys.*, **32** (1960), 176.
328. O. CHALVET and R. DAUDEL, *J. Chimie Phys.*, **49** (1952), 629; H. C. LEFKO-

VITS, H.C.FAIN and F.A.MATSEN, *J. Chem. Phys.*, **23** (1955), 1690; J.HI-GUCHI, *J. Chem. Phys.*, **26** (1957), 151; H.D.HUNT, D.L.PETERSON and W.T.SIMPSON, *J. Chem. Phys.*, **27** (1957), 20.

329. J.N.MURRELL, *J. Chem. Phys.*, **26** (1957), 1738.

330. A.D.LIEHR, *Z. für Phys. Chemie*, **9** (1956), 338.

331. C.A.COULSON and J.JACOBS, *Proc. Roy. Soc.*, A **206** (1951), 287; R.LE-FEBVRE, *C.R.*, **237** (1953), 1158; A.PULLMAN, *J. Chimie Phys.*, **51** (1954), 188; A.PULLMAN and J.BAUDET, *C.R.*, **238** (1954), 241; R.K.NESBET, *Proc. Roy. Soc.*, A **230** (1955), 312, 322; A. PULLMAN and H.BERTHOD, *J. Chimie Phys.*, **52** (1955), 771; J.FAIN and F.A.MATSEN, *J. Chem. Phys.*, **26** (1957), 376; R.S.BERRY, *J. Chem. Phys.*, **26** (1957), 1660.

332. D.P.CRAIG, *Proc. Roy. Soc.*, A **200** (1950), 474; R. McWEENY, *Proc. Roy. Soc.*, A **227** (1955), 288; A.D.LIEHR (*loc. cit.*).

333. R.G.PARR, D.P.CRAIG and I.G.ROSS, *J. Chem. Phys.*, **18** (1950), 1561; C.W.L.BEVAN and D.P.CRAIG, *Trans. Far. Soc.*, **47** (1951), 564; R. McWEENY (*loc. cit.*); W.KOLOS, *J. Chem. Phys.*, **27** (1957), 592.

334. C.M.MOSER and R.LEFEBVRE, *J. Chem. Phys.*, **23** (1955), 598.

335. A.JULG and A.PULLMAN, *J. Chimie Phys.*, **50** (1953), 459.

336. R.PARISER, *J. Chem. Phys.*, **25** (1956), 1112.

337. L.PAULING and G.W.WHELAND, *J. Am. Chem. Soc.*, **57** (1935), 2086.

338. B.BAK, D.CHRISTENSEN, L.HANSEN and J.RASTRUP ANDERSEN, *J. Chem. Phys.*, **24** (1956), 720.

339. R.S.MULLIKEN, *J. Chem. Phys.*, **2** (1934), 782; **3** (1935), 573.

340. L.PAULING, *J. Am. Chem. Soc.*, **54** (1932), 3570; O.K.RICE, *Electron structure and chemical binding*, McGraw-Hill (1940), p. 196; W.GORDY, *J. Chem. Phys.*, **14** (1946), 305.

341. J.BELLUGUE and R.DAUDEL, *Rev. Sci.*, **84** (1946), 541 (see also: M.HAÏS-SINSKY, *J. Phys. Radium*, **7** (1946), 5).

342. R.S.MULLIKEN, *J. Chimie Phys.*, **46** (1949), 497, 675.

343. A.LAFORGUE, *J. Chimie Phys.*, **46** (1949), 568.

344. J.E.LENNARD-JONES, *Proc. Roy. Soc.*, A **158** (1931), 280.

345. See, for example: H.O.PRITCHARD and F.H.SUMNER, *Proc. Roy. Soc.*, A **235** (1956), 136.

346. C.A.COULSON and H.C.LONGUET-HIGGINS, *Proc. Roy. Soc.*, A **191** (1947), 39; A **192** (1947), 16.

347. H.C.LONGUET-HIGGINS, **18** (1950), 265, 275, 283; F.A.MATSEN, *J. Am. Chem. Soc.*, **72** (1950), 5243; H.H.JAFFÉ, *J. Am. Chem. Soc.*, **77** (1955), 274; **76** (1954), 3843; J.L.MASSE, *Cah. de Phys.*, **70** (1956), 31; M.J.S.DE-WAR, *J. Am. Chem. Soc.*, **74** (1952), 3341; *J. Chem. Soc.* (1950), 2329; K.FUKUI, C.NAGATA, T.YONEZAWA, H.KATO and K.MOROKUMA, *J. Chem. Phys.*, **31** (1959), 287.

348. K.NISHIMOTO and R.FUJISHIRO, *Bull. Chem. Soc. Japan*, **32** (1959), 699.

349. O.CHALVET and C.SANDORFY, *C.R.*, **228** (1949), 566; P.O.LÖWDIN, *J. Chem. Phys.*, **19** (1951), 123; B.W.DAVIES, *Trans. Far. Soc.*, **51** (1955), 449.

350. R.McWEENY and T.E.PEACOCK, *Proc. Phys. Soc.*, **70** (1957), 41.

351. S.ODIOT and M.ROUX, *J. Chim. Phys.*, **50** (1953), 141; J.I.FERNANDEZ-ALONSO, *C.R.*, **233** (1951), 56.

352. H.O.PRITCHARD and F.H.SUMNER, *Proc. Roy. Soc.*, A **235** (1956), 136.

353. R.D.BROWN and H.L.HEFFERNAN, *Aust. J. Chem.*, **10** (1957), 211.

354. R. D. BROWN and M. L. HEFFERMAN, *Aust. J. Chem.*, **10** (1957), 483.
355. R. D. BROWN and M. L. HEFFERMAN, *Trans. Far. Soc.*, **54** (1958), 757.
356. R. D. BROWN and M. L. HEFFERNAN, *Aust. J. Chem.*, **12** (1959), 554.
357. M. KASHA, *Phys. Rev.*, **76** (1949), 161; *Disc. Far. Soc.*, **9** (1950), 14.
358. J. H. RUSH and H. SPONER, *J. Chem. Phys.*, **20** (1952), 1847.
359. J. R. PLATT, *J. Chem. Phys.*, **19** (1951), 101; L. E. ORGEL, *J. Chem. Soc.* (1955), 121.
360. L. GOODMAN and R. W. HARRELL, *J. Chem. Phys.*, **30** (1959), 1131.
361. L. GOODMAN and H. SHULL, *J. Chem. Phys.*, **22** (1954), 1138; **22** (1955), 33.
362. T. ANNO, *J. Chem. Phys.*, **29** (1958), 1161.
363. H. F. HAMEKA and A. M. LIQUORI, *Kon. Nederl. Akad. Van Wetenschappen* (Amsterdam), **59** (1956), 242.
364. T. ANNO and A. SADÔ, *J. Chem. Phys.*, **29** (1958), 1170; **32** (1960), 619.
365. T. ANNO, *J. Chem. Phys.*, **32** (1960), 867.
366. L. E. ORGEL, *J. Chem. Soc.*, (1955), 121.
367. N. MATAGA and S. TSUNO, *Naturwissenschaften*, **45** (1958), 333; N. MATAGA, *Bull. Chem. Soc. Japan*, **31** (1958), 453; S. MATAGA and N. MATAGA, *Bull. Chem. Soc. Japan*, **32** (1959), 521; *Z. Phys. Chemie*, **19** (1959), 231.
368. K. CHANDRA and S. BASU, *J. Chem. Soc.*, (1959), 1623.
369. J. N. MURRELL, *Mol. Phys.*, **1** (1958), 384.
370. G. FAVINI and S. CARRA, *Gazz. Chim. It.*, **87** (1957), 1367; S. CARRA, S. POLEZO and M. SIMONETTA, *Rend. Acc. Lincei*, **23** (1957), 429; S. CARRA, E. GIANINETTI and M. SIMONETTA, *Rend. Acc. Lincei*, **24** (1958), 723.
371. L. PAOLONI, *J. Chem. Phys.*, **25** (1956), 1277; *Gaz. Chim. It.*, **87** (1957), 313.
372. S. MATAGA and N. MATAGA, *Bull. Chem. Soc. Japan*, **32** (1959), 511.
373. N. MATAGA and K. NISHIMOTO, *Z. Phys. Chem.*, **13** (1957), 140; N. MATAGA, *Z. Phys. Chem.*, **18** (1958), 19; N. MATAGA, *Bull. Soc. Chim. Japan*, **31** (1958), 463.
374. G. FAVINI, V. PIERPAOLI and M. SIMONETTA, *Rend. Acc. Naz. Lincei*, **24** (1958), 66.
375. J. I. FERNANDEZ-ALONSO and L. CARBONELL VILA, *Ann. Real. Soc. Fis. Chim.*, **52** (1956), 617.
376. T. E. PEACOCK, *J. Chem. Soc.*, (1959), 3645.
377. R. D. BROWN and B. A. W. COLLER, *Mol. Phys.*, **2** (1958), 159.
378. S. CARRA and S. POLEZZO, *Gazz. Chim. It.*, **88** (1958), 1103.
379. R. D. BROWN and M. L. HEFFERNAN, *Aust. J. Chem.*, **12** (1959), 319.
380. J. I. FERNANDEZ-ALONSO, R. DOMINGO, L. CARBONELL VILA and F. PERADEJORDI, *Ann. Real. Soc. Fis. Chim.*, **53** (1957), 109.
381. J. I. FERNANDEZ-ALONSO, R. DOMINGO and L. CARBONELL VILA, *Rec. Trav. Chim. Pays-Bas*, **78** (1959), 215.
382. L. PAOLONI and G. B. MARINO-BETTOLO, *Nature*, **179** (1957), 42.
383. M. J. S. DEWAR, *J. Chem. Soc.*, (1950), 329; (1952), 3532, 3534; M. J. S. DEWAR and H. C. LONGUET-HIGGINS, *Proc. Roy. Soc.*, A **214** (1952), 482.
384. NAGAKURA and TANAKA, *J. Chem. Phys.*, **22** (1954), 236; NAGAKURA, *J. Chem. Phys.*, **23** (1955), 1441; TANAKA, NAGAKURA and KOBAYSHI, **24** (1956), 311.
385. N. MATAGA and S. MATAGA, *Bull. Chem. Soc. Japan*, **32** (1959), 600.
386. J. W. SIDMAN, *J. Chem. Phys.*, **27** (1957), 429; T. ANNO and A. SADÔ, *J. Chem. Phys.*, **26** (1957), 1759.

387. L. PAOLINI, *J. Chim. Phys.*, **51** (1954), 385.

388. A. KUBOYAMA, *Bull. Chem. Soc. Japan*, **31** (1958), 752.

389. G. PAYETTE and C. SANDORFY, *J. Chem. Soc.*, **30** (1959), 168.

390. R. BLINC and E. PIRKMAJER, *Reports J. Stefan Institute*, **4** (1957), 133.

391. T. ANNO, I. MATUBARA and A. SADÔ, *Bull. Chem. Soc. Japan*, **29** (1957), 168; T. ANNO, A. SADÔ and I. MATUBARA, *J. Chem. Phys.*, **26** (1957), 967; T. ANNO and A. SADÔ, *Bull. Chem. Soc. Japan*, **31** (1958), 728; T. ANNO and A. SADÔ, *Bull. Chem. Soc. Japan*, **31** (1958), 734.

392. S. BESNAINOU and S. BRATOZ, *J. Chem. Phys.*, **34** (1961), 1142.

393. J. J. KAUFMAN and W. S. KOSKI, *J. Am. Chem. Soc.*, **82** (1960), 3262.

394. T. H. GOODWIN. *J. Chem. Soc.*, (1955), 4451.

395. K. NISHIMOTO and R. FUJISHIRO, *Bull. Chem. Soc. Japan*, **31** (1958), 1036.

396. S. SENENT and F. J. IGEA, *Ann. Real. Soc. Fis. Quim.*, **52** (1956).

397. K. NISHIMOTO and R. FUJISHIRO, *Bull. Chem. Soc. Japan*, **32** (1959), 445.

398. J. I. FERNANDEZ-ALONSO, *C.R.*, **233** (1951), 403.

399. G. FAVINI and S. CARRA, *Gaz. Chim. It.*, **85** (1955), 1029.

400. M. KUBO, Y. KURITA and M. KIMURA, *Molecular Structure and Related Problems*, no. 4 (1954), 1.

401. R. D. BROWN and B. A. W. COLLER, *Aust. J. Chem.*, **12** (1959), 52.

402. H. C. LONGUET-HIGGINS, *Trans. Far. Soc.*, **41** (1949), 173; L. MELANDER, *Arkiv f. Kemi*, **8** (1955), 361.

403. A. PULLMAN and J. METZGER, *Bull. Soc. Chim. France* (1948), 1021; J. METZGER and A. PULLMAN, *ibidem* (1948), 1166; G. BERTHIER and B. PULMAN, *C.R.*, **231** (1950), 774; M. M. KREEWOY, *J. Am. Chem. Soc.*, **80** (1958), 5543.

404. J. KOUTECKY, R. ZAHRADNIK and J. PALDUS, *J. Chem. Phys.*, (1959), 455.

405. M. KREEVOY, *J. Am. Chem. Soc.*, **80** (1958), 5543.

406. G. BERGSON, *Arkiv f. Kemi*, **12** (1958), 233.

407. G. GIACOMETTI and G. RIGATTI, *J. Chem. Phys.*, **30** (1959), 1633.

408. G. BERGSON, *Arkiv f. Kemi*, **13** (1958), 11.

409. W. T. ASTBURY and H. J. WOODS, *Phil. Trans. Roy. Soc.*, A **232** (1933), 333.

410. L. PAULING, R. B. COREY and H. R. BRANSON, *Proc. Nat. Acad. Sci. U.S.*, **37** (1951), 205.

411. A. SZENT GYORGI, *Nature*, **148** (1941), 157.

412. BAYLISS, *J. Chem. Phys.*, **16** (1948), 287.

413. M. G. EVANS and J. GERGELY, *Biochim. Biophys. Acta*, **3** (1949), 188.

414. R. B. COREY, *Chem. Revs.*, **26** (1940), 227.

415. VARTANYAN, *Chem. Abst.*, **43** (1949), 1272.

416. AKAMATU and INOKUCHI, *J. Chem. Phys.*, **18** (1950), 810; AKAMATU, INOKUCHI and HANDA, *Nature*, **168** (1951), 520; INOKUCHI, *J. Chem. Soc. Japan*, **54** (1951), 222.

417. ELEY, PARFITT, PERRY and TAYSUM, *Trans. Far. Soc.*, **49** (1953), 79; ELEY, *Discus. Far. Soc.*, no. **20** (1955); M. H. CARDEW and D. D. ELEY, *Discus. Far. Soc.*, no. **27** (1959), 115; D. D. ELEY and D. I. SPIVEY, *Trans. Far. Soc.*, **56** (1960), 1432.

418. P. DOUZOU and J. M. THUILLIER, *J. Chimie Phys.*, **57** (1960), 96.

419. B. GRABE, *Arkiv f. Kemi*, **9** (1955), 29; *Exp. Cell. Res.*, **10** (1956), 447; *Arkiv f. Fysik*, **15** (1959), 207; *Exp. Cell. Res.*, **13** (1957), 588; *Biochim. Biophys.*

Acta, **30** (1958), 560; *Arkiv f. Fysik*, **17** (1960), 97; *Arkiv f. Kemi*, **15** (1960), 323.

420. B. GRABE, *Arkiv f. Fysik*, **15** (1959), 207.
421. H. A. SKINNER and H. O. PRITCHARD, *Trans. Faraday Soc.*, **49** (1953), 1254.
422. B. and A. PULLMAN, *C.R.*, **249** (1959), 1827; *Radiation Research*, Sup. 2 (1960), 161.
423. B. and A. PULLMAN, *Proc. Nat. Acad. Sci.*, **45** (1959), 136.
424. B. GRABE, *Arkiv f. Fysik*, **17** (1960), 97.
425. LONGUET-HIGGINS, RECTOR and PLATT, *J. Chem. Phys.*, **18** (1950), 1174; S. L. MATLOW, *J. Chem. Phys.*, **23** (1955), 673; G. R. SEELY, *J. Chem. Phys.*, **27** (1957), 125.
426. H. KUHN, *Chimia*, **4** (1950), 215; T. NAKAJIMA and H. KON, *J. Chem. Phys.*, **20** (1952), 750.
427. B. PULLMAN, C. SPANJAARD and G. BERTHIER, *Proc. Nat. Acad. Sci.*, **46** (1960), 1011.
428. J. S. GRIFFITH, *Disc. Far. Soc.*, **26** (1958), 81.
429. J. R. PLATT, *Science*, **129** (1959), 372.
430. L. G. S. BROOKER *et al.*, *J. Am. Chem. Soc.*, **73** (1951), 5332, 5350.
431. R. S. MULLIKEN, *J. Am. Chem. Soc.*, **72** (1950), 600; **74** (1952), 8113; *J. Chem. Phys.*, **19** (1951), 514.
432. B. and A. PULLMAN, *Biochim. Biophys. Acta*, **36** (1959), 343.
433. A. and B. PULLMAN, *Soc. Chim.*, (1958), 766.
434. A. and B. PULLMAN, *Soc. Chim.*, (1959), 594.
435. A. PULLMAN, *C.R.*, **251** (1960), 808, 1430.

Index